SYNOPSIS OF GROSS ANATOMY

with 81 illustrations

JOHN B. CHRISTENSEN, PH.D.
Associate Professor of Anatomy

IRA ROCKWOOD TELFORD, PH.D.
Professor of Anatomy

The George Washington University
School of Medicine
Washington, D. C.

HOEBER MEDICAL DIVISION
HARPER & ROW, PUBLISHERS, NEW YORK, EVANSTON, AND LONDON

PUBLISHED OCTOBER 1966

Synopsis of Gross Anatomy
Copyright © 1966 by Hoeber Medical Division,
Harper & Row, Publishers, Incorporated
Printed in the United States of America

LIBRARY OF CONGRESS CATALOG CARD NUMBER: 66–25533

CONTENTS

PREFACE

This synoptic volume of regional anatomy presents the basic facts and concepts in the study of gross anatomy considered essential for students of medicine and associated sciences. It meets the need of the student for a concise, straightforward textbook, uncluttered by minutiae. This synopsis is intended, not to replace selective reading in large conventional textbooks, but rather to give the student an initial appreciation of important body structures and relations.

Many original illustrations have been especially prepared to enhance this epitomized approach to the study of anatomy. The line drawings are keyed to the text and can be readily correlated with regional dissections.

For the student who finds gross anatomy difficult, this compact text may provide all that he can or need comprehend of the subject. However, for those who wish to pursue the subject more deeply, it will serve as a framework for the building of a broader and firmer foundation in anatomy.

Because of its regional approach, we suggest that this book could be used as *1)* a study guide in conjunction with anatomical atlases and larger textbooks, *2)* a companion text in gross dissection, or *3)* a review of the fundamentals of gross anatomy.

In brief, we have endeavored to present, in the most succinct form, the essentials of human gross anatomy that we believe every medical student should know.

We gratefully acknowledge the kindness of our colleagues, Dr. Frank D. Allan, Associate Professor of Anatomy, George Washington University, and Dr. W. Montague Cobb, Chairman and Professor of Anatomy, Howard University, in reading and offering constructive suggestions for improvement of our original text.

We are deeply indebted to Mr. David S. Kern and his daughter Bonnie for the excellent rendering of most of the illustrations, to Mr. Michael S. Murtaugh for his splendid diagrammatic sketches and drawings, and to Dr. William A. Rush, Jr., Mrs. Margaret Dupree, and Miss Joan Ruback for their contributions to the artwork.

By the kind permission of various authors and their publishers, we have borrowed a few illustrations from the sources acknowledged in the individual legends.

JOHN B. CHRISTENSEN

IRA ROCKWOOD TELFORD

Washington, D. C.

vii

SUPERIOR EXTREMITY

The superior extremity consists of shoulder, arm, forearm, and hand, the latter being specially adapted for prehension. The muscles of the shoulder and arm act to place the grasping hand in almost any desired position. The rich nerve supply of the fingertips makes the hand a sensitive tactile organ. The muscles of the hand permit complex activity of the digits, which are moved primarily by muscles in the forearm. The superior extremity articulates with the trunk at the small sternoclavicular joint and is firmly anchored to the chest by a series of muscles covering the thorax. Thus the superficial muscles of the trunk (back and pectoral regions) acting upon this member must be considered in any description of the upper extremity.

SUPERFICIAL BACK AND SCAPULAR REGION

Surface Anatomy

The most superior structure palpable in the midline of the upper back is the spinous process of the seventh cervical vertebra, or **vertebra prominens.** Above this level the spinous processes of the cervical vertebrae are covered by the **ligamentum nuchae,** while inferiorly all vertebral spinous processes are palpable.

The **spine** of the scapula is subcutaneous through most of its extent, although its medial triangular portion is covered by the trapezius muscle. Laterally it is continuous with the **acromion,** which forms the point of the shoulder. The **vertebral border** and the **inferior** and **superior angles** of the scapula can be felt deep to the superficial musculature of the back. In a muscular individual there is a diamond-shaped depression between the two scapulae formed by the lack of muscle fibers in the aponeurosis of the trapezius muscle in this area.

Inferolaterally the **crests of the ilia** project as bony ridges below the waist and are palpable posteriorly to the **posterior superior iliac spines.** Further inferiorly in the midline of the lower back, the posterior surface of the **sacrum** is subcutaneous, and at its inferior extent the **coccyx** can be felt in the cleft between the buttocks. On each side the **lumbar triangle** (of Petit), a small area low in the back, is bounded by the crest of the ilium, the anterior border of the latissimus dorsi, and the posterior extent of the external abdominal oblique muscles.

1

Cutaneous Innervation (Figs. 1 and 4)

The cutaneous innervation of the shoulder, superior portion of the back, and upper pectoral region is derived from the **supraclavicular branches** of the cervical plexus. Inferior to this region the posterior body wall is supplied by cutaneous branches of the posterior primary rami of segmental spinal nerves; cutaneous branches of the intercostal or thoracoabdominal nerves, continuations of the anterior primary rami of spinal nerves, supply the anterolateral body wall. At consecutive spinal levels the **intercostal nerves** arise from anterior primary rami to supply segmental bands of skin over the ribs and intercostal spaces, with branches of a single spinal nerve sending overlapping twigs to adjacent skin areas. From these nerves **lateral cutaneous branches** penetrate the skin near the mid-axillary line and divide into anterior and posterior branches. The intercostal nerve then continues anteriorly in the intercostal space and terminates as **perforating branches** emerging just lateral to the sternum to divide into **medial** and **lateral cutaneous twigs.**

The **posterior primary rami** of spinal nerves divide into medial and lateral branches. Above the level of the sixth thoracic vertebra the **medial branch** supplies the skin over the back, while the **lateral branch** is entirely muscular. Below the level of the sixth thoracic vertebra the distribution of these branches is reversed.

SUPERFICIAL BACK

Muscles (Table I, Fig. 1)

The muscles of the back are arranged in layers. Those of the first and second layers, although related topographically to the back, afford attachment of the upper limb to the vertebral column, are innervated by anterior primary rami of spinal nerves, and should be considered as belonging to the upper extremity. The first, or most superficial, layer is composed of the trapezius and the latissimus dorsi muscles.

The **trapezius muscle,** with its companion of the opposite side, forms a large trapezoid over the upper back. Its anterior border in the cervical region gives the sloping contour to the neck and bulges in the action of shrugging the shoulders. Inferiorly in the midline, it overlaps the upper origin of the latissimus dorsi. With the scapula drawn forward, the lateral border of the trapezius, the superior border of the latissimus dorsi, and the medial border of the scapula bound the **triangle of auscultation,** an area often utilized in listening to respiratory sounds with the stethoscope. In this position the underlying ribs become essentially subcutaneous.

The **latissimus dorsi** gives the lateral taper to the chest. With the teres major, the latissimus dorsi forms the posterior wall of the axilla, or armpit. Inferiorly its lateral fibers interdigitate with those of the obliquus externus abdominis. Its inferior edge spirals or turns under in passing to its insertion on the humerus. The latissimus dorsi acting with the pectoralis major muscle draws the flexed arm back to the anatomical position, as in the action of rowing a boat or climbing a rope.

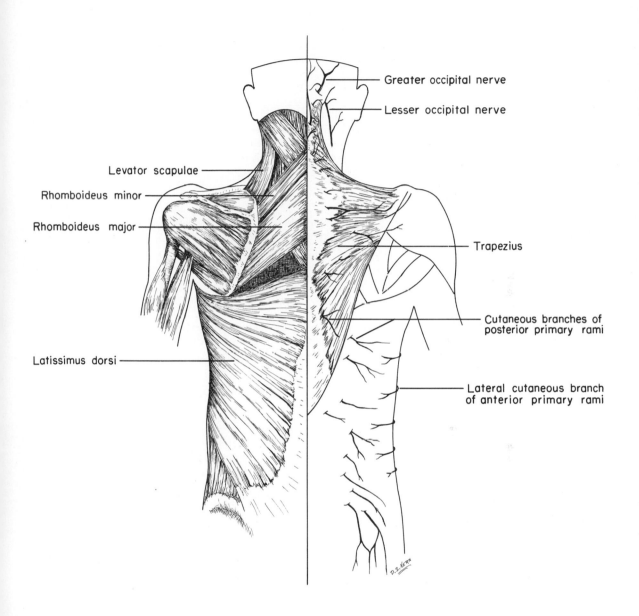

Fig. 1. Cutaneous innervation and superficial muscles of the back.

TABLE I. MUSCLES OF THE SUPERFICIAL BACK

Muscle	Origin	Insertion	Action	Nerve
Trapezius	External occipital protuberance, superior nuchal line, ligamentum nuchae, seventh cervical and all thoracic spinous processes	Anterior border of spine of scapula, acromion, and lateral third of posterior border of clavicle	Adducts and rotates scapula; upper part elevates scapula; lower part depresses scapula	Spinal accessory and twigs from third and fourth cervical nerves
Latissimus dorsi	Spinous processes of all vertebrae below sixth thoracic, lumbodorsal fascia, crest of ilium, and lower three or four ribs	Floor of intertubercular groove of humerus	Lowers, rotates medially, and draws arm posteriorly	Thoracodorsal
Levator scapulae	Transverse processes of first through fourth cervical vertebrae	Posterior lip of vertebral border of scapula	Elevates scapula and inclines head	Twigs from cervical plexus and dorsal scapular
Rhomboideus major	Spinous processes of second through fifth thoracic vertebrae	Posterior lip of lower half of vertebral border of scapula	Adducts and rotates scapula laterally	Dorsal scapular
Rhomboideus minor	Spinous processes of seventh cervical and first thoracic vertebrae	Root of spine of scapula	Adducts and rotates scapula laterally	Dorsal scapular
Serratus anterior	Digitations from lateral surfaces of upper eight ribs	Anterior lip of vertebral border of scapula	Holds scapula to chest wall; draws scapula anteriorly; and rotates inferior angle laterally	Long thoracic

Deep to the trapezius a sheet of three relatively thin strap-like muscles, the **levator scapulae** and the **rhomboideus minor** and **major,** inserts serially into the posterior lip of the vertebral border of the scapula. The levator scapulae and the rhomboideus minor are usually fused at their insertion and therefore somewhat difficult to differentiate. These muscles elevate the scapula, draw it toward the midline, and assist in lateral rotation. The rhomboideus major draws the inferior angle of the scapula superiorly to depress the lateral angle, which assists in adduction of the arm.

A fourth muscle, the **serratus anterior,** inserts into the anterior lip of the vertebral border of the scapula. From its origin on the upper eight or nine ribs this muscle follows the contour of the thoracic cage as it passes to its insertion. It acts to hold the scapula onto the rib cage, and loss of its action results in a flaring out of the vertebral border (winged scapula).

Fasciae

The superficial fascia over the back has no special characteristic features. The deep fascia, in addition to forming muscular envelopes, specializes in the lower back as the thickened lumbodorsal fascia, which will be described with the deep muscles of the back and the abdominal musculature.

Arteries and Nerves (Fig. 2)

The arterial supply to the trapezius, levator scapulae, and rhomboidei muscles is derived from the transverse cervical artery, a branch of the thyrocervical trunk from the first part of the subclavian artery. The **transverse cervical artery** crosses the posterior triangle of the neck to reach the anterior border of the trapezius, where it divides into a **superficial branch** ramifying on the deep surface of the muscle and a **deep branch** passing parallel to the vertebral border of the scapula, deep to and supplying the levator scapulae and rhomboidei.

Innervation of the trapezius is derived from the **spinal accessory nerve** together with twigs from the third and fourth cervical nerves; the latter are probably sensory in function. The spinal accessory emerges from the deep surface of the sternocleidomastoid and crosses the posterior triangle of the neck, passing deep to the trapezius to ramify on its deep surface. The levator scapulae and rhomboidei are supplied by the **dorsal scapular nerve,** a branch of the brachial plexus. After piercing the scalenus medius muscle, this nerve passes deep to, and supplies, the levator scapulae and rhomboidei, passing with the deep branch of the transverse cervical artery parallel to the vertebral border of the scapula.

The latissimus dorsi receives its blood supply from the **thoracodorsal artery,** a terminal branch of the subscapular from the third part of the axillary. This vessel passes along the axillary border of the scapula to its distribution in the muscle. The nerve supply of the latissimus dorsi is from the **thoracodorsal nerve,** a branch of the posterior cord of the brachial plexus, which passes anterior to the subscapularis and teres major muscles to descend along the axillary border of the scapula to its termination in the muscle.

The serratus anterior is supplied by the **lateral thoracic artery,** a branch of the second part of the axillary. This vessel arises near, and descends along, the lower border of the pectoralis minor muscle to ramify on the superficial surface of the serratus anterior muscle. Innervation of the latter is by the **long thoracic nerve,** a branch of the brachial plexus, which descends posterior to the brachial plexus to follow the lateral thoracic artery into the muscle.

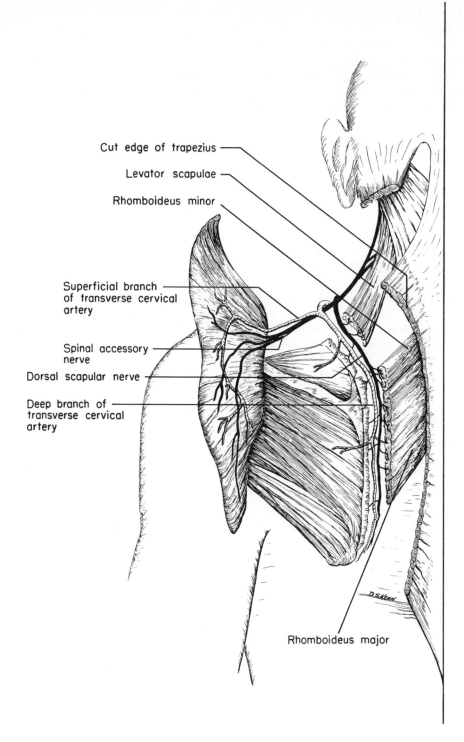

Cut edge of trapezius

Levator scapulae

Rhomboideus minor

Superficial branch
of transverse cervical
artery

Spinal accessory
nerve

Dorsal scapular nerve

Deep branch of
transverse cervical
artery

Rhomboideus major

D.S.KERN

Fig. 2. Innervation and arterial supply to the superficial muscles of the back.

SCAPULAR REGION

Muscles (Table II)

Three muscles, the **supraspinatus, infraspinatus,** and **subscapularis,** originate from, and cover, the three shallow fossae of the scapula. The tendons of these muscles, as well as that of the teres minor, pass over the glenohumeral articulation, deep to the deltoideus muscle, to fuse with and strengthen the joint capsule as they insert into the tubercles of the humerus. Their insertions form the **musculotendinous cuff** of the shoulder joint. The supraspinatus initiates, then assists the deltoideus, in abduction of the arm. The infraspinatus and subscapularis rotate the arm laterally and medially, respectively.

TABLE II. MUSCLES OF THE SHOULDER

Muscle	Origin	Insertion	Action	Nerve
Supraspinatus	Medial two-thirds of supraspinous fossa	Superior portion of greater tubercle of humerus	Initiates abduction of arm and augments deltoid function	Suprascapular
Infraspinatus	Medial three-fourths of infraspinous fossa	Midportion of greater tubercle of humerus	Acts as main lateral rotator of arm	Suprascapular
Subscapularis	Medial two-thirds of subscapular fossa	Lesser tubercle of humerus	Acts as main medial rotator of arm; aids in flexion, extension, adduction, and abduction of arm	Upper and lower subscapular
Deltoideus	Lateral third of anterior border of clavicle, acromion, and posterior border of spine of scapula	Deltoid tuberosity of humerus	Acts as main abductor of arm; aids in flexion, extension, adduction, and medial and lateral rotation of arm	Axillary (circumflex)
Teres major	Posterior surface of inferior angle and lower portion of axillary border of scapula	Medial lip of intertubercular groove of humerus	Adducts and rotates arm medially	Lower subscapular
Teres minor	Upper portion of axillary border of scapula	Inferior portion of greater tubercle of humerus	Rotates arm laterally and acts as weak adductor of arm	Axillary (circumflex)

The superficial **deltoideus muscle** forms the lateral mass of the shoulder. From its extensive origin on the clavicle, the acromion, and spine of the scapula, it acts primarily as an abductor, but segments working independently function also in adduction, extension, flexion, and internal and external rotation of the arm.

The teres major, teres minor, and long head of the triceps have a lineal origin along the axillary border of the scapula, whereas the omohyoideus arises from the scapular notch. Note that with respect to muscular attachments to the scapula, all the muscles attaching to the fossae, including the omohyoid attachment at the lesser scapular notch, are attachments of origin. Muscles attaching to the vertebral border are all insertions, whereas muscles attaching to the axillary border are all origins, including the supraglenoid tubercular attachment of the long head of the biceps. The trapezius and deltoideus attach to both the spine of the scapula and the clavicle, parallel each other, and form a U- or V-shaped inner insertion for the trapezius and outer origin for the deltoideus.

Arteries and Nerves (Fig. 3)

The supraspinatus and the infraspinatus muscles are supplied by branches of the same artery and nerve. The artery, the **transverse scapular,** crosses the posterior triangle of the neck to arrive at the scapular notch. Here it passes over

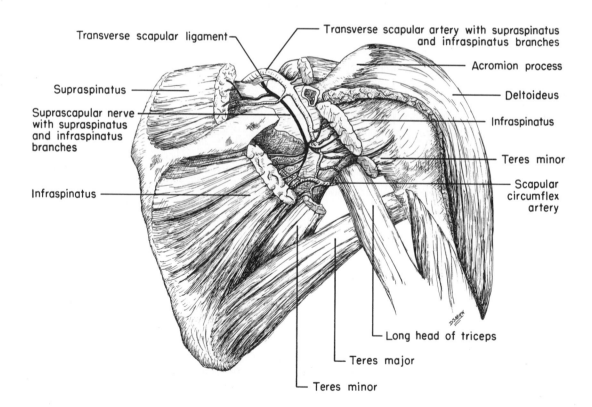

Fig. 3. Innervation and arterial supply to the shoulder muscles.

the transverse scapular ligament, which bridges the scapular notch, then terminates as **supraspinatus** and **infraspinatus branches** to these respective muscles. The **suprascapular nerve,** a branch of the brachial plexus, also crosses the posterior triangle of the neck to the scapular notch, but passes deep to the transverse scapular ligament, after which its distribution follows that of the arterial supply.

The subscapularis, teres major, and teres minor muscles receive their blood supply from a single vessel, the **scapular circumflex,** a terminal branch of the subscapular artery from the third part of the axillary. The **lower subscapular nerve,** a branch of the posterior cord of the brachial plexus, innervates the teres major and sends twigs to the subscapularis, which receives additional innervation from the **upper subscapular nerve** of the brachial plexus. The teres minor is supplied by a branch of the **axillary nerve** from the posterior cord of the brachial plexus.

Blood is distributed to the deltoideus muscle via the **anterior** and **posterior humeral circumflex arteries** and small deltoid branches of the thoracoacromial. The humeral circumflex arteries, from the third part of the axillary, pass anterior and posterior, respectively, to the neck of the humerus. The posterior humeral circumflex, the larger branch, passes through the **quadrangular space** with the **axillary nerve** which innervates the deltoideus.

PECTORAL REGION

Surface Anatomy

On the anterior surface of the thorax, demarcating the chest from the neck, the **clavicle** is subcutaneous in its entire length from the manubrium to its articulation with the acromion process of the scapula. A depression in the midline at the base of the neck, the **suprasternal notch,** is bounded inferiorly by the manubrium and laterally by the tendons of the sternal heads of the sternocleidomastoid muscles. In the midline a palpable ridge demarcates the **sternal angle** (of Louis) and corresponds to the junction of the manubrium with the body of the sternum. Laterally this junction affords articulation for the costal cartilage of the second rib and therefore can be utilized for accurate superficial determination of rib number or intercostal space. The **nipple** of the breast usually lies over the fourth intercostal space about a hand's breadth from the midline. The inferior and lateral margins of the thoracic cage are easily palpable, and in the midline the **xiphoid process** can be felt at the inferior extent of the body of the sternum.

Muscles (Table III, Fig. 4)

The **pectoralis major,** a large fan-shaped muscle, covers the anterior chest wall from an extensive origin on the clavicle, sternum, and ribs. Near its insertion into the humerus it forms the anterior wall of the axilla. The superior border of this muscle meets the deltoideus to form the **deltopectoral triangle,** a small triangular depression bounded by the anterior border of the deltoid, the superior border of the pectoralis major, and the midportion of the clavicle. It contains fat,

TABLE III. MUSCLES OF THE PECTORAL REGION

Muscle	Origin	Insertion	Action	Nerve
Pectoralis major	Clavicular head from medial half of clavicle; sternal head from sternum and costal cartilages; abdominal head from aponeurosis of external abdominal oblique	Lateral lip of intertubercular groove of humerus	Flexes, adducts, and medially rotates arm	Lateral and medial pectoral
Pectoralis minor	Anterior aspect of third, fourth, and fifth ribs	Coracoid process of scapula	Draws scapula inferiorly and elevates ribs	Medial pectoral
Subclavius	Junction of first rib and costal cartilage	Inferior surface of clavicle	Draws clavicle inferiorly and anteriorly	Nerve to subclavius

the deltopectoral lymph nodes, the cephalic vein, and the deltoid branch of the thoracoacromial artery.

The **pectoralis minor,** lying immediately deep to the pectoralis major, is a much less extensive muscle and acts as a muscle of forced respiration by elevating the chest wall. As it passes toward its insertion, it crosses superficially the axillary artery dividing it, for descriptive purposes, into three parts. The small **subclavius muscle** lies deep to the clavicle. In fracture of the clavicle this muscle may afford protection for the deeper lying subclavian vessels and the brachial plexus.

Fasciae

Over the pectoral region the **superficial fascia** contains abundant fat, especially in the female, where it surrounds the mammary gland and gives the gross configuration to the breast.

The membranous **deep fascia** in the pectoral region specializes as the **clavipectoral fascia.** This specialization is attached to the clavicle, encloses the subclavius muscle, fuses to span the gap between the clavicle and the pectoralis minor, then separates to enclose the latter. Lateral to the pectoralis minor, the fascia fuses again and thickens to form the **suspensory ligament of the axilla,** which passes to the floor of the axilla where it blends with the axillary fascia. Between the subclavius and the pectoralis minor this fascial sheet is pierced by branches of the thoracoacromial artery and medial and lateral pectoral nerves.

Arteries and Nerves

Blood is supplied to both pectoralis major and minor muscles by **pectoral branches** from the thoracoacromial, the **lateral thoracic,** and **perforating branches** of the anterior intercostal arteries. Additional supply to the pectoralis major is derived from the **perforating branches** of the internal thoracic artery.

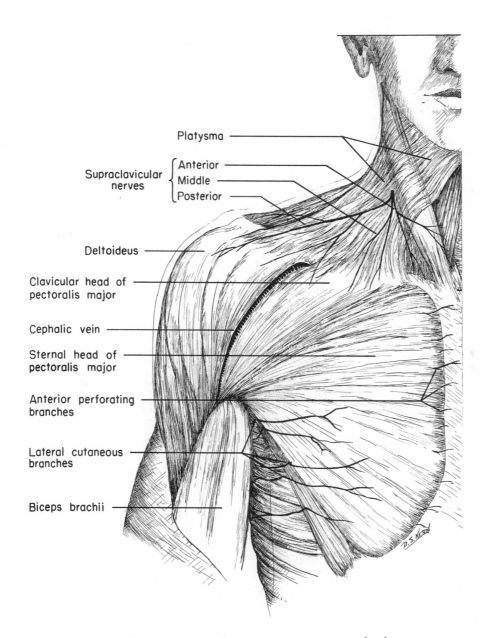

Platysma

Supraclavicular nerves
{ Anterior
  Middle
  Posterior

Deltoideus

Clavicular head of pectoralis major

Cephalic vein

Sternal head of pectoralis major

Anterior perforating branches

Lateral cutaneous branches

Biceps brachii

Fig. 4. Pectoralis major and cutaneous innervation over the chest.

The **medial** and **lateral pectoral nerves,** branches from, respectively, medial and lateral cords of the brachial plexus, pierce the clavipectoral fascia to innervate the pectoral muscles. The medial pectoral nerve passes through the pectoralis minor to the pectoralis major to supply both muscles. The lateral pectoral nerve courses medial to the pectoralis minor, usually supplying only the pectoralis major.

The blood supply to the subclavius is the **clavicular branch** of the thoraco-acromial trunk. The **nerve to the subclavius** is a branch of the upper trunk of the brachial plexus as the latter passes deep to the clavicle.

BREAST (FIG. 5)

The female **breast,** a modified sweat gland, is located in the superficial fascia of the pectoral region, where it rests upon the deep fascia covering the pectoralis major. It extends between the second and sixth rib and from the lateral border of the sternum to the axilla. It consists of glandular tissue, stroma, and fat. The **mammary gland** has no distinct capsule and is composed of fifteen to

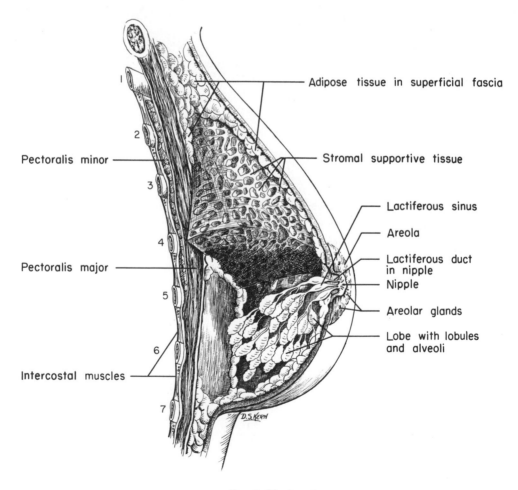

Pectoralis minor

Pectoralis major

Intercostal muscles

Adipose tissue in superficial fascia

Stromal supportive tissue

Lactiferous sinus

Areola

Lactiferous duct in nipple

Nipple

Areolar glands

Lobe with lobules and alveoli

Fig. 5. The breast.

twenty **lobes** radiating from the **nipple.** Each lobe has a single **lactiferous duct** which converges toward the **areola,** dilating near its termination to form a secretory reservoir, the **lactiferous sinus,** then constricting to open individually on the surface of the nipple. The stroma of the mammary gland consists of fibrous connective tissue which loosely envelopes the entire gland, extending into the gland to enclose the parenchyma. Condensations of the collagenous fibers form the **suspensory ligaments** (of Cooper), which extend from the skin through the mammary gland to the underlying fascia.

The arterial supply to the breast is from **pectoral branches of the thoracoacromial,** the **lateral thoracic,** perforating branches of the **internal thoracic,** and the third through the sixth **anterior intercostal** arteries.

Lymphatic drainage from **subareolar** and **circumareolar plexuses** is continuous with the general cutaneous drainage of the thoracic region and may drain toward the neck or the abdomen. **Perilobular** and **interlobular lymphatic plexuses** in the breast proper drain the deeper tissue and communicate with the subareolar plexus. The deeper drainage of the breast is regional. The lateral half of the mammary gland drains to the axillary and pectoral nodes. Lymph drainage from the medial side passes into the thorax to nodes along the internal thoracic artery or may cross the midline to the opposite breast. Inferiorly the lymph may flow toward the abdomen and drain into nodes in the upper abdomen.

ARM, FOREARM, AND HAND

Surface Anatomy

The **biceps brachii muscle** makes the anterior, and the **triceps** the posterior, bulge on the arm. Medial and lateral intermuscular septa, extensions of the investing fascia of the arm, separate the flexor (anterior) and extensor (posterior) compartments. These septa pass deeply to attach to the humerus, and are deep to the **superficial grooves** on either side of the arm. At the elbow, the **medial** and **lateral epicondyles** are easily palpable. The **olecranon process** of the ulna forms the posterior prominence of the elbow. Pressure on the medial side of the olecranon process elicits a tingling sensation which demonstrates the superficial position of the ulnar nerve passing along the ulnar groove of the medial epicondyle.

The **antecubital fossa** forms a triangular depression anterior to the elbow joint. The **tendon of the biceps** can be palpated within its boundaries, and the **lacertus fibrosus** (bicipital aponeurosis), a strong band of fibrous tissue, passes inferomedially from the tendon to the deep fascia of the forearm. The **median cubital vein,** forming a connection between the basilic and cephalic veins, can be seen crossing the fossa superficially. Just distal to the elbow the increased width of the forearm results from a massing of the bellies of the **flexor muscles** of the wrist and fingers **medially** and the **extensor group laterally.**

The **ulna** is subcutaneous along its entire length including its prominent head and distal styloid process. The radius is palpable in its distal half, and its **styloid process** can be felt at the lateral side of the wrist. Extension of the thumb results in a prominent ridge on the dorsum of the wrist formed by the **tendon of the extensor pollicis longus muscle.** With the thumb extended this tendon with that of the **abductor pollicis longus** forms a lateral depression, the "anatomical snuff box," across the bottom of which the radial artery courses. When the wrist is flexed against pressure, its palmar aspect reveals in the midline the **tendon of the palmaris longus,** and half an inch laterally, the **tendon of the flexor carpi radialis.**

The palmar aspect of the hand reveals transverse creases at the metacorpophalangeal joints. Note that the webbing of the fingers is distal to these articulations. The **thenar eminence** (ball of the thumb) is formed by the small muscles to the thumb, the **hypothenar eminence** (heel of the hand) by the small muscles to the little finger. The interval between the thumb and the index finger contains the adductor muscle of the thumb anteriorly and the first dorsal interosseus muscle posteriorly. The skin of the palm is thick, with little subcutaneous fat, and is firmly bound to deeper structures; over the dorsum of the hand the skin is more delicate and freely movable. Upon maximal extension of the wrist and fingers, the tendons of the **extensor digitorum communis muscle** form prominent ridges on the dorsum of the hand.

Cutaneous Innervation (Figs. 6 and 7)

The cutaneous innervation to the arm, forearm, and hand is supplied by branches of the brachial plexus with some contribution from the cervical plexus. The branches of the cervical plexus are the **posterior supraclavicular nerves,** which supply skin over the upper portion of the deltoideus muscle.

Three major branches of the brachial plexus are distributed to the arm. The **lateral brachial cutaneous,** a branch of the axillary nerve, supplies skin over the lower half of the deltoideus and the long head of the triceps. The **posterior brachial cutaneous,** from the radial nerve, innervates skin on the posterior aspect of the arm below the deltoideus, and the **medial brachial cutaneous,** from the medial cord, is distributed to the posteromedial aspect of the lower third of the arm. The arm receives additional cutaneous innervation from the lateral cutaneous branch of the second thoracic nerve, the **intercostobrachial,** supplying the posteromedial surfaces of the arm from the axilla to the olecranon process.

Cutaneous branches to the forearm from the brachial plexus include the **lateral antebrachial cutaneous,** a continuation of the musculocutaneous nerve, giving anterior and posterior branches to the radial half of the forearm; the **posterior antebrachial cutaneous,** from the radial nerve, supplying an upper branch to the distal half of the anterolateral aspect of the arm and a lower branch to the middorsum of the forearm; and the **medial antebrachial cutaneous,** a branch of the medial cord, giving anterior and posterior branches to the medial aspect of the forearm.

The ulnar, median, and radial nerves all contribute to the cutaneous innervation of the hand. The cutaneous branches of the **ulnar nerve** supply both surfaces of the hand and fingers medial to a line passing through the center of the ring finger. The **median nerve** gives cutaneous branches to the remainder of the palmar surface of the hand and fingers and to the dorsal surface of the fingers to

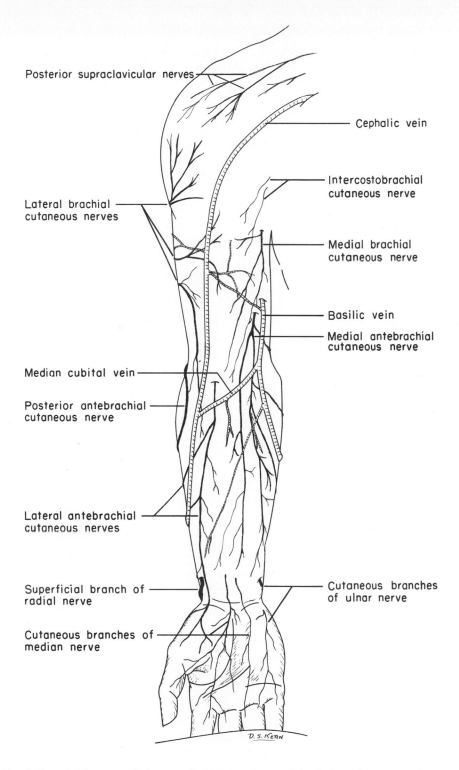

Posterior supraclavicular nerves

Cephalic vein

Intercostobrachial cutaneous nerve

Lateral brachial cutaneous nerves

Medial brachial cutaneous nerve

Basilic vein

Medial antebrachial cutaneous nerve

Median cubital vein

Posterior antebrachial cutaneous nerve

Lateral antebrachial cutaneous nerves

Superficial branch of radial nerve

Cutaneous branches of ulnar nerve

Cutaneous branches of median nerve

D. S. KERN

Fig. 6. Superficial venous drainage and cutaneous innervation of the volar aspect of the superior extremity.

the middle phalanx. Cutaneous branches from the **radial nerve** supply the remainder of the dorsal surface of the hand and fingers, as well as a small area over the lateral aspect of the thenar eminence.

Venous Drainage (Fig. 6)

The superficial venous drainage of the arm, forearm, and hand begins as **palmar** and **dorsal digital veins** on the respective surfaces of the digits. These veins join to form the **dorsal metacarpal veins,** which anastomose to form the **dorsal venous arch** lying proximal to the heads of the metacarpal bones.

The **cephalic vein** is the lateral continuation of the dorsal venous arch. It ascends along the radial side of the forearm receiving tributaries from the posterior surface. Above the elbow it continues in the lateral bicipital groove, then follows the interval between the deltoideus and the pectoralis major muscles into the deltopectoral triangle. It terminates by perforating the clavipectoral fascia and drains into either the axillary or subclavian vein.

The **basilic vein** is the medial continuation of the dorsal venous arch. It ascends on the ulnar side of the forearm, receiving tributaries from both the anterior and posterior surfaces. In the arm it ascends a short distance in the medial bicipital groove, then penetrates the brachial fascia and unites with the brachial vein to form the axillary vein.

In the antecubital fossa the **median cubital vein** passes obliquely across the fossa connecting the cephalic and basilic veins. It may conduct the bulk of the blood from the cephalic to the basilic vein. The median cubital is the vein most commonly used for venepuncture.

The deep venous drainage of the upper extremity originates from **deep venous arcades** of the hand which parallel the arterial arches. The radial, ulnar, and brachial arteries have **venae comitantes,** which receive blood from the areas supplied by these vessels. Deep and superficial veins communicate extensively with each other. The veins accompanying the radial and ulnar arteries join to form the venae comitantes of the brachial artery, which unite with the basilic vein to form the axillary vein.

Lymphatic Drainage

The **superficial lymphatics** of the upper extremity begin as a meshwork around the fingers as the **digital lymphatic plexus,** which is drained by vessels following the digital arteries, and turn onto the dorsum of the hand where they form the **dorsal plexus.** The radial half of this plexus drains along the radial side, and the ulnar half along the ulnar side, of the forearm. Lymphatics draining the palm pass to the sides of the hand to join either ulnar or radial channels, or may drain along channels which ascend in the midline of the volar aspect of the forearm. One or two **cubital lymph nodes,** located just above the medial epicondyle, are interposed in the ulnar channels. Their efferent vessels accompany the basilic vein to the **axillary lymph nodes.** The radial and posterior channels of the forearm follow the cephalic vein to terminate in the **apical node** of the axilla. There may be a **deltopectoral node** interposed before they reach the axilla.

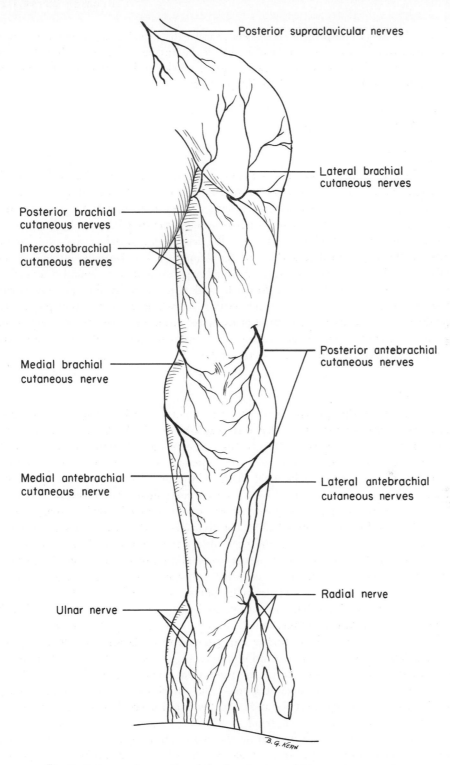

Posterior supraclavicular nerves

Lateral brachial cutaneous nerves

Posterior brachial cutaneous nerves

Intercostobrachial cutaneous nerves

Medial brachial cutaneous nerve

Posterior antebrachial cutaneous nerves

Medial antebrachial cutaneous nerve

Lateral antebrachial cutaneous nerves

Ulnar nerve

Radial nerve

B. G. KERN

Fig. 7. Cutaneous innervation of the dorsal aspect of the superior extremity.

The **deep lymphatic channels** parallel the arteries in the hand and fore-arm and drain into five or six small nodes in the antecubital fossa. Efferent vessels accompany the brachial veins as two or three trunks and ascend to drain into the **lateral and central groups of axillary nodes.**

ARM

Axilla

The axilla is a potential space, pyramidal in shape, consisting of four walls, an apex, and a base. The **anterior wall** is formed by the pectoralis major and minor muscles and the clavipectoral fascia; the **posterior wall** by the subscapularis, teres major, and the latissimus dorsi muscles; the **medial wall** by the serratus anterior muscle, the first five ribs, and the intercostal muscles; and the **lateral wall** by the upper medial surface of the humerus. The **base** is formed by the axillary fascia; the truncated **apex,** directed superomedially, is bounded anteriorly by the clavicle, medially by the first rib, and posteriorly by the superior border of the scapula. Through the apex the axillary vessels and the brachial plexus, ensheathed in the **cervicoaxillary fascia,** pass from the neck to the upper extremity. The axilla contains the axillary artery and vein, most of the brachial plexus, axillary lymph nodes, fat, and connective tissue.

Brachial Plexus (Fig. 8)

The **brachial plexus** is a network of nerves derived from the **anterior primary rami of the fifth through eighth cervical** (C_5 through C_8) and **first thoracic** (T_1) **nerves.** It may also receive contributions from the fourth cervical (C_4) and second thoracic (T_2) nerves. The brachial plexus supplies muscular, sensory, and sympathetic fibers to the upper extremity. The plexiform arrangement permits intermingling of nerve components from several segments of the spinal cord to form composite nerves which supply individual structures. It is composed of five roots, three trunks, six divisions, three cords, and sixteen named branches. It is located partly in the neck, under the clavicle, and in the axilla.

The **roots** of the brachial plexus are continuations of the anterior primary rami of its component spinal nerves which emerge between the scalenus anterior and medius muscles in line with similar, but more cranially placed, roots constituting the cervical plexus. The roots of C_5 and C_6 unite to form the **upper trunk,** C_7 becomes the **middle trunk,** and C_8 and T_1 constitute the **lower trunk.** Each trunk divides distally into **anterior** and **posterior divisions,** which anastomose to form lateral, medial, and posterior cords, so named for their relation to the second part of the axillary artery. The **posterior cord** is formed by the union of the posterior divisions of all three trunks; the anterior divisions of the upper and middle trunks form the **lateral cord;** and the **medial cord** is the continuation of the anterior division of the lower trunk.

Two branches are derived from the roots: the dorsal scapular and the long thoracic. The **dorsal scapular** (C_5) pierces the scalenus medius to course parallel to the/vertebral border of the scapula and deep to the levator scapulae and the

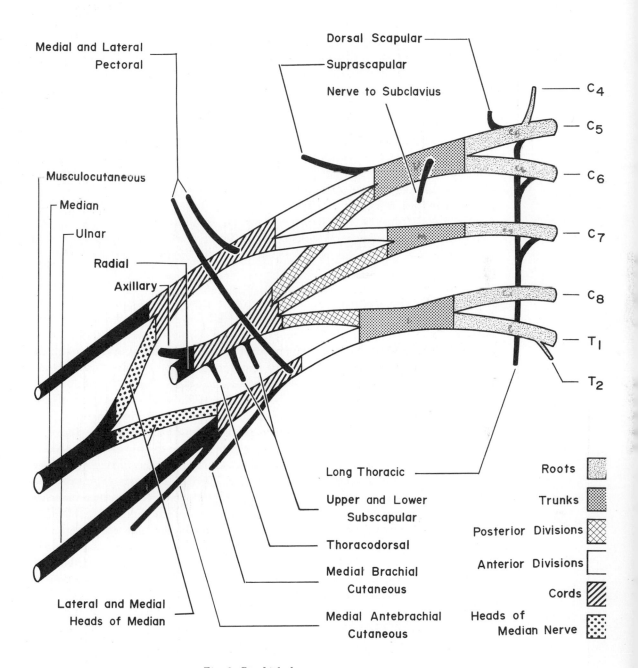

Medial and Lateral Pectoral

Dorsal Scapular

Suprascapular

Nerve to Subclavius

Musculocutaneous

Median

Ulnar

Radial

Axillary

C_4

C_5

C_6

C_7

C_8

T_1

T_2

Long Thoracic

Upper and Lower Subscapular

Thoracodorsal

Medial Brachial Cutaneous

Medial Antebrachial Cutaneous

Lateral and Medial Heads of Median

Roots

Trunks

Posterior Divisions

Anterior Divisions

Cords

Heads of Median Nerve

Fig. 8. Brachial plexus.

rhomboidei to supply these muscles. The **long thoracic** (C_5, C_6, and C_7) descends posterior to the roots of the plexus to ramify on and supply the serratus anterior muscle.

Two nerves are also derived from the upper trunk. The **nerve to the subclavius** (C_5 and C_6) descends anterior to the plexus and posterior to the clavicle to supply the subclavius muscle. The **suprascapular** (C_5 and C_6) crosses the posterior triangle of the neck to the lesser scapular notch, where it divides into **supraspinatus** and **infraspinatus branches** to supply muscles in their respective scapular fossae.

Two nerves originate from the lateral cords. The **lateral pectoral** (C_5, C_6, and C_7) pierces the clavipectoral fascia to supply the pectoralis major; the **musculocutaneous** (C_5, C_6, and C_7) enters the coracobrachialis, supplying it and the two other flexor muscles in the arm, then continues into the skin on the lateral side of the forearm as the **lateral antebrachial cutaneous nerve.** The **lateral head of the median nerve** is also derived from the lateral cord. It joins with the **medial head** from the medial cord to form the **median nerve** (C_6, C_7, C_8, and T_1), which supplies flexor muscles in the forearm, most of the short muscles of the thumb, and skin of the lateral two-thirds of the palm of the hand and the fingers.

In addition to the medial head of the median nerve, the medial cord gives rise to the **medial pectoral** (C_8 and T_1), which passes through and supplies the pectoralis minor as well as the overlying pectoralis major; the **medial brachial cutaneous** (C_8 and T_1), which supplies skin over the medial and posterior aspect of the distal third of the arm; the **medial antebrachial cutaneous** (C_8 and T_1), which innervates skin of the medial and posterior aspect of the forearm; and the **ulnar** (C_8 and T_1), which is distributed to some of the flexors in the forearm, the intrinsic muscles of the hand, the skin of the medial side of the hand, all the skin of the little finger, and the skin of the medial half of the ring finger.

The posterior cord gives origin to the **upper subscapular** (C_5 and C_6), which passes posteriorly to enter the subscapularis muscle; the **lower subscapular** (C_5 and C_6), which descends to supply the subscapularis to terminate in the teres major; and the **thoracodorsal** (C_5, C_6, and C_7), which descends anterior to the subscapularis and teres major to terminate in the latissimus dorsi. Other branches include the **axillary** (C_5 and C_6), which passes posteriorly through the quadrangular space and innervates the deltoideus and teres minor, and the **radial** (C_5, C_6, C_7, C_8, and T_1), which descends posterior to the axillary artery to innervate the extensors of the arm and forearm and the skin on the posterior aspect of the arm, forearm, lateral two-thirds of the dorsum of the hand, and the dorsum of the fingers over the proximal and intermediate phalanges.

Axillary Artery (Fig. 9)

The **axillary artery,** a continuation of the **subclavian,** extends from the lateral border of the first rib to the lower border of the teres major, where it becomes the **brachial artery.** It is subdivided, for descriptive purposes, into **three parts** by the overlying pectoralis minor muscle. The first portion lies proximal, the second deep, and the third distal to this muscle.

Six branches originate from the axillary artery, one branch from the first segment, two from the second, and three from the third. The single branch from the **first part,** the **superior thoracic** (highest thoracic), is distributed to the first intercostal space.

The branches from the **second portion** are the thoracoacromial trunk and the lateral thoracic. The **thoracoacromial artery** pierces the clavipectoral fascia to divide into four branches: The **acromial branch** passes laterally over the coracoid process, gives twigs to the deep surface of the deltoideus, and finally rami-

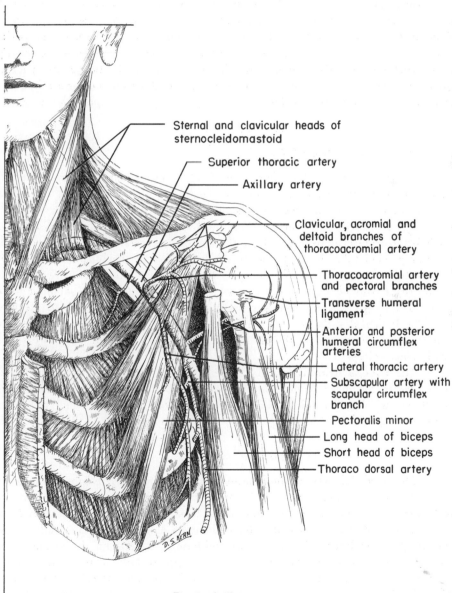

Fig. 9. Axillary artery.

fies on the acromial process; the **deltoid branch** courses in the deltopectoral triangle to supply the deltoideus and pectoralis major; the **pectoral branches** pass between and supply both pectoral muscles and, in the female, distribute deep branches to the mammary gland; and the **clavicular branch** supplies the sternoclavicular joint and the subclavius muscle. The **lateral thoracic artery** arises near and descends along the lower border of the pectoralis minor, supplying pectoral muscles and the serratus anterior. In the female it sends deep branches to the mammary gland.

Branches from the **third part** of the axillary artery include the smaller **anterior** and the larger **posterior humeral circumflex arteries,** which encircle the humerus to supply the deltoideus and anastomose with the ascending branch of the profundus brachii artery. The largest branch of the axillary, the **subscapular artery,** arises opposite the lower border of the subscapularis muscle. It divides into the **scapular circumflex artery,** which passes through the triangular space to supply muscles on the dorsum of the scapula, and the **thoracodorsal branch,** which continues along the axillary border of the scapula to supply the latissimus dorsi.

Muscles of the Arm (Table IV)

The four muscles of the arm, three flexors and one extensor, are located in flexor (anterior) and extensor (posterior) compartments delineated by the lateral and medial intermuscular septa. In the flexor compartment the fusiform **biceps brachii** originates by two heads, a short head (in common with the medially situated **coracobrachialis muscle**) from the coracoid process, and a long head from the supraglenoid tubercle of the scapula. The tendon of the long head, lying in the intertubercular groove, passes deep to the transverse humeral ligament, where it acquires a synovial sheath as it traverses the joint cavity of the shoulder to its origin. The biceps is a powerful supinator as well as the main flexor of the forearm. The **brachialis,** the pure flexor of the forearm, covers the lower half of the humerus and the capsule of the elbow joint, forming a bed for the more superficially placed biceps.

The **triceps brachii** fills the posterior compartment. Its long and lateral heads obscure the more deeply placed medial head. Both biceps and triceps cross the elbow and shoulder joints, and hence, act upon both. The small triangular **anconeus muscle** is located superficially at the lateral aspect of the elbow joint.

Arteries and Nerves in the Arm (Fig. 10)

The **brachial artery,** the continuation of the axillary, begins at the lower border of the teres major, passes obliquely from a medial to a midline position in the arm, and terminates in the antecubital fossa by dividing into the radial and ulnar arteries. It may be palpated throughout its entire course. Laterally it lies against the coracobrachialis and biceps; posteriorly it rests on the medial intermuscular septum and medial head of the triceps; distally it is located on the brachialis muscle medial to the tendon of the biceps and lateral to the median nerve. Four named branches arise from this vessel. The largest, the **profunda**

TABLE IV. MUSCLES OF THE ARM				
Muscle	*Origin*	*Insertion*	*Action*	*Nerve*
Biceps brachii	Long head, supraglenoid tubercle; short head, tip of coracoid process	Tuberosity of radius	Flexes forearm and arm; supinates hand	Musculocutaneous
Coracobrachialis	Tip of coracoid process	Middle third of medial surface of humerus	Flexes and adducts arm	Musculocutaneous
Brachialis	Distal two-thirds of anterior surface of humerus	Coronoid process and tuberosity of ulna	Flexes forearm	Musculocutaneous and small branch of radial
Triceps brachii	Long head, infraglenoid tubercle; lateral head, posterior surface and lateral border of humerus; medial head, posterior surface of distal half of humerus	Posterior aspect of olecranon process of ulna	Extends forearm; long head aids in extension and adduction of arm	Radial
Anconeus	Lateral epicondyle of humerus	Lateral aspect of olecranon and upper fourth of posterior surface of ulna	Acts as weak extensor of forearm	Radial

brachii (deep brachial) accompanies the radial nerve in the radiospiral groove of the humerus. Posteriorly this vessel divides into an ascending branch which courses proximally between the lateral and long heads of the triceps, and a descending branch which runs with the medial head of the triceps to the posterior aspect of the elbow. The small **nutrient artery** of the humerus arises about the middle of the arm to enter the nutrient canal on the anteromedial aspect of the bone. The **superior ulnar collateral branch** begins about the middle of the arm, pierces the medial intermuscular septum, accompanies the ulnar nerve, and sends branches to either side of the medial epicondyle. The **inferior ulnar collateral artery** arises about an inch proximal to the medial epicondyle. It divides into a posterior branch which pierces the intermuscular septum to descend deep to the triceps, and an anterior branch which passes inferiorly between the biceps and the brachialis muscles.

The **median nerve** arises from the brachial plexus lateral to the axillary

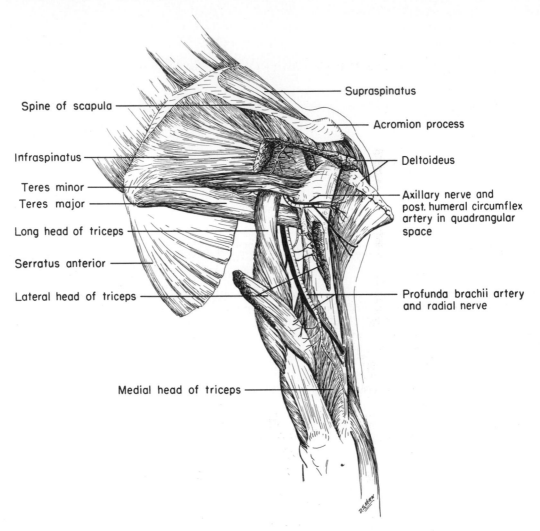

Spine of scapula

Infraspinatus

Teres minor

Teres major

Long head of triceps

Serratus anterior

Lateral head of triceps

Medial head of triceps

Supraspinatus

Acromion process

Deltoideus

Axillary nerve and post. humeral circumflex artery in quadrangular space

Profunda brachii artery and radial nerve

Fig. 10. Innervation and arterial supply to the muscles on the posterior aspect of the arm.

artery, descends crossing the brachial artery in the midarm, and proceeds into the cubital fossa, where it then lies medial to the artery. The **ulnar nerve,** the terminal branch of the medial cord, courses distally medial to the brachial artery. In the midarm it pierces the medial intermuscular septum, and at the elbow passes between the olecranon process and the medial epicondyle, where it is superficial and easily palpable. Impingement upon the nerve at this point gives rise to the sensation interpreted as arising from the "crazy bone" of the elbow. The median and ulnar nerves have no branches in the arm.

The **musculocutaneous nerve,** from the lateral cord, courses lateral to the axillary artery, pierces the coracobrachialis muscle, and continues distally between the biceps and the brachialis to innervate all three muscles. Crossing to the lateral side of the arm between the biceps and the brachialis, it pierces the deep fascia above the biceps tendon to continue distally as the **lateral antebrachial cutaneous nerve.**

The **axillary** (circumflex) **nerve,** arising from the posterior cord at the lower border of the subscapularis muscle, passes posteriorly through the quadrangular space with the posterior humeral circumflex artery to supply the teres minor and ramify on the deep surface of the deltoideus muscle. It gives a branch, the **lateral brachial cutaneous,** which supplies skin over the deltoideus.

The **radial nerve,** the largest branch of the brachial plexus and the continuation of the posterior cord, initially lies posterior to the axillary artery. It passes distally between the teres major and the long head of the triceps, spirals around the posterior aspect of the humerus in the radiospiral groove between the lateral and medial heads of the triceps, and is accompanied in this part of its course by the profunda brachii artery. It pierces the lateral intermuscular septum and follows the interval between the brachialis and brachioradialis muscles into the antecubital fossa. Along its course it supplies the triceps and, just proximal to the elbow, sends branches to the brachialis, brachioradialis, extensor carpi radialis longus, and anconeus muscles.

ANTECUBITAL FOSSA (FIG. 11)

The **antecubital fossa** is a triangular depression at the anterior aspect of the elbow joint. Its base is formed by a line passing through the epicondyles of the humerus. Its apex is directed distally, with the brachioradialis muscle forming the lateral side and the pronator teres muscle the medial side. The floor of the fossa is formed by the brachialis and the supinator muscles. The fossa is covered by deep and superficial fasciae and skin. The **median cubital vein** (utilized in drawing blood and for intravenous injection) crosses the fossa obliquely, superficial to the deep fascia. Descending through the middle of the fossa, the tendon of the biceps brachii inserts into the radial tuberosity and sends a fibrous expansion, the **bicipital aponeurosis,** as a secondary insertion into the deep fascia of the flexor muscles. The brachial artery passes through the fossa medial to the biceps tendon to bifurcate into the radial and ulnar arteries. Entering the fossa between the brachioradialis and brachialis muscles, the median nerve descends medial to the brachial artery and the radial nerve.

FOREARM

Muscles (Table V)

The flexor muscles of the forearm are subdivided into superficial and deep groups. The superficial group, the **palmaris longus, pronator teres, flexor carpi radialis,** and **flexor carpi ulnaris,** form the muscle mass at the medial side of the proximal forearm. The superficial group and the **flexor digitorum superficialis** originate, in part, from a common tendon from the medial epicondyle of the humerus. In the deep group, the **flexor pollicis longus** and **flexor digitorum profundus** pass superficial to the more distally placed **pronator quadratus.** With the exception of the flexor carpi ulnaris and the ulnar half of the flexor

TABLE V. MUSCLES OF THE FOREARM

Muscle	Origin	Insertion	Action	Nerve
Palmaris longus	Medial epicondyle of humerus	Flexor retinaculum and palmar aponeurosis	Flexes hand	Median
Pronator teres	Humeral head, medial epicondyle; ulnar head, coronoid process of ulna	Middle of lateral surface of radius	Pronates hand	Median
Flexor carpi radialis	Medial epicondyle of humerus	Bases of second and third metacarpals	Flexes hand and elbow; slightly pronates and abducts hand	Median
Flexor carpi ulnaris	Humeral head, medial epicondyle; ulnar head, medial border of olecranon process and posterior border of ulna	Pisiform, hook of hamate, and base of fifth metacarpal	Flexes and adducts hand	Ulnar
Flexor digitorum superficialis	Humeral head, medial epicondyle; ulnar head, coronoid process; radial head, anterior border of radius	Palmar surface of middle phalanges of fingers	Flexes middle phalanx; continued action flexes proximal phalanx and hand; aids in flexion of elbow	Median
Flexor digitorum profundus	Medial and anterior surface of ulna and adjacent interosseus membrane	Base of distal phalanges of fingers	Flexes terminal phalanx; continued action flexes proximal phalanges and hand	Ulnar and median
Flexor pollicis longus	Anterior surface of radius, adjacent interosseus membrane, and coronoid process of ulna	Base of distal phalanx of thumb	Flexes thumb	Median
Pronator quadratus	Anterior surface of distal fourth of ulna	Anterior surface of distal fourth of radius	Pronates hand	Median
Brachioradialis	Lateral supracondylar ridge of humerus and lateral intermuscular septum	Lateral side of base of styloid process of radius	Flexes forearm	Radial

continued

TABLE V.   MUSCLES OF THE FOREARM *continued*

Muscle	*Origin*	*Insertion*	*Action*	*Nerve*
Extensor carpi radialis longus	Lateral supracondylar ridge of humerus	Posterior surface of base of second metacarpal	Extends and abducts hand	Radial
Extensor carpi radialis brevis	Lateral epicondyle of humerus	Posterior surface of base of third metacarpal	Extends and abducts hand	Radial
Extensor digitorum communis	Lateral epicondyle of humerus	Forms extensor expansion on fingers	Extends fingers and hand	Radial
Extensor carpi ulnaris	Lateral epicondyle and posterior border of ulna	Base of fifth metacarpal	Extends and adducts hand	Radial
Extensor digiti minimi	From extensor digitorum communis and interosseus membrane	Extensor expansion on proximal phalanx of fifth digit	Extends fifth digit	Radial
Supinator	Lateral epicondyle of humerus, ligaments of elbow joint, and supinator crest and fossa of ulna	Lateral surface of upper third of radius	Supinates hand	Radial
Abductor pollicis longus	Posterior surface of ulna and middle third of posterior surface of radius	Base of first metacarpal	Abducts thumb and hand	Radial
Extensor pollicis longus	Middle third of posterior surface of ulna and adjacent interosseus membrane	Base of distal phalanx of thumb	Extends distal phalanx and abducts hand	Radial
Extensor pollicis brevis	Posterior surface of middle third of radius	Base of proximal phalanx of thumb	Extends and abducts hand	Radial
Extensor indicis	Posterior surface of ulna	Extensor expansion on index finger	Extends index finger	Radial

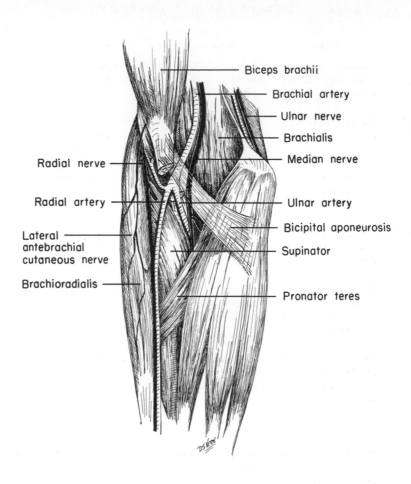

Fig. 11. Antecubital fossa.

digitorum profundus, which are supplied by the **ulnar nerve,** all the flexors are supplied by the **median nerve.** The flexors are separated from the extensor muscles by the **interosseous membrane** passing between the radius and ulna.

The extensor muscles are also divided into groups. The superficial group, consisting of the **brachioradialis, extensor carpi radialis longus** and **brevis, extensor digitorum communis, extensor digiti minimi,** and the **extensor carpi ulnaris,** forms the muscle mass at the lateral aspect of the proximal forearm. Two of these muscles, the brachioradialis and the extensor carpi radialis longus, extend above the elbow joint, taking origin from the lateral supracondylar ridge of the humerus; the remainder arise, in part, by a common tendon attached to the lateral epicondyle of the humerus. The **brachioradialis,** while grouped with the extensors and innervated by the radial nerve, is functionally a flexor of the forearm. The deep extensor group distal to the **supinator** (the **abductor pollicis longus,** the **extensor pollicis brevis** and **longus,** and the **extensor indicis**) lie parallel to each other in the above order extending obliquely across the interosseous space. All the extensors are supplied by the deep branch (posterior interosseous) of the radial nerve.

Arteries and Nerves (Fig. 12)

One of the terminal branches of the brachial artery, the **radial artery,** courses distally in the forearm between the brachioradialis and the pronator teres, passes to the anterior aspect of the radius, and becomes superficial at the wrist where the pulse is usually taken. It gives a **radial recurrent branch** in the cubital fossa which courses proximally anterior to the lateral epicondyle, to anastomose with the profunda brachii artery. Muscular branches of the radial artery are distributed to the superficial extensor muscles. At the wrist it gives **palmar** and **dorsal carpal branches** which aid in the formation of the **carpal arches** which supply the wrist and carpal joints before passing into the hand.

The **ulnar artery,** larger of the two terminal branches of the brachial, passes deep to the pronator teres and the superficial flexors to course on the surface of the flexor digitorum profundus, where it is overlapped distally by the flexor carpi ulnaris. At the wrist it passes into the hand deep to the volar carpal ligament after giving **palmar** and **dorsal carpal** branches to the **carpal arches.** At the origin of the ulnar artery, **anterior** and **posterior ulnar recurrent branches** arise that course proximally, pass respectively anterior and posterior to the medial epicondyle, and anastomose with superior and inferior ulnar collateral branches of the brachial artery. The largest ulnar branch, the **common interosseous,** arises about an inch distal to the bifurcation of the brachial. A **recurrent branch** of the common interosseous artery turns proximally, deep to the supinator, to join the anastomosis around the elbow joint. The common interosseous artery terminates by dividing into the **anterior** and **posterior interosseous branches,** which pass to their respective sides of the interosseous membrane to supply the deep flexor and deep extensor muscles. The **anterior interosseous artery,** extending further distally than the posterior branch, pierces the interosseous membrane in the distal third of the forearm, supplies the muscles on the dorsum of the forearm, and anastomoses with the carpel arches.

The **median nerve** leaves the antecubital fossa by passing between the heads of the pronator teres to gain a position deep to the flexor digitorum superficialis, where it continues distally between this muscle and the flexor digitorum profundus. In the forearm it supplies the pronator teres, the pronator quadratus, and all the flexors except the flexor carpi ulnaris and the ulnar half of the flexor digitorum profundus, which are innervated by the ulnar nerve. At the wrist the median nerve becomes superficial to lie at the ulnar side of the tendon of the palmaris longus muscle, then passes deep to the flexor retinaculum to enter the hand.

From its position between the olecranon process and the medial epicondyle, the **ulnar nerve** enters the forearm by passing between the heads of the flexor carpi ulnaris. It continues distally in the forearm deep to this muscle, lying on the flexor digitorum profundus. In the distal half of the forearm it parallels the course of the ulnar artery to pass to the lateral side of the tendon of the flexor carpi

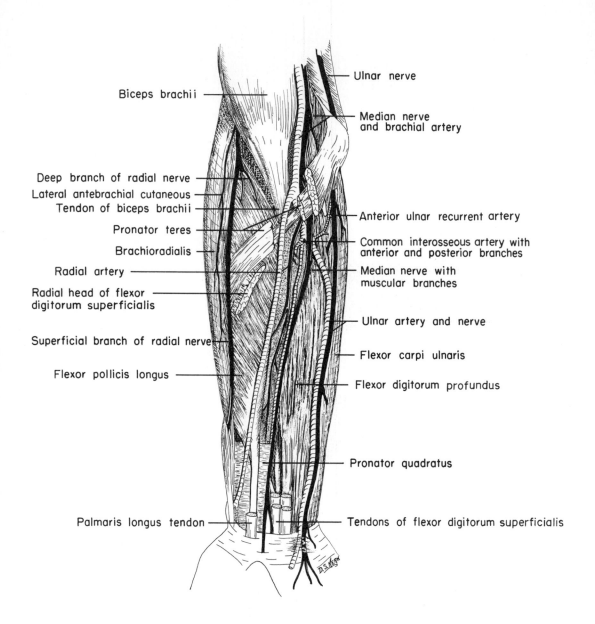

Biceps brachii

Deep branch of radial nerve
Lateral antebrachial cutaneous
Tendon of biceps brachii
Pronator teres
Brachioradialis
Radial artery
Radial head of flexor
digitorum superficialis

Superficial branch of radial nerve

Flexor pollicis longus

Palmaris longus tendon

Ulnar nerve
Median nerve
and brachial artery

Anterior ulnar recurrent artery
Common interosseous artery with
anterior and posterior branches
Median nerve with
muscular branches

Ulnar artery and nerve

Flexor carpi ulnaris

Flexor digitorum profundus

Pronator quadratus

Tendons of flexor digitorum superficialis

Fig. 12. Innervation and arterial supply to the volar aspect of the forearm.

ulnaris and enters the hand deep to the volar carpal ligament. In the forearm it supplies the flexor carpi ulnaris and the ulnar half of the flexor digitorum profundus.

After entering the antecubital fossa, the **radial nerve** divides into superficial and deep branches. The **superficial branch** passes distally, deep to the brachioradialis, to the dorsum of the wrist, where it divides into medial and lateral branches. Its distribution is the sole cutaneous innervation to the dorsum of the hand. The **deep branch** of the radial (posterior interosseous) nerve pierces the supinator muscle to be distributed to all the extensors muscles within the forearm.

HAND

Muscles (Table VI)

The intrinsic muscles of the hand are divided into three groups: the thenar muscles, the hypothenar muscles, and the interossei and lumbricales.

The **thenar eminence** (ball of the thumb) is formed by the superficial laterally placed **abductor pollicis brevis,** the intermediate **opponens pollicis,** and the more deeply placed **flexor pollicis brevis.** The latter is divided into a deep and superficial portion by the tendon of the flexor pollicis longus. The **hypothenar eminence** (heel of the hand) is composed of the medially situated **abductor digiti minimi,** the more lateral **flexor digiti minimi brevis** lying superficial to and usually blending with the **opponens digiti minimi.**

The seven interossei are disposed in two layers and are composed of three palmar and four dorsal muscles. These muscles are located in the spaces between the metacarpal bones. The unipennate **palmar interossei** arise from single metacarpals, and the bipennate **dorsal interossei** from two adjacent metacarpals. All the interossei insert into bases of proximal phalanges and act as abductors or adductors of the digits. Abduction and adduction of the digits is relative to a line passing through the central axis of the middle finger, and the insertions of the interossei make abduction from this plane a function of the dorsal interossei and adduction a function of the palmar interossei. The **adductor pollicis** in the same plane as the palmar interossei, a relatively extensive muscle arising by two heads, is sometimes referred to as the fourth palmar interosseous.

The four **lumbricales** consist of muscular slips which originate from the four tendons of the flexor digitorum profundus. They course to the radial side of the metacarpophalangeal joint to insert into the extensor expansion. Their action is to flex the metacarpophalangeal and extend the interphalangeal joints, thus placing the fingers at right angles to the palm of the hand.

Synovial Tendon Sheaths (Fig. 13)

At the wrist and in the hand, lubricating synovial sheaths surround tendons as the latter extend from the forearm to the hand. The **ulnar bursa** is a large synovial sac invaginated on the radial side by tendons of the flexor digitorum profundus and superficialis muscles. It extends from approximately an inch above the flexor retinaculum to the middle of the palm, except around the tendons of the

TABLE VI. MUSCLES OF THE HAND

Muscle	Origin	Insertion	Action	Nerve
Palmaris brevis	Medial aspect of flexor retinaculum	Skin of palm	Wrinkles skin of palm	Ulnar
Abductor pollicis brevis	Flexor retinaculum, scaphoid, and trapezium	Lateral side of base of proximal phalanx of thumb	Abducts thumb; assists in flexion of proximal phalanx	Median
Flexor pollicis brevis	Flexor retinaculum and trapezium	Base of proximal phalanx of thumb with sesamoid interposed	Flexes thumb; assists in apposition	Median
Opponens pollicis	Flexor retinaculum and trapezium	Entire length of lateral border of first metacarpal	Draws first metacarpal toward center of palm	Median
Abductor digiti minimi	Pisiform and tendon of flexor carpi ulnaris	Medial side of base of proximal phalanx of fifth digit	Abducts fifth digit	Ulnar
Flexor digiti minimi brevis	Flexor retinaculum and hook of hamate	Medial side of base of proximal phalanx of fifth digit	Flexes proximal phalanx of fifth digit	Ulnar
Opponens digiti minimi	Flexor retinaculum and hook of hamate	Medial border of fifth metacarpal	Draws fifth metacarpal forward in cupping of hand	Ulnar
Adductor pollicis	Oblique head from capitate and bases of second and third metacarpals; transverse head from anterior surface of third metacarpal	Medial side of base of proximal phalanx of thumb	Adducts thumb; assists in apposition	Ulnar
Lumbricales (4)	Tendons of flexor digitorum profundus	Extensor expansion distal to metacarpophalangeal joint	Flex metacarpophalangeal joint; extend interphalangeal joints	Two lateral muscles by median; two medial by ulnar
Dorsal interossei (4)	By two heads from adjacent sides of metacarpal bones	Lateral sides of bases of proximal phalanges of index and middle fingers; medial sides of bases of middle and ring fingers	Abduct index, middle, and ring fingers; aid in extension of interphalangeal and flexion of metacarpophalangeal joints	Ulnar
Palmar interossei (3)	Medial side of second metacarpal; lateral sides of fourth and fifth metacarpals	Base of proximal phalanx in line with its origin	Adduct index, ring, and little fingers; aid in extension of interphalangeal and flexion of metacarpophalangeal joints	Ulnar

fifth finger, where it continues to their insertions. **Digital synovial sheaths,** separate from the ulnar bursa, invest the digital parts of the deep and superficial flexor tendons to the second, third, and fourth fingers. These sheaths extend from the heads of the metacarpals to the insertion of the long flexor tendons.

The **radial bursa** surrounds the flexor pollicis longus tendon, extending from an inch proximal to the flexor retinaculum to the insertion of this tendon. A separate synovial sheath surrounds the tendon of the flexor carpi radialis from a point proximal to the flexor retinaculum to its insertion into the base of the second metacarpal bone.

Synovial sheaths surround **extensor tendons** within six osseofibrous

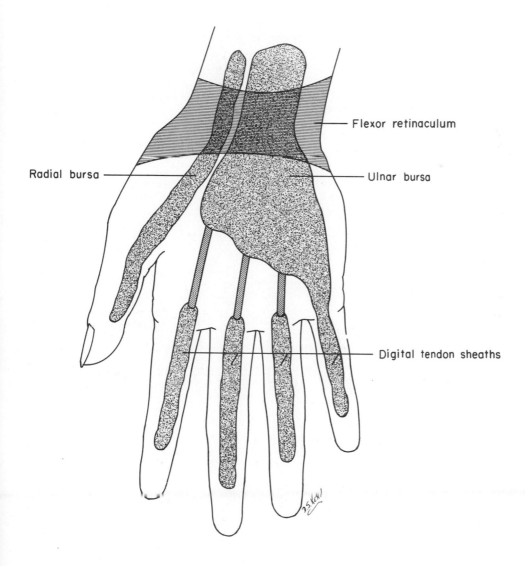

Fig. 13. Radial and ulnar bursae.

compartments or tunnels located deep to the extensor retinaculum. The sheaths, enclosing the tendons of the extensor carpi radialis longus and brevis and the extensor carpi ulnaris, extend from the proximal border of the extensor retinaculum to the insertions of these tendons. Sheaths of the digital extensors, including the extensors of the thumb and the abductor pollicis longus, terminate at about the middle third of the metacarpal bones.

Arteries and Nerves (Fig. 14)

After passing deep to the volar carpal ligament, the **ulnar artery** enters the hand by passing to the radial side of the pisiform bone to give muscular branches to the hand. It terminates by dividing into a **deep branch** which joins

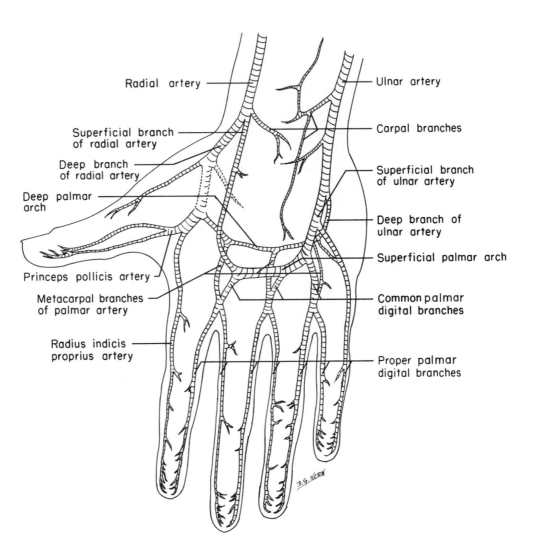

Fig. 14. Arterial supply of the hand.

with a similar branch of the radial artery to form the **deep palmar arch,** and a **superficial branch** joining with a similar branch of the radial forming the **superficial palmar arch.** The latter, predominately from the ulnar artery, lies transversely in the palm immediately under the skin and palmar aponeurosis in line with the fully extending thumb. It gives a **proper digital branch** to the medial side of the little finger and three **common palmar digital branches,** which subsequently divide into **proper digital branches** to supply contiguous sides of the four fingers.

Passing from the anterior surface of the radius medial to the styloid process, the **radial artery** enters the hand deep to the tendons of the abductor pollicis longus and the extensor pollicis longus and brevis muscles. It pierces the first dorsal interosseous to lie between this muscle and the adductor pollicis. Branches of the radial artery include the **superficial palmar,** which with a similar branch of the ulnar, completes the **superficial palmar arch.** The **princeps pollicis** and the **radius indicis proprius branches** both arise as the radial artery pierces the first dorsal interosseous muscle. They supply, respectively, both sides of the thumb and the radial side of the index finger. The **deep branch** of the radial artery forms most of the **deep palmar arch,** which lies on the carpal bones a thumb's breadth proximal to the superficial arch. Branches of the deep arch are the **palmar metacarpal vessels,** which join the **common palmar digital arteries** of the superficial arch to supply the fingers.

The **median nerve,** on entering the hand deep to the flexor retinaculum, gives a **lateral** (muscular) **branch** to the muscles of the thenar eminence, namely, the opponens pollicis and the abductor pollicis brevis, as well as the two lateral lumbricales. Terminally the nerve supplies cutaneous innervation to the central area of the palm and palmar surface of the thumb, index, middle, and lateral half of the ring fingers, and all of the skin on the distal phalanges of these digits.

At the wrist the **ulnar nerve** divides into a **superficial branch** which supplies the palmaris brevis and the cutaneous innervation to both surfaces of the hand medial to a line passing through the center of the ring finger, and a **deep branch** which supplies all the intrinsic muscles of the hand except those supplied, as listed above, by the median nerve.

The **radial nerve** supplies no muscles in the hand. Its terminal distribution is the cutaneous innervation to a small area on the palmar surface of the thenar eminence and the dorsum of the hand lateral to a line passing through the center of the ring finger, except for skin over the distal phalanges.

FASCIAE (FIG. 15)

The **investing layer** of deep fascia completely ensheathes the upper extremity. In the arm it sends distinct **lateral** and **medial intermuscular septa** to attach to the humerus which separate the musculature of the arm into extensor and flexor compartments. At the wrist this layer of deep fascia condenses and thickens to form a distinct band surrounding the wrist as the flexor and extensor retinacula. The **extensor retinaculum** has deep attachments to the lateral side of the dorsum of the radius, the pisiform and triquetrum bones, and the styloid process of the ulna. It sends septa to attach to ridges on the dorsum of the radius and forms **six osseofibrous compartments** for the extensor tendons passing from the forearm to the hand. The six compartments transmit tendons, from the radial to the ulnar side respectively, as follows: The tendons of the abductor pollicis longus and extensor pollicis brevis traverse the **first compartment,** located on the lateral border of the styloid process of the radius; the **second compartment,** situated on the radial side of the tubercle of the radius, contains the tendons of the extensor carpi radialis longus and brevis muscles; the **third,** on the ulnar side of the tubercle of the radius, conveys the tendon of the extensor pollicis longus muscle. The **fourth** and largest compartment, covering the ulnar third of the dorsum of the radius, transmits the four tendons of the extensor digitorum communis and the extensor indicis proprius; the **fifth,** located over the distal radioulnar articulation, contains the tendon of the extensor digiti minimi; and the **sixth,** located on the head of the ulnar bone, affords passage for the tendon of the extensor carpi ulnaris.

The **flexor retinaculum** (transverse carpal ligament) stretches across the concavity formed by the articulated carpal bones and attaches to the tuberosity of the scaphoid and trapezium bones laterally, and the hamate and pisiform medially. One **large** and one **small osseofibrous tunnels** are formed to transmit the tendons of the flexor muscles and the median nerve. The smaller compartment contains the tendon of the flexor carpi radialis, while the larger transmits the tendons of the flexor digitorum superficialis and profundus. The tendons of the superficialis to the third and fourth digits lie superficial, those to the second and

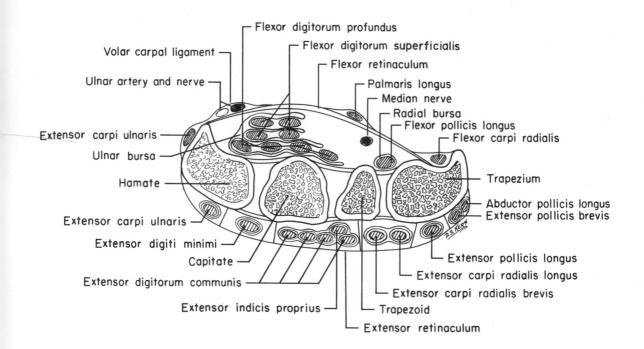

Fig. 15. Relations of flexor and extensor retinacula.

fifth digits lie intermediate, and the deeply placed tendons of the profundus lie side by side in the compartment. Superficial to the flexor retinaculum the palmaris longus muscle passes distally in the midline, and the ulnar nerve and artery course to its ulnar side between the retinaculum and the **volar carpal ligament.**

Deep fascia is also specialized on the palmar aspect of the hand to form compartments. The **thenar compartment** is formed by fascia surrounding the small muscles of the thumb and attaches to both sides of the first metacarpal. Structures within this space include the abductor, flexor, and opponens muscles of the thumb; the muscular branch of the median nerve; and the superficial palmar branch of the radial artery. The **hypothenar compartment,** formed by fascia surrounding the small muscles of the little finger, attaches to both sides of the fifth metacarpal. It contains the abductor, flexor brevis, and opponens of the fifth digit and the deep branches of the ulnar artery and nerve. The **central,** or intermediate, **compartment** (midpalmar space) is bounded superficially by the **palmar aponeurosis,** medially and laterally by fascia covering hypothenar and thenar muscles, and dorsally by the interosseous adductor compartment. The central space is incompletely divided by septa separating flexor tendons and associated lumbricale muscles. It contains the long flexor tendons, the lumbricales, median and ulnar nerves, and the superficial palmar arch. The **interosseous adductor compartment,** bounded by dorsal and palmar interosseous fasciae, encloses the interossei muscles and the metacarpal bones, and contains the interossei muscles, metacarpal bones, the adductor of the thumb, the deep palmar arch, the deep branch of the ulnar nerve, and the arterial arch on the dorsum of the hand.

JOINTS OF THE SUPERIOR EXTREMITY

SHOULDER JOINT

The multiaxial, **ball-and-socket** shoulder joint, consisting of the **head of the humerus** articulating with the much smaller, relatively flat **glenoid fossa** of the scapula, has the greatest freedom of movement of any joint of the body. The osteological configurations result in a mobile but inherently unstable joint. This anatomical instability is compensated for by the presence of an **articular cuff of muscles and tendons** which holds the humeral head in place and reinforces the joint capsule. A fibrocartilaginous rim around the glenoid cavity, the **glenoidal labrum,** deepens the articular fossa. The **articular capsule** attaches proximally to the margins of the glenoid fossa and distally at the anatomical neck of the humerus. The joint cavity, lined by synovial membrane, is traversed by the **tendon of the long head of the biceps** ensheathed by a synovial membrane. This tendon continues distally in the **intertubercular groove,** which is bridged by the **transverse humeral ligament** to hold the tendon in place. The **glenohumeral ligaments** are three bands of tissue which blend with the articular capsule to strengthen it. The **coracohumeral ligament** passes from the coracoid process to unite with the upper posterior part of the capsule and attaches to the anatomical neck and greater tubercle of the humerus. The **coracoclavicular ligament** forms the strongest union between the scapula and the clavicle. Passing from the coracoid process of the scapula, its lateral **trapezoid portion** attaches to the trapezoid ridge of the clavicle, while medially the **conoid portion** passes to the conoid tubercle of the clavicle.

ELBOW JOINT

The elbow is a double **hinge (ginglymus) joint.** The spool-shaped **trochlea** of the humerus articulates with the **trochlear notch** of the ulna, and the **capitulum** of the humerus articulates with the **head of the radius.** A single articular capsule encloses this double joint. Anteriorly and posteriorly the capsule is relatively thin and membranous, but it is reinforced laterally and medially by strong **radial** and **ulnar collateral ligaments.** The synovial membrane lining the joint capsule is extensive and passes distally under the **annular ligament** to permit free rotation of the radius.

Radioulnar joints form the proximal and distal articulations between the radius and ulna which permit rotation of the radius in pronation and supination of the forearm. The **superior radioulnar** articulation is enclosed in the articular capsule of the elbow joint and shares its synovial membrane. The **radial notch** of the ulna and the annular ligament of the radius form a ring in which the radial head rotates. The **annular ligament** forms four-fifths of the ring and attaches to the margins of the radial notch cupping the head of the radius and blending with the articular capsule and the **radial collateral ligament.** The **quadrate ligament** forms a loose band extending from the distal border of the radial notch to the medial surface on the neck of the radius.

The **interosseous membrane,** a strong tendinous sheet connecting the shafts of the radius and ulna, separates the extensor from the flexor compartment of the forearm and gives attachment to deep muscles of both groups. It extends proximally to within an inch of the tuberosity of the radius and distally to the inferior radioulnar articulation.

WRIST JOINT

The **inferior radioulnar articulation** is a **pivot-type joint** lying between the head of the ulna and the ulnar notch of the radius. An **articular disc** of fibrocartilage, attaching to the medial edge of the distal end of the radius and the internal surface of the styloid process of the ulna, is interposed between the ulna and the proximal row of carpal bones. The articular capsule is relatively weak.

A **condyloid joint** is present between the distal end of the radius, the articular disc, and the proximal row of carpal bones, namely, the **scaphoid** (navicular), **lunate,** and **triquetrum** (triangularis). The articular capsule enclosing the joint is strengthened by **dorsal** and **palmar radiocarpal ligaments** and the **radial** and **ulnar collateral ligments.**

CARPAL JOINTS

The intercarpal articulations are **gliding joints** between the two transverse rows of carpal bones, with **dorsal** and **palmar intercarpal ligaments** passing transversely, and interosseous **intercarpal ligaments** linking the lateral borders of the proximal row to the distal row of bones. The **midcarpal joint** between the proximal and distal rows allows a considerable range of movement. The central portion of this articulation forms a limited ball-and-socket type of joint, with the **scaphoid** and **lunate** forming the socket proximally and the **capitate** and **hamate** forming the ball distally. The lateral portions are **gliding joints** between the **trapezium** and **trapezoid** articulating with the **scaphoid** laterally and the **hamate** with the **triquetrum** medially. **Collateral ligaments** of the radial and ulnar borders connect the scaphoid with the trapezium and the triquetrum with the hamate. The **pisiform** articulates with the **triquetrum** surrounded by a separate articular capsule.

JOINTS OF THE HAND

The **carpometacarpal joint** of the thumb forms a **saddle-shaped articulation** between the **trapezium** and the **first metacarpal** and is surrounded by an articular capsule. The remaining carpometacarpal joints have a common synovial cavity between the **intercarpal** and **intermetacarpal joints** linked by **dorsal, palmar,** and **interosseus ligaments.**

The **intermetacarpal joints** formed by contiguous sides of the bases of **second through fifth metacarpals** are joined by **dorsal, palmar,** and **interosseous ligaments.** The **deep transverse metacarpal ligaments** connect the heads of the **second, third,** and **fourth metacarpals** on the palmar aspect and thereby limit the abduction of these bones.

The condyloid **metacarpophalangeal joints** are formed by the rounded **head of the metacarpal bones** articulating with the concavities of the **proximal phalanges.** These joints are linked by articular capsules which are reinforced dorsally by the extensor tendons. **Palmar ligaments** bridge the joints on the palmar aspect of the hand and are continuous laterally with the strong cord-like **collateral ligaments,** which attach proximally to the tubercle and distally to the lateral aspect of the base of the phalanx.

The **interphalangeal joints** are **hinge-type joints,** structurally the same as the metacarpophalangeal articulations, with a **palmar ligament** and two **collateral ligaments** which are reinforced dorsally by the extensor expansion.

BURSAE

Synovial bursae of the upper extremity are associated with the joints and sometimes communicate with the articular synovial cavity. The **subacromial (subdeltoid) bursa,** about an inch in diameter, is located deep to the deltoid between the tendon of the supraspinatus and the joint capsule. This bursa sends an extension deep to the acromial process and the coracoacromial ligament and may communicate with the joint cavity. The **subscapular bursa** between the tendon of the subscapularis and the neck of the scapula frequently communicates with the cavity of the shoulder joint. The **olecranon bursa** is in the subcutaneous tissue spaces over the olecranon process, and the **subtendinous olecranon bursa** is located between the tendon of the triceps and the olecranon process. The **bicipitoradial bursa** is a small but constant structure between the tendon of the biceps and the radial tuberosity.

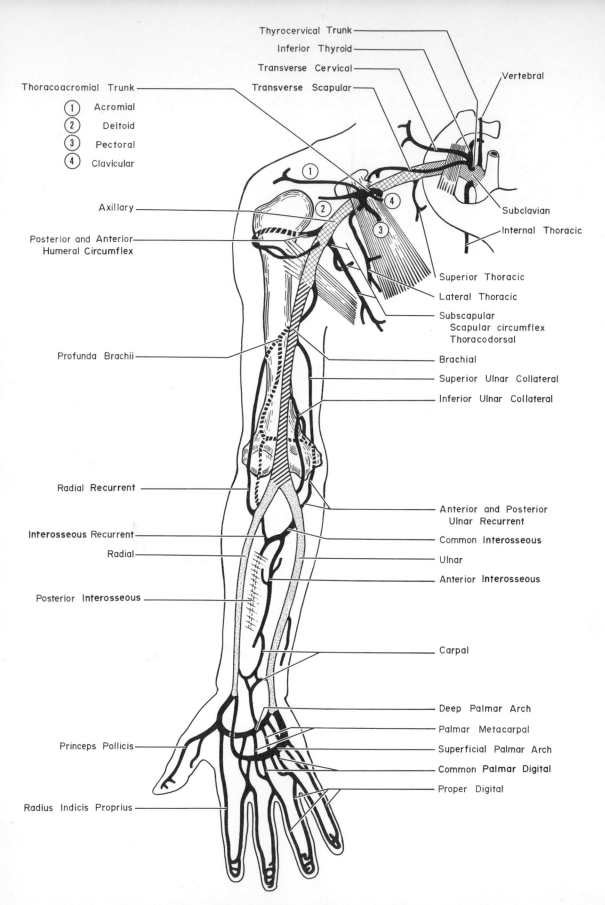

Fig. 16. Summary of arterial supply of the upper extremity.

THORAX

THORACIC CAGE

The thoracic cage, formed by the sternum, the ribs, and the thoracic vertebrae, gives protection for the lungs and heart and affords attachment for muscles
of the thorax, upper extremity, back, and diaphragm.

Skeleton of the Thorax

The **sternum** is a flat bone consisting of three parts, the manubrium, the
body, and the xiphoid process. The **manubrium,** united with the body by fibrocartilage at the **sternal angle** (of Louis), presents a superior **suprasternal
notch** and articulates laterally with the clavicle and the first costal cartilage. At
its junction with the body of the sternum, lateral demifacets are present for articulation with the second costal cartilage. The **body,** forming the bulk of the sternum,
articulates with the second through seventh costal cartilages and is united with the
xiphoid process inferiorly at the **xiphisternal junction.** The **xiphoid process,**
the smallest part of the sternum, is thin, flattened, and elongated, and presents a
demifacet for the seventh costal cartilage. In youth the xiphoid process consists
of hyaline cartilage; this is gradually replaced with a core of bone.

There are twelve pair of ribs. The first seven are **true ribs** in that they
attach by way of their costal cartilages to the sternum. The remaining five pair
are called **false ribs** because their attachment anteriorly is via the costal cartilage
of the rib above, rather than directly to the sternum. The eleventh and twelfth ribs
have no anterior attachment and are called **floating ribs.** Ribs one through seven
increase progressively in length, while the remaining ribs decrease. The first rib
has the greatest curvature and thereafter the curvature diminishes.

A **typical rib** (third through ninth) can be divided into three parts: head,
neck, and shaft. The **head** is wedge-shaped with a crest at the apex presenting two
facets that articulate with the numerically corresponding thoracic vertebra and
the vertebra above. At the **junction of the neck and shaft,** a **tubercle** on the
posterior surface articulates with the transverse process of the numerically corresponding vertebra. The **shaft,** or body, is long, thin, curved, and twisted on its
long axis, and forms the **angle** at its point of maximal curvature. The **costal
groove** on the inferior border of the rib gives protection to intercostal nerves and
vessels.

The first, second, tenth, eleventh, and twelfth ribs are classified as **atypical.**
The **first rib** is short, broad, and flat and has a long neck and only one facet on

its head. There is a prominent tubercle on this rib for articulation with the transverse process of the first thoracic vertebra. The tubercle is separated by a groove
formed by the subclavian artery and the brachial plexus from the **scalene tubercle,**
which affords attachment for the anterior scalenus muscle. The **second rib** is
appreciably longer but similar to the first. Its shaft is not twisted but is still
strongly curved, and the costal groove is indistinct. Its roughened external surface
gives partial origin for the serratus anterior muscle. The **tenth rib** is atypical
only in that it has a single facet for articulation with the tenth vertebra. The
eleventh rib is short, presents a slight angle, but has no neck or tubercle. The
twelfth rib is very short and lacks neck, tubercle, angle, and costal groove.

The **costal cartilages,** bars of hyaline cartilage, prolong the ribs anteriorly.
The upper seven cartilages articulate with the sternum, the next three with the
costal cartilages immediately above; the last two terminate in abdominal wall
musculature.

The ribs and intercostal spaces constitute the thoracic wall. The **intercostal
space** is filled by muscles between which arteries, veins, and nerves course. The
intercostal muscles elevate the ribs and receive their nerve supply from corresponding intercostal or thoracoabdominal nerves.

Intercostal Muscles (Table VII, Fig. 17)

The intercostal muscles are disposed in three layers. The most superficial,
the **external intercostal muscle** partially fills the intercostal space from the
vertebral column to the costochondral junction, where its muscle fibers are lost

TABLE VII. MUSCLES OF THE THORAX

Muscle	Origin	Insertion	Action	Nerve
External intercostals	Inferior border of rib	Superior border of rib below origin	Elevate rib	Segmentally by intercostals
Internal intercostals	Superior border of rib	Inferior border of rib above origin	Elevate rib	Segmentally by intercostals
Innermost intercostals	Variable in extent, sometimes considered as deep portion of internal intercostals, being separated by intercostal nerves and vessels			
Transversus thoracis	Posterior surface of xiphoid process and lower third of sternum	Inner surface of costal cartilage of second to sixth ribs	Draw costal cartilage inferiorly	Segmentally by intercostals
Subcostales	Inner surface of lower ribs near their angle	Inner surface of second or third rib below rib of origin	Draw adjacent ribs together	Segmentally by intercostals

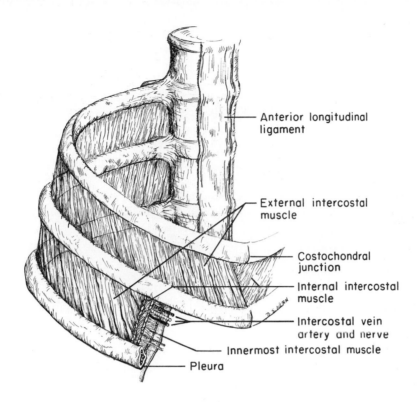

Anterior longitudinal
ligament

External intercostal
muscle

Costochondral
junction

Internal intercostal
muscle

Intercostal vein
artery and nerve

Innermost intercostal muscle

Pleura

Fig. 17. Intercostal muscles.

but its fascia continues to the sternum as the **anterior intercostal membrane.**
The **internal intercostal muscle** forms the middle layer of muscle. Its muscular
fibers extend from the sternum anteriorly to the angle of the ribs posteriorly, where
its fascia continues to the vertebral column as the **posterior intercostal membrane.** The third muscular layer is discontinuous and is described as three individual muscles: anteriorly the **transverse thoracis** (sternocostalis), laterally the
innermost intercostals (sometimes considered as a splitting of the internal intercostal), and posteriorly the **subcostalis.** The nerves, arteries, and veins within the
intercostal space course between the second and third layers of muscles.

Intercostal Arteries and Nerves (Fig. 18)

Arteries passing in the intercostal space supply intercostal muscles; send
twigs to the overlying pectoral muscles, mammary gland, and skin; and at the
lower intercostal spaces give branches to the diaphragm. The **internal thoracic**
(internal mammary) **artery,** arising in the root of the neck as a branch of the
first part of the subclavian, descends vertically at the side of the sternum to divide
behind the sixth intercostal space into **musculophrenic** and **superior epigastric
branches.** The **anterior intercostal arteries** supplying the first six intercostal
spaces are branches of the internal thoracic artery. The remaining spaces are sup-

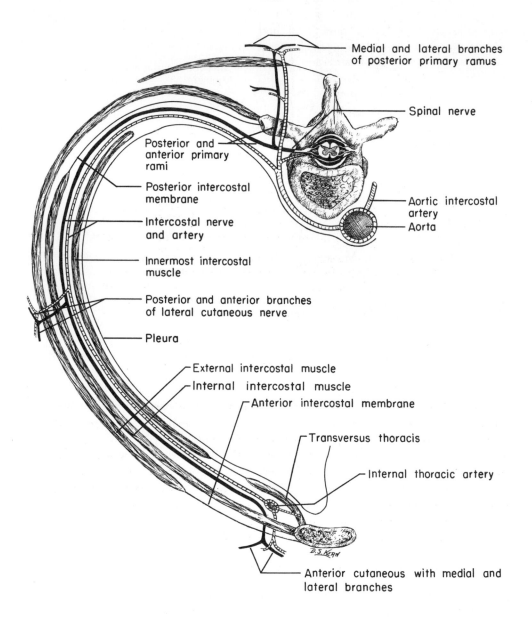

Medial and lateral branches of posterior primary ramus

Spinal nerve

Posterior and anterior primary rami

Posterior intercostal membrane

Intercostal nerve and artery

Innermost intercostal muscle

Posterior and anterior branches of lateral cutaneous nerve

Pleura

Aortic intercostal artery

Aorta

External intercostal muscle

Internal intercostal muscle

Anterior intercostal membrane

Transversus thoracis

Internal thoracic artery

D.S.KERN

Anterior cutaneous with medial and lateral branches

Fig. 18. Typical intercostal nerve and intercostal arteries.

plied by similar branches of the musculophrenic artery. The **posterior intercostal arteries** to the first two intercostal spaces are branches of the **superior intercostal,** a branch of the costocervical trunk from the subclavian. The remaining intercostal spaces receive their posterior (aortic) intercostal branches directly from the descending aorta. Additional branches from the posterior intercostals pass posteriorly to supply the deep muscles of the back, the vertebral column, and the spinal cord. The **subcostal artery,** the most inferior paired branch of the thoracic aorta arising in line with the posterior intercostals, passes inferiorly to supply structures in the abdominal wall, as do the lower six posterior intercostal vessels.

The **intercostal nerves** are anterior primary rami of thoracic spinal nerves. The **typical intercostal nerves** (third through sixth thoracic) course along the posterior intercostal membrane to enter the **costal groove** on the inferior border of the rib between the internal and innermost intercostal muscles and inferior to the intercostal vessels. They supply all the intercostal muscles and in the midlateral line give **lateral cutaneous nerves,** which send **anterior** and **posterior branches** to supply the skin of the lateral chest wall. The intercostal nerves then proceed anteriorly to penetrate the anterior body wall just lateral to the sternum as the **anterior cutaneous nerves,** which divide into **medial** and **lateral branches** and supply the skin on the anterior aspect of the thorax.

Atypical intercostal nerves are anterior primary rami, but have several distinctive characteristics. The **first thoracic nerve** is short and thick and divides unevenly into two branches. The small inferior branch supplies the first intercostal space, while the much larger superior branch joins the brachial plexus. The cutaneous innervation over the first intercostal space is not supplied by this nerve but by the **anterior** and **middle supraclavicular nerves.** The lateral cutaneous branch of the second thoracic nerve joins the brachial plexus as the **intercostobrachial branch** and supplies cutaneous innervation to the floor of the axilla as well as to the posteromedial aspect of the arm. At the point where the costal cartilages course upward, the seventh through eleventh thoracic (thoracoabdominal) nerves continue anteriorly, passing between the external and internal abdominal oblique muscles. They supply the anterolateral abdominal wall musculature and overlying skin. The **twelfth thoracic nerve,** the **subcostal,** passes anterior to the quadratus lumborum muscle to the abdominal wall, where its distribution is similar to that of the lower intercostal nerves.

PLEURAL CAVITY

PLEURA

The thorax contains three serous cavities, the two lateral pleural sacs and the midline pericardial cavity. The two **pleural cavities** are completely closed, separate, and lined by a serous membrane, the **pleura.** This membrane is one continuous sheet, but is subdivided for descriptive purposes into parietal and visceral portions. The **parietal pleura** applied to the thoracic cage is designated the **costal parietal pleura;** the portion fused to the diaphragm, the **diaphramatic**

parietal pleura; and the portion adjacent to the mediastinum, the **mediastinal parietal pleura.** The **visceral pleura** is intimately adherent to the lung, covering its entire surface and continuing deeply into its fissures. In the adult the lung lies free in the cavity except at the root of the lung and the pulmonary ligament, where the visceral pleura reflects to become the parietal plura. The **pulmonary ligament** extends inferiorly from the root of the lung as a fusion of two layers of mediastinal pleura. Near the diaphragm the ligament ends in a free falciform border. Anteriorly the costal parietal pleura reflects to become the mediastinal parietal pleura forming the **costomediastinal recess;** inferiorly it is reflected onto the diaphragm to form the **costodiaphragmatic (phrenicocostal) recess.** These recesses do not contain lung except in maximal inspiration.

Projection of the **pleural reflection** to the surface of the chest coincides with certain landmarks of the second, fourth, sixth, eighth, tenth, and twelfth ribs or costal cartilages. The anterior border of the parietal pleura passes inferiorly from the cupola (pleura over the apex of the lung) to the sternoclavicular joint, continues obliquely across the manubrium, and proceeds inferiorly along the midline of the sternum from the level of the second to the fourth costal cartilage. Here the margin of the left pleural reflection moves laterally, then inferiorly at the cardiac notch to reach the sixth costal space or cartilage at the midclavicular line. On the right side, the pleural reflection continues inferiorly to the sixth or seventh costal cartilage before it angles laterally to the midclavicular line at the level of the eighth costal cartilage. From this level the pleura on both sides follows the same line of reflection, crossing the tenth rib at the midaxillary line and the twelfth rib at the midscapular line.

LUNGS (FIG. 19)

The lungs are organs of respiration. **Inspiration,** an active process, results from a decrease in the intrathoracic pressure as the thoracic cavities increase their volume by the activity of the chest muscles and the diaphragm. Normal **expiration** is passive. Relaxation of the chest muscles results in a resilient recoil of the ribs with a concomitant intrathoracic volume decrease and pressure increase. The most extensive movement of the lung occurs in the lateral, anterior, and inferior directions. Each lung is accurately adapted to the space in which it lies and, when hardened in situ, bears impressions of structures in contact with its surfaces.

The **shape of the lung,** described as a bisected cone, presents an apex; a base; costal and mediastinal surfaces; and anterior, inferior, and posterior borders. The rounded **apex** lying behind the middle third of the clavicle and rising an inch and a half above the first rib, is grooved by the subclavian artery and separated from structures in the neck by the suprapleural membrane, or Sibson's fascia. The concave semilunar **base** is adapted to the upper surface of the diaphragm. The convex and extensive **costal surface** follows the contour of the rib cage. The **mediastinal surface** is adjacent to, and marked by, structures in the mediastinum and presents a large centrally depressed area, the **hilus,** through which bronchi, nerves, vessels, and lymphatics enter or leave the lung.

The **right lung** is shorter than the left, owing to the high position of the right lobe of the liver, and is related superiorly to the superior vena cava, the

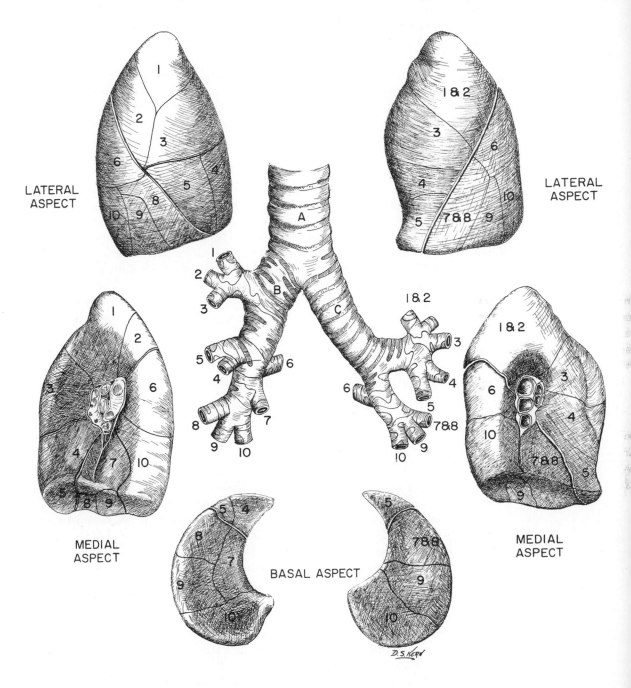

Fig. 19. Lung and tracheobronchial tree: *A*, trachea; *B*, right primary bronchus; *C*, left primary bronchus.

Tertiary bronchi and bronchopulmonary segments

RIGHT LUNG		LEFT LUNG	
1. apical	6. superior	1.⎰ apicoposterior	6. superior
2. posterior	7. medial basal	2.⎱	7.⎰ anteromedial basal
3. anterior	8. anterior basal	3. anterior	8.⎱
4. medial	9. lateral basal	4. superior	9. lateral basal
5. lateral	10. posterior basal	5. inferior	10. posterior basal

brachiocephalic and azygos veins, and, anterior to these structures, the ascending aorta. Posterior to the hilus the right lung is grooved by the esophagus and more superiorly by the arch of the aorta and the trachea.

The **left lung** displays a deep depression for the apex and left surface of the heart and is grooved widely above and behind the hilus by the arch of the aorta and the descending aorta. Superiorly the left lung is grooved by the sub-clavian and common carotid arteries. The **anterior borders** of both lungs are comparatively short and thin and extend into the costomediastinal recesses. On the left lung this border is displaced laterally by the heart to form the cardiac notch. The rounded, thick **posterior borders** form an indistinct confluence of costal and mediastinal surfaces occupying a deep hollow on either side of the vertebral column. Along its **inferior border** the mediastinal portion is blunt and related to the lower border of the pericardium. Anteriorly, laterally, and posteriorly this border is thin and sharp and extends into the costodiaphragmatic recess.

Each lung is partially transected by an **oblique fissure** from its surface to within a short distance of the hilus. On the left lung this fissure extends from the posterior border approximately two and one-half inches below the summit, runs obliquely and inferiorly to cross the fifth rib in the midaxillary line, and ends anteriorly opposite the sixth costal cartilage. On the right lung the oblique fissure begins slightly lower. The oblique fissure in each lung separates the **upper** (supero-anterior) **lobe** from the **lower** (posteroinferior) **lobe.** The right lung is further subdivided by the **horizontal fissure,** which extends from the anterior border of the lung at the fourth interspace to follow the upper border of the fifth rib to the oblique fissure and form a wedge-shaped **middle lobe.** In the left lung the **lingula** represents the homologous structure to the middle lobe of the right lung and consists of a small tongue-like appendage between the cardiac notch and the oblique fissure.

Air-conduction System

The **trachea,** a wide tube four to five inches long, is kept patent by a series of sixteen to twenty U-shaped horizontal cartilaginous bars embedded in its con-nective tissue wall. Posteriorly the open cartilages of the tube are closed by the **trachealis muscle** and fibrous tissue. The trachea, continuous superiorly in the neck with the larynx, terminates between the fourth and fifth thoracic vertebrae by dividing into right and left primary bronchi. In inspiration the respiratory shift carries the bifurcation as low as the seventh vertebra. The trachea is related pos-teriorly to the esophagus and inferior laryngeal nerves; anteriorly to the left innominate vein, left common carotid artery, and arch of the aorta; and laterally on the right to the pleura, vagus nerve, and arch of the azygos vein, and on the left to the common carotid and subclavian arteries, phrenic and vagus nerves, and the arch of the aorta.

The **right primary bronchus,** a more direct continuation of the trachea, is shorter, straighter, and larger than the left; therefore foreign bodies are more apt to pass into the right than into the left lung. The right primary bronchus enters the lung at the hilus, where it divides into **secondary bronchi** passing to the upper, middle, and lower lobes, with the superior lobe bronchus passing above the pulmonary artery as the epiarterial bronchus. Secondary bronchi give rise to **tertiary bronchi** named for the **bronchopulmonary segments** they supply. The secondary bronchus to the right upper lobe divides into apical, posterior, and anterior tertiary bronchi; the secondary bronchus to the right middle lobe divides into lateral and medial tertiary bronchi; and the secondary bronchus to the right lower lobe divides into superior, medial basal, anterior basal, lateral basal, and posterior basal tertiary bronchi. Thus ten bronchopulmonary segments are present in the right lung.

The **left primary bronchus** is smaller in caliber but roughly twice as long as the right. It passes initially superior to the pulmonary artery, but divides inferior to the artery, into upper and lower lobe **secondary bronchi.** The secondary bronchus to the upper lobe subdivides into apicoposterior, anterior, superior, and inferior tertiary bronchi; the lower lobe bronchus subdivides into superior, anteromedial basal, lateral basal, and posterior basal tertiary bronchi. This results in eight bronchopulmonary segments in the left lung.

The **root of the lung,** formed by structures entering or leaving the viscus, consists of the bronchi, the pulmonary artery (carrying venous blood), pulmonary veins (carrying arterial blood), bronchial arteries supplying the bronchial tree, lymph vessels and nodes, and the pulmonary plexus of nerves. These structures are held together by connective tissue and are surrounded by pleura reflecting from the surface of the lung as the visceral pleura to become the parietal pleura. The superior vena cava and right atrium are anterior to the root of the right lung, and the azygos vein arches above it. The root of the left lung lies anterior to the descending aorta and inferior to the arch of the aorta. The phrenic nerves, pericardiophrenic arteries and veins, and the anterior pulmonary plexuses are located anterior to both roots; the posterior pulmonary plexuses and the vagus nerves are posterior to both roots.

Blood Vessels, Lymphatics, and Nerves

The **right** and **left pulmonary arteries** are branches of the **pulmonary trunk,** which, in turn, stems from the right ventricle. The **right branch,** longer and of larger caliber than the left, passes posterior to the ascending aorta and superior vena cava and anterior to the right bronchus. It divides into two branches, one to the upper lobe and a second to the middle and lower lobes. The **left pulmonary artery** passes horizontally and anteriorly to the descending aorta and left bronchus and divides into branches to the upper and lower lobes. Further subdivisions of the pulmonary arteries correspond to the divisions of the bronchial tree.

Pulmonary veins begin from alveolar capillaries and coalesce at the periphery of the lung lobule. They maintain a peripheral relation in bronchopulmonary segments running in intersegmental connective tissue draining adjacent, rather than single, segments. On the right side the middle lobe vein joins the lower lobe vein at the hilus, usually resulting in two veins from each lung draining into the left atrium.

The **bronchial arteries,** small vessels coursing along the posterior aspect of the bronchi, supply the bronchi to the level of the respiratory bronchiole. Two

left bronchial arteries arise from the anterior aspect of the descending aorta, while a single **right bronchial artery** arises from the first right aortic intercostal or the upper left bronchial artery.

The **lymphatics** of the lungs are disposed as a **superficial plexus** lying immediately under the visceral pleura, and a **deep plexus** arising in the submucosa of the bronchi and peribronchial connective tissue. The efferent lymph vessels of the superficial plexus follow the surface of the lung to the bronchopulmonary trunks; those of the deep plexus follow the pulmonary vessels to the hilus. The **nodes** of the lung are disposed in five groups: the tracheal or paratracheal nodes along the trachea, the superior tracheobronchial nodes in the angle between the trachea and bronchi, the inferior tracheobronchial nodes in the angle between the bronchi, the bronchopulmonary nodes at the hilus of each lung, and the pulmonary nodes in the substance of the lung.

Innervation to the lung is supplied by the vagus and thoracic sympathetic nerves distributed through the **anterior** and **posterior pulmonary nerve plexuses,** located on corresponding surfaces of the root of the lung. The cell bodies of the preganglionic sympathetic neurons are located in the upper three to five thoracic segments of the spinal cord. Postganglionic nerve cell bodies in the middle and inferior cervical sympathetic ganglia descend through the neck as the **cardiac nerves** to reach (via lateral extensions of the cardiac plexus) the pulmonary plexuses.

PERICARDIAL CAVITY

The **pericardial cavity,** a conical fibroserous sac, surrounds the heart and proximal portions of the great cardiac vessels. The **pericardium** is disposed into three layers: an external strong **fibrous layer,** which superiorly and inferiorly blends with the adventitia of the great vessels; a **parietal layer** of serous pericardium lining the inner surface of the fibrous layer and closely adherent to it; and a **visceral layer** of serous pericardium which reflects onto and is intimately applied to the heart and great vessels. Superiorly the pericardial cavity is pierced by the aorta, the pulmonary trunk, and the superior vena cava. Near the median plane the base of the pericardial cavity rests on, and fuses with, the central tendon of the diaphragm. The right posteroinferior aspect of the base is pierced by the inferior vena cava and posteriorly, at the junction of the upper part of the posterior and lateral surfaces, by the pulmonary veins.

Anteriorly the pericardium is separated from the sternum and the second to sixth costal cartilages by the lungs and pleura, except in the region of the fifth intercostal space, where the left lung is deficient at the **cardiac notch.** In this area, known as the "bare area," the pericardium comes in contact with the anterior chest wall. **Superior** and **inferior sternopericardial ligaments** attach the pericardium to the sternum. Laterally the pericardium is adjacent to the mediastinal parietal pleura, with the phrenic nerve and pericardiophrenic vessels interposed between them. Posteriorly it is related to the descending aorta, the esophagus, and the bronchi.

The **transverse sinus** of the pericardium, a space within the pericardial cavity situated between the aorta and pulmonary trunk and the superior vena cava, is formed by the reflection of the serous pericardium. The **oblique sinus** of the pericardium, a box-like diverticulum of the pericardial cavity within the irregularities of the pericardial reflection, is between the right and left pulmonary veins and the inferior vena cava.

HEART (FIG. 20)

Anteriorly the heart presents a **sternocostal surface** formed superiorly by the right and left auricular appendages and by the infundibulum. Inferiorly two-thirds of this aspect of the heart is formed by the right ventricle and one-third by the left ventricle, with the **apex** of the heart being formed entirely by the left ventricle. The **lower border** of the sternocostal surface presents a sharp margin (margo acutis) formed almost entirely by the right ventricle. The **right border,** formed by the right atrium, is continuous superiorly with the superior vena cava and inferiorly with the inferior vena cava. The more convex **left border** is formed

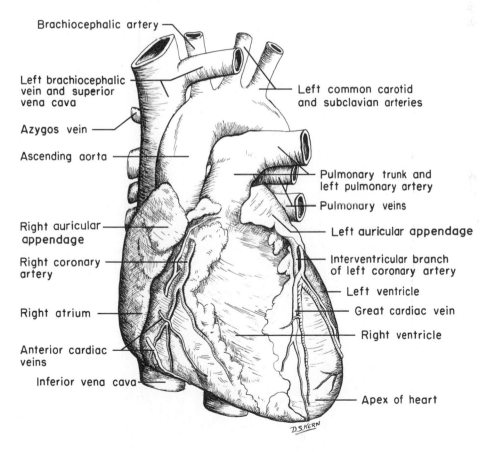

Fig. 20. Anterior aspect of the heart.

mostly by the left ventricle. The **diaphragmatic surface** of the heart rests on the diaphragm and is formed entirely by the ventricles, with the greatest contribution by the left ventricle. The **base** of the heart, or **posterior surface,** is formed by both atria, but mostly by the left. The **atrioventricular groove** completely encircles the heart and separates the atria, which lie superiorly and to the right, from the ventricles, which lie inferiorly and to the left.

Blood Vessels (Fig. 21)

The nutrient vessels of the heart, the **coronary arteries,** may be considered as greatly enlarged vasa vasorum. They originate from the **aortic sinuses** (dilations of the aorta) immediately above the aortic cusps. The **right coronary artery** originates from the anterior aortic sinus, courses forward between the pulmonary trunk and the right auricular appendage, then passes inferiorly to the atrioventricular groove, in which it runs posteriorly to anastomose with the left coronary. It gives small branches to the root of the aorta, the pulmonary trunk, and the walls of the right atrium and ventricle. A **marginal branch** of the right coronary passes from right to left along the lower border and anterior aspect of the heart. A **posterior interventricular** (posterior descending) **branch** extends anteriorly on the diaphragmatic surface in the interventricular groove. The large **left coronary,** originating from the left posterior aortic sinus, passes a short distance to the left behind the pulmonary trunk, then between the pulmonary trunk and the left auricular appendage, where it divides into an anterior interventricular (anterior descending) branch and the circumflex branch. The **anterior interventricular branch** descends in the interventricular groove on the anterior aspect of the

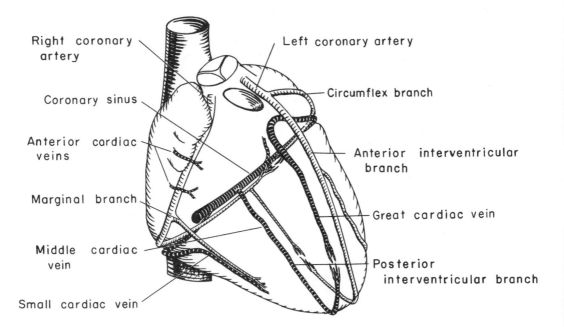

Fig. 21. Vasculature of the heart.

heart toward the apex, where it anastomoses with the posterior interventricular branch. The **circumflex artery** continues in the atrioventricular groove to the lower border of the base of the heart to anastomose with the right coronary.

The **coronary sinus,** the largest vein draining the heart, runs posteriorly from left to right in the atrioventricular groove. At the upper end of the anterior interventricular groove it receives the **great cardiac vein,** the companion vein of the anterior descending branch of the left coronary artery. The **middle cardiac vein,** accompanying the posterior descending branch of the right coronary artery, empties into the coronary sinus near its termination. The **small cardiac vein,** coursing with the marginal branch of the right coronary artery, curves around the lower margin and right border of the heart to empty into the coronary sinus at its termination. The small **oblique vein of the left atrium,** descends over the posterior surface of this chamber to drain into the midportion of the coronary sinus. **Valves** in the coronary sinus are usually present at the junction of the great and small cardiac veins and at its termination. The **anterior cardiac veins** are small vessels on the right atrial and ventricular surface which empty directly into the right atrium near the atrioventricular groove. A small part of the blood is collected from the heart musculature by small veins, the **venae cordis minimae,** which lie in the substance of the heart wall and drain directly into all chambers of the heart, but mainly into the right atrium.

Nerves

Modification of the intrinsic rhythm of heart muscle is produced through autonomic nerve plexuses. **Parasympathetic innervation,** from the vagus nerve, slows the rate and reduces the force of the heart beat. **Sympathetic innervation,** from the thoracic ganglia and the cervical chain, has the opposite effects. The **superficial cardiac plexus** lies in the concavity of the aortic arch, proximal to the ligamentum arteriosum, and receives the inferior cervical cardiac branch of the left vagus and the superior cervical cardiac branch of the left sympathetic trunk. The more extensive **deep cardiac plexus** is located on the base of the heart posterior to the aortic arch and anterior to the tracheal bifurcation. From the cervical sympathetic chain it receives all the cardiac branches on the right side and the middle and inferior cardiac branches on the left. From the right vagus the deep cardiac plexus receives the superior and inferior cervical branches, and from the left vagus, the superior cervical branch. In the thorax additional vagal and sympathetic branches pass directly to the deep cardiac plexus.

Coronary plexuses, surrounding and accompanying the coronary arteries, are extensions from the cardiac plexus. Vagal fibers within the coronary plexus produce vasoconstriction, while sympathetic fibers cause vasodilatation, of the arterioles. **Visceral afferent fibers** from the heart and coronary arteries end almost entirely in the first four thoracic segments of the spinal cord.

Conduction (Purkinje) System

The orderly sequence in which ventricular contraction follows atrial contraction and proceeds from the apex to the base of the heart is due to a specialized conduction system composed of two aggregates of nodal tissue and a band of specialized cardiac muscle. The **sinoatrial node** is a small collection of specialized myocardial tissue at the junction of the right atrium and the superior vena cava, at the superior end of the sulcus terminalis. This node, the **pace-maker,** appears to initiate the heart beat, and the impulse is propagated over the atria. The **atrioventricular node** is a nodule of similar tissue located in the septal wall of the right atrium immediately above the opening of the coronary sinus. Activity at this node is probably initiated by stimuli reaching it through the atrial musculature. The impulse is then directed toward the apical portions of the ventricles via the **atrioventricular bundle of His.** This structure is a strand of specialized myocardium (Purkinje fibers) passing from the atrioventricular node into the interventricular septum, where it divides into a right and left bundle within the septal musculature. The **right bundle branch** follows the endocardium along the septum of the right ventricle giving branches to the septum, then extends across the ventricular cavity, traversing the **moderator band** to reach the anterior papillary muscle of the right ventricle. The **left bundle branch** follows the endocardium of the left ventricle to the apex, where it is distributed to the anterior and posterior papillary muscles and the ventricular myocardium.

Interior of the Heart (Fig. 22)

The interior of the heart is divided into right and left atria with auricular appendages, and right and left ventricles.

The **right atrium** is described as having two parts, the sinus venarum and the atrial portion. The sinus venarum, a large quadrangular cavity with smooth walls, is between the two venae cavae and is continuous inferiorly with the right ventricle. The auricle (proper) is a small conical muscular pouch which projects from the upper front part of the sinus venarum to overlap the root of the aorta. The crista terminalis is a vertical ridge extending from the orifice of the superior vena cava to the opening of the inferior vena cava. The **musculi pectinati** are parallel muscular ridges at right angles to the crista terminalis and extend into the auricular appendage.

Openings into the right atrium include the superior vena cava, devoid of valves, opening into the superoposterior part of the chamber; the inferior vena cava, with a thin rudimentary valve along the anterior margin between its orifice and the atrioventricular orifice, opening into the inferoposterior part; the opening of the coronary sinus, guarded by a crescentic valve directly posterior to the atrioventricular orifice; and the right atrioventricular aperture, closed by the tricuspid valve in the anteroinferior part of the atrium, opening into the right ventricle. The rudimentary valve of the inferior vena cava is continuous on its left with the **annulus ovalis** of the interatrial septum, which surrounds a wide shallow depression, the **fossa ovalis.** The upper end of the fossa was open in fetal circulation as the **foramen ovale** and permitted passage of blood from the right to the left atrium.

The **right ventricular cavity** is triangular in shape. Its funnel-shaped superior portion, the **infundibulum,** or **conus arteriosus,** leads into the pulmonary trunk. The infundibulum has smooth internal walls, while the remainder of the cavity possesses projecting muscular bundles, the **trabeculae carneae.** **Papillary muscles,** conical projections from the wall into the cavity, are con-

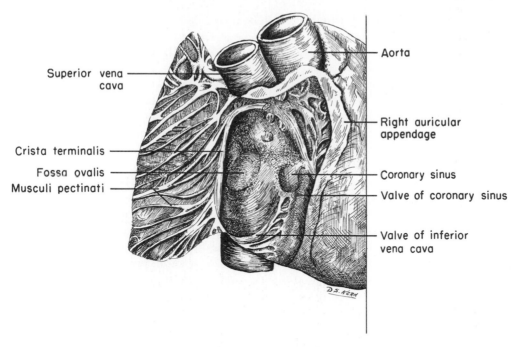

Superior vena cava

Aorta

Crista terminalis

Right auricular appendage

Fossa ovalis

Musculi pectinati

Coronary sinus

Valve of coronary sinus

Valve of inferior vena cava

Fig. 22. Internal aspect of the right atrium.

nected at their apices to the tricuspid valve by the **chordae tendineae.** The **moderator band,** a well-marked trabeculum, projects from the interventricular septum to the base of the anterior papillary muscle and may act to prevent over-distention of this chamber. The **right atrioventricular orifice,** about an inch in diameter, is guarded by a valve with three triangular cusps, the **tricuspid valve.** The anterior cusp intervenes between the atrioventricular orifice and the infundibulum, the medial cusp lies in relation to the septal wall, and the inferior cusp is adjacent to the inferior wall. The bases of the cusps are attached continuously to a fibrous ring, the **annulus fibrosus,** a deeply lying structure at the periphery of the atrioventricular orifice. The apex of each cusp extends into the ventricle and is attached by chordae tendineae to papillary muscles. The **pulmonary orifice,** at the apex of the infundibulum, is surrounded by a thinner fibrous ring to which the bases of three cup-like **pulmonary semilunar cusps** are attached. The center of the free margin of each semilunar cusp is thickened to form a **nodule** (corpus Arantii), and the **lunulae** of the valves are the thinner crescentic regions at either side of the nodules. When the valve is closed the three nodules meet at the center of the orifice, effecting complete occlusion.

The **left atrium,** forming most of the base of the heart, consists of the atrium proper and its auricular appendage. Four **pulmonary veins,** two on each side, enter this chamber at its superolateral aspect. The internal surface of the wall of the left atrium is generally devoid of muscular ridges except in the auricular appendage. Anteroinferiorly the left atrioventricular orifice, guarded by the bicuspid valve, opens into the left ventricle.

The cone-shaped cavity of the **left ventricle** is longer and narrower than the right and has much thicker walls. The internal surface is covered with a dense meshwork of muscular ridges, **trabeculae carneae,** which are finer and more numerous than those of the right ventricle. The **papillary muscles,** much larger and stronger than in the right ventricle, are usually two in number. The interventricular septum and the upper portion of the anterior wall are relatively free of muscular ridges. The **left atrioventricular orifice,** slightly smaller than the right, is closed by the **bicuspid (mitral) valve.** The cusps are set obliquely, with the larger anterior cusp to the right and the smaller posterior cusp to the left. The bases of the cusps are attached to the **annulus fibrosus** surrounding the left atrioventricular orifice, and their apices project into the cavity, with **chordae tendineae** extending from each cusp to both papillary muscles. The **aortic vestibule** is that portion of the left ventricle immediately below the aortic orifice. Its walls, composed mainly of fibrous tissue, are quiescent during ventricular contraction so that rapid closure of the aortic valve is not affected. The **aortic orifice,** in the upper right posterior part of the cavity, is surrounded by an **annulus fibrosus** for the attachment of the bases of the three **semilunar aortic cusps** guarding the opening. This valve is similar to the previously described pulmonary valve. The musculomembranous **interventricular septum** separates the ventricles as well as separating the left ventricle from the inferiormost part of the right atrium. The muscular portion is thickest near the apex and gradually thins to become membranous near the aortic opening.

The **fibrous skeleton** of the heart consists of fibrous rings, the annuli fibrosi, surrounding the atrioventricular, aortic, and pulmonary orifices; intervening fibrous connections, namely, the right and left trigona fibrosa and the conus tendon. The **right trigonum fibrosum,** situated between the two atrioventricular orifices, sends a strong dense expansion into the membranous portion of the interventricular septum. The **left trigonum fibrosum** lies between the left atrioventricular orifice and the root of the aorta, and the **conus tendon** extends between the root of the aorta and the pulmonary artery. In addition to giving attachment to the bases of the valves of the heart, this fibrous skeleton also serves for the attachment of the various muscle bundles composing the myocardium.

MEDIASTINUM (FIG. 23)

The **mediastinum** is a midline septum between the two pleural cavities and contains all the thoracic structures except the lungs. The heart occupies a central subdivision of this area, the middle mediastinum. The rest of the mediastinum is subdivided with respect to the relation to the heart (or pericardial cavity) into superior, anterior, and posterior portions. The anterior, middle, and posterior mediastina are sometimes referred to collectively as the **inferior mediastinum.**

The **superior mediastinum** is the area above the fibrous pericardium, extending from an imaginary line passing from the sternal angle to the intervertebral disc between the fourth and fifth thoracic vertebrae. It contains all structures passing between the neck and the thorax and includes the remnant of the thymus; the brachiocephalic (innominate) veins and superior vena cava; the aortic arch and its three branches; the thoracic duct; the trachea; the esophagus; phrenic,

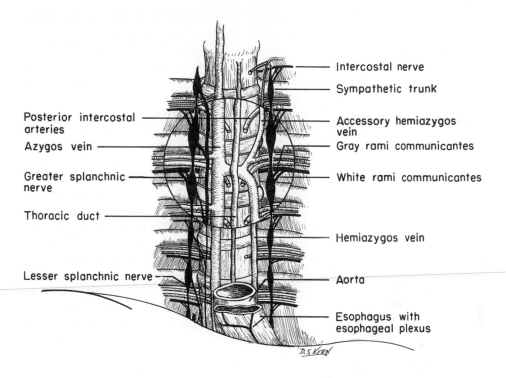

Posterior intercostal arteries

Azygos vein

Greater splanchnic nerve

Thoracic duct

Lesser splanchnic nerve

Intercostal nerve

Sympathetic trunk

Accessory hemiazygos vein

Gray rami communicantes

White rami communicantes

Hemiazygos vein

Aorta

Esophagus with esophageal plexus

D.S.KERN

Fig. 23. Structures within the posterior mediastinum.

vagus, and cardiac nerves; and the sympathetic trunk. The **anterior mediastinum** is a limited area anterior to the pericardium and contains connective tissue with some remains of the thymus, fat, and lymph nodes. The **middle mediastinum,** centrally located and limited by the fibrous pericardium, contains the heart and its eight great vessels, namely, the aorta, the pulmonary artery, the superior and inferior venae cavae, and the four pulmonary veins. Laterally, to either side of the pericardium, the phrenic nerve and the pericardiophrenic vessels course between the parietal pericardium and the mediastinal parietal pleura. The **posterior mediastinum,** posterior to the pericardium and the diaphragm, contains the descending (thoracic) aorta, the posterior intercostal vessels, the azygos and hemiazygos veins, the thoracic duct, the vagus and splanchnic nerves, the sympathetic trunk, and the esophagus.

Aorta

In the thorax the **aorta** is divided for descriptive purposes into the ascending, arch, and descending parts. The **ascending aorta,** originating at the aortic orifice, passes superiorly to the level of the second costal cartilage, where it becomes the arch. At its origin its lumen is not uniform owing to the aortic sinuses, which are opposite the cusps of the aortic semilunar valves. From two of these dilatations the right and left coronary arteries originate. The **arch of the aorta** begins at the level of the second costal cartilage, ascends to the level of the middle of the manubrium, and then arches to the left and anteroposteriorly to reach the lower border of the fourth thoracic vertebra, where it becomes the descending aorta. The **brachiocephalic** (innominate), **left common carotid,** and **left subclavian arteries** arise from the arch. The **ligamentum arteriosum,** the remnant of the ductus arteriosus, passes from the inferior aspect of the arch to the left pulmonary artery. The **left recurrent branch** (inferior laryngeal) of the vagus nerve loops around the arch adjacent to the ligamentum arteriosum, to pass to the tracheo-esophageal groove, where it ascends to reach the larynx. The **descending aorta** continues from the arch to pass through the posterior mediastinum, inclining to the right and then anteriorly to gain a position anterior to the vertebral column. It passes into the abdomen through the aortic opening in the diaphragm, opposite the lower border of the twelfth thoracic vertebra, to become the abdominal aorta. Its branches include, from the anterior aspect, **two left bronchial** and several small branches to the esophagus, mediastinum, diaphragm, and pericardium, and from the posterior aspect, nine pair of **posterior** (aortic) **intercostal** and the two **subcostal arteries.** The posterior intercostal arteries divide to send one branch anteriorly into the intercostal space and a second branch posteriorly to the deep muscles of the back, the vertebral column, and the spinal cord. The subcostal arteries follow the lower border of the twelfth rib to supply the abdominal wall musculature.

Azygos System of Veins

The **azygos system of veins** drains most of the blood from the thorax, back, and posterior wall of the abdomen. The **azygos vein,** formed by the junction of the right subcostal and the right ascending lumbar veins, ascends through the posterior and superior mediastina receiving blood from the posterior intercostal veins as high as the level of the third intercostal space. Arching over the root of the right lung, it empties into the superior vena cava. It may deviate to the right, cleaving the developing right lung to demarcate an **azygos lobule.** The **hemiazygos vein,** formed by the junction of the left subcostal and the left ascending lumbar veins, receives the posterior intercostal veins draining the ninth, tenth, and eleventh left intercostal spaces. It crosses the midline to empty into the azygos vein. The **accessory hemiazygos** usually begins at the fourth intercostal vein on the left side, descends to the eighth or ninth space receiving the intervening intercostal veins, to empty into the azygos or hemiazygos. The **superior intercostal veins** drain the second and third intercostal spaces. The right vessel joins the azygos, and the left vein drains into the left brachiocephalic vein. The **first intercostal veins** on both sides drain directly into both brachiocephalic veins.

Sympathetic Trunk, Phrenic and Vagus Nerves

The **sympathetic trunk,** or vertebral chain, is a series of ganglia (collections of nerve cell bodies) connected by interganglionic nervous tissue. It extends from the **superior cervical ganglion** at the base of the skull to the **ganglion impar** at the coccyx. The cell bodies of the preganglionic fibers passing to the chain ganglia are located in the **intermediolateral cell column** of gray matter of the spinal cord from the **first thoracic to the second or third lumbar spinal level.** The **preganglionic fibers** leave the central nervous system by way of the anterior root of a spinal nerve to pass to the ganglia via the **white rami communicantes.** The cell bodies of the **postganglionic neurons,** located within the chain ganglia, send their fibers by way of **gray rami communicantes** back to the spinal nerve to be distributed with its peripheral branches. Preganglionic fibers may also form **splanchnic nerves** by passing through the chain ganglia without synapsing and continue to para- or preaortic ganglia, where they synapse with the postganglionic cell bodies. In the thorax the **greater splanchnic nerve** is formed by filaments from the fifth through tenth ganglia, the **lesser splanchnic** from the tenth and eleventh, and the **least splanchnic** from the twelfth ganglion. These nerves descend anteromedially and pass through the diaphragm to terminate at **preaortic** or **para-aortic ganglia** in the abdomen. Preganglionic fibers may also pass up or down the chain to synapse in ganglia at higher or lower levels, where gray rami communicantes carry the postganglionic fiber to the spinal nerves.

The **phrenic nerve,** which arises from the fourth cervical spinal nerve (with additional twigs from the third and fifth cervical spinal nerves) descends obliquely across the scalenus anterior muscle, passing anterior to the first part of the subclavian artery to enter the thorax. It descends through the thorax between the mediastinal parietal pleura and the fibrous pericardium to supply the diaphragm.

After traversing the neck, the **vagus nerves** enter the thorax anterior to the subclavian arteries. The right vagus gives a **recurrent branch** which loops around the corresponding subclavian artery, while the recurrent branch from the left vagus loops around the arch of the aorta. Both vagi pass posterior to the root of the lung, giving branches to the **pulmonary plexus,** and thoracic cardiac branches to the **cardiac plexus,** after which they become plexiform around the esophagus. As the **esophageal plexus** the vagi continue through the thorax to pass through the esophageal hiatus of the diaphragm, where they are reconstituted from their plexiform arrangement, the left vagus becomes the **anterior,** and the right the **posterior, gastric nerve.**

Esophagus

The **esophagus** originates at the level of the cricoid cartilage or sixth cervical vertebra as a continuation of the pharynx. It descends through the thorax, posterior to the trachea and anterior to the vertebral bodies, to pass through the **esophageal hiatus** of the diaphragm at the level of the tenth or eleventh thoracic vertebra.

Thoracic Duct

The **thoracic duct** begins in the abdomen as a dilatation, the **cysterna chyli,** which receives lymph drainage from the abdomen, pelvis, and inferior extremities. Traversing the **aortic hiatus** of the diaphragm, it ascends in the thorax between the aorta and the azygos vein. In the neck it arches above the subclavian artery to empty into the junction of the subclavian and internal jugular veins. In addition to draining the lower half of the body, the thoracic duct receives the lymphatic drainage from the left side of the thorax, head, and left upper extremity. The **right lymphatic duct,** a short, half-inch-long vessel, is formed by the junction of the right jugular and subclavian lymphatic trunks and empties at the origin of the right brachiocephalic vein. It drains the right side of the head and thorax and the right upper extremity.

Thymus

The **thymus gland,** a prominent organ in the infant with its greatest relative size at two years and greatest absolute size at puberty, occupies the anterior mediastinum and the anterior part of the superior mediastinum. At puberty it undergoes **involution** and is largely replaced by adipose tissue. It is included among the lymphoid organs, as its only well-established function is lymphocyte production.

ABDOMEN

ABDOMINAL WALL

Surface Anatomy

The **linea alba,** a linear depression in the median plane extending from the xiphoid process to the pubic symphysis, is formed by the fused insertions of the aponeuroses of the anterolateral muscles of the abdominal wall. The **umbilicus** (navel), a puckered, yet depressed scar, is interposed in the linea alba and results from the closure of the umbilical cord shortly after birth. The **linea semilunaris** indicates the lateral extent of the rectus abdominis muscle and its sheath, and the point at which this line meets the ninth costal cartilage on the right indicates the position of the more deeply placed gallbladder. Transverse bands of connective tissue, the **tendinous inscriptions,** are interposed segmentally within the rectus abdominis and are visible as transverse lines in the muscular individual. The **xiphoid process** can be palpated in the midline at the thoracic outlet. The **crests of the ilia,** the **superior** and **inferior anterior iliac spines,** and the **pubic tubercle** are all palpable at the inferior extent of the abdominal wall. **Pubic hair** distribution differs in the two sexes. In the male it is dispersed in a diamond-shaped area and extends from the pubis to the umbilicus, while in the female it is triangular, with the base of the triangle above the mons pubis.

Muscles and Rectus Sheath (Table VIII, Fig. 24)

The anterolateral abdominal wall between the thoracic outlet and innominate bone is composed of the three abdominal muscles (the **obliquus externus abdominis,** the **obliquus internus abdominis,** and the **transversus abdominis**), the transversalis fascia, peritoneum, and overlying skin. Anteriorly the abdominal wall is formed by the **rectus abdominis muscle** and its sheath, and posteriorly by the **quadratus lumborum** and the **psoas major** and **minor muscles.**

The muscles of the anterolateral wall are disposed in three layers. The fibers of the outermost external oblique pass inferomedially; those of the intermediate internal oblique, inferolaterally; and those of the innermost transversus abdominis, transversely. Their insertions by broad aponeuroses into the midline envelop the rectus abdominis and form the rectus sheath. Nerves and vessels to the anterolateral wall course between the internal oblique and transversus abdominis muscles. The posterior abdominal wall muscles, namely, the quadratus

TABLE VIII. MUSCLES OF THE ABDOMINAL WALL

Muscle	Origin	Insertion	Action	Nerve
Obliquus externus	External surface of lower eight ribs	Anterior half of iliac crest and linea alba	Compresses and supports abdominal viscera; rotates and flexes vertebral column	Lower five intercostals, subcostal, and iliohypogastric
Obliquus internus abdominis	Lateral two-thirds of inguinal ligament, iliac crest, and lumbodorsal fascia	Cartilages of lower three or four ribs, linea alba, and by conjoined tendon into pubis	Compresses and supports abdominal viscera; flexes and rotates vertebral column	Lower five intercostals, subcostal, iliohypogastric, and ilioinguinal
Transversus abdominis	Lateral one-third of inguinal ligament, iliac crest, lumbodorsal fascia, and cartilages of lower six ribs	Linea alba and by conjoined tendon into pubis	Compresses and supports abdominal viscera	Lower five intercostals, subcostal, iliohypogastric, and ilioinguinal
Rectus abdominis	Xiphoid process and fifth to seventh cartilages	Crest and symphysis of pubis	Tenses abdominal wall and flexes vertebral column	Lower five intercostals and subcostal
Pyramidalis	Front of pubis and anterior pubic ligament	Linea alba midway between umbilicus and pubis	Tenses linea alba	Subcostal
Quadratus lumborum	Lumbar vertebrae, lumbodorsal fascia, and iliac crest	Lower border of twelfth rib and transverse processes of upper four lumbar vertebrae	Draws last rib toward pelvis and flexes vertebral column laterally	Subcostal and first three or four lumbar
Psoas major	Transverse processes, intervertebral discs and bodies of all lumbar vertebrae	Lesser trochanter of femur	Flexes and medially rotates thigh; flexes vertebral column	Second and third lumbar
Psoas minor	Bodies and intervening discs of twelfth thoracic and first lumbar vertebrae	Pectineal line and iliopectineal eminence	Flexes vertebral column	First lumbar

lumborum and the psoas major and minor, are the deepest lying structures in the small of the back and extend from the twelfth rib to the iliac crest, with the psoas muscles continuing inferiorly into the iliac fossa.

The **rectus sheath** extends from the xiphoid process and adjacent costal cartilages to the pubic bone. It holds the rectus abdominis muscle in place but does not restrict its movement owing to the presence of anterior and posterior fascial clefts. The **anterior wall** of the rectus sheath covers the muscle from end to end, but the **posterior wall** is incomplete superiorly and inferiorly. In the uppermost part of the abdomen the anterior wall of the sheath is formed by the aponeurosis of the external oblique; the posterior wall in this area is absent. From the lower margin of the thoracic outlet to the midpoint between the umbilicus and

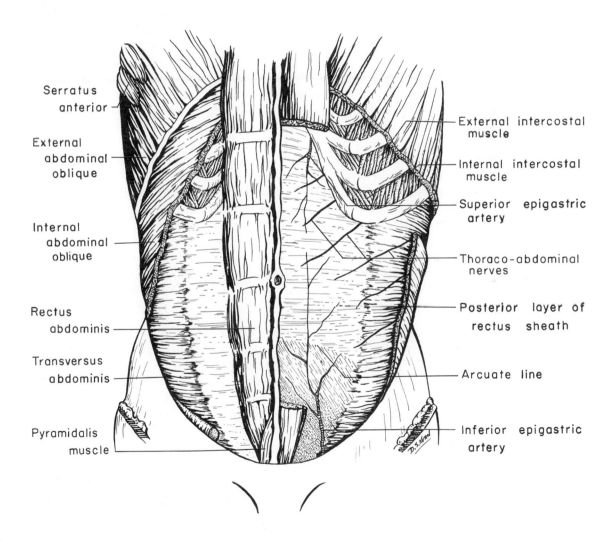

Fig. 24. Abdominal wall musculature and rectus sheath.

pubis, the aponeurosis of the internal oblique splits into two laminae. In this area the anterior wall of the sheath is formed by the aponeurosis of the external oblique and the superficial lamina of the aponeurosis of the internal oblique, while the posterior wall is composed of the deep lamina of the aponeurosis of the internal oblique and the aponeurosis of the transversus abdominis. Inferiorly the anterior wall is formed by the aponeuroses of all three abdominal muscles, whereas posteriorly the wall is lacking and the rectus abdominis rests directly on the **transversalis fascia,** the fascia lining the entire abdominal cavity. The **arcuate line** (semicircular line of Douglas) is the lower edge of the aponeurotic components of the posterior wall of the rectus sheath. **Contents of the sheath** include the rectus abdominis and pyramidalis muscles, terminations of the lower five intercostal and subcostal nerves, and the inferior and superior epigastric arteries and their venae comitantes.

Fasciae

The superficial fascia of the abdominal wall is divided into a **superficial (Camper's layer),** with an increased content of adipose tissue, and a **deep membranous (Scarpa's) layer.** In the male Scarpa's fascia extends over the pubic symphysis and thickens to form the **fundiform ligament** of the penis, which extends inferiorly to attach to the dorsum and sides of this structure. Camper's fascia extends over the inguinal ligament as the **superficial fascia of the thigh.** It continues over the groove between the external genitalia and thigh as the **superficial fascia of the perineum.** Over the scrotum Camper's fascia fuses with Scarpa's, and the superficial fat is lost as this combined layer becomes the **dartos tunic** of the scrotum. This same combined layer, devoid of fat, elongates to ensheathe the penis. Inferiorly Scarpa's fascia passes over the inguinal ligament and is continuous with the **fascia cribrosa** in the thigh; over the perineum it becomes the **external perineal (Colles') fascia.**

Deep fascia of the abdominal wall above the inguinal region is characteristic in that it affords increased freedom of movement.

Inguinal Region (Fig. 25)

Inferiorly the abdominal muscles contribute to the formation of the inguinal ligament and inguinal canal. The **inguinal** (Poupart's) **ligament,** formed by the inferior free border of the aponeurosis of the external abdominal oblique muscle, attaches laterally to the **anterior superior iliac spine** and medially to the **pubic tubercle** and adjacent area. Medially the inguinal ligament splits to form a triangular gap with a **superior** and an **inferior crus.** Intercrural fibers transform this triangular gap into the **superficial inguinal ring,** and extensions from the deep surface of the inguinal ligament pass to the superior pubic ramus to gain additional attachment and separate structures passing from the abdomen into the thigh.

The **lacunar** (Gimbernat's) **ligament** is a portion of the medial end of the inferior crus that rolls under the spermatic cord to attach to the **pectineal line** on the superior pubic ramus lateral to the pubic tubercle. This portion is

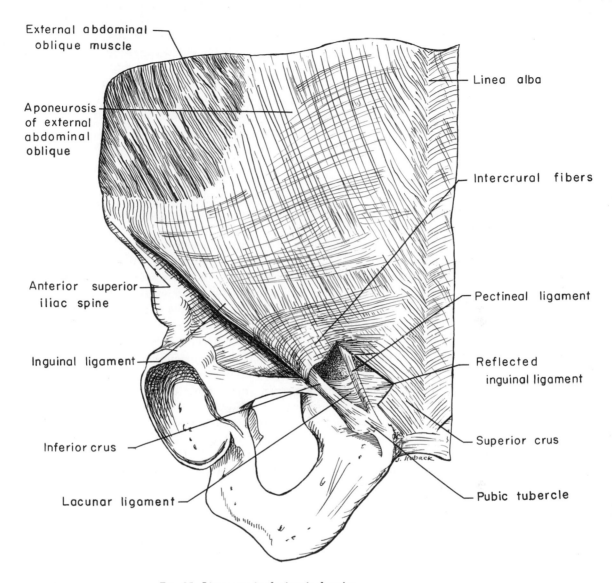

Fig. 25. Ligaments in the inguinal region.

triangular in form and has a lateral crescentic base and an apex directed medially towards the pubic tubercle. The **pectineal ligament** (of Cooper), a lateral extension from the lacunar ligament, forms a strong narrow band attaching along the **pectineal line.** A tendinous medial expansion continuous with the lacunar ligament sweeps beneath the superficial inguinal ring to the linea alba as the **reflected** (reflex) **inguinal ligament.**

The **superficial inguinal ring,** easily palpable in the living subject, allows passage of the spermatic cord in the male or the round ligament in the female from the inguinal canal to the scrotum or labium majus. The **deep inguinal**

ring is an opening in the transversalis fascia, a half inch above the midinguinal point, immediately lateral to the inferior epigastric vessels. The **inguinal canal** is a narrow channel an inch and a half in length, passing between the deep and superficial rings. This passage is formed when the **processus vaginalis** evaginates the abdominal wall during the descent of the testes into the scrotum. The inguinal canal, directed inferiorly, medially, and anteriorly, has a floor, a roof, and anterior and posterior walls. In the male it transmits the spermatic cord, cremasteric vessels, genital branch of the genitofemoral nerve, and cutaneous branches of the ilioinguinal nerve. In the female the round ligament of the uterus with its vessels and nerves traverse the canal.

The grooved surface of the inguinal ligament, supplemented laterally by the pectineal ligament and medially by the lacunar ligament, forms the **floor** of the inguinal canal. The **anterior wall** is formed by the aponeurosis of the external abdominal oblique muscle, and in its lateral half by the muscle fibers of the internal abdominal oblique muscle. The canal is **roofed** by the arching fibers of the internal abdominal oblique and its medial continuation, the cremaster muscle. Transversalis fascia covers the entire **posterior wall,** reinforced laterally by the aponeurosis of the transversus abdominis muscle and medially by the conjoint tendon (falx inguinalis), lacunar ligament, and reflected inguinal ligament.

The inguinal canal and the superficial and deep rings are potential areas of weakness in the abdominal wall through which inguinal hernias pass. The anterior wall of the canal is strongest opposite the deep inguinal ring because of the presence of the muscle fibers of the internal oblique; similarly the posterior wall is strongest opposite the superficial ring because of the presence of the conjoint tendon and the lacunar ligament.

A **hernia** is an abnormal protrusion of any structure beyond its normal site. In the inguinal region hernias are classified as direct or indirect, depending upon their course through the abdominal wall. A **direct inguinal hernia** bypasses the deep inguinal ring to penetrate the posterior wall of the inguinal canal medial to the inferior epigastric artery. This area of direct inguinal hernia, **Hesselbach's triangle,** is formed medially by the rectus abdominis, laterally by the inferior epigastric artery, and inferiorly by the inguinal ligament. The direct inguinal hernia occurs more frequently in elderly people and is usually limited to the region of the superficial ring. The wall of the hernial sac of a direct hernia is composed, from within outward, of peritoneum, extraperitoneal connective tissue, transversalis fascia, fascia of the transversus abdominis, cremasteric muscle and fascia, external spermatic fascia, subcutaneous fascia, and skin.

The **indirect inguinal hernia** is three times more common in the male than the direct hernia. It traverses the deep inguinal ring (lateral to the inferior epigastric artery) and passes through the inguinal canal to exit through the superficial ring into the scrotum. Thus, the indirect inguinal hernia follows the same course as the spermatic cord. This type is also known as the **congenital hernia,** since failure of closure of the processus vaginalis predisposes to this type of hernia. The coverings of the indirect hernia are the same as the coverings of the spermatic cord.

The internal aspect of the anterior abdominal wall presents five longitudinal ridges of peritoneum. The single median ridge, the **median umbilical ligament,** encloses a slender fibrous cord, the remnant of the **urachus,** which passes from the apex of the bladder to the umbilicus between the peritoneum and the transversalis fascia. Two **lateral umbilical ligaments,** representing the **obliterated umbilical arteries,** continue from the superior vesicular branch of the internal iliac artery to pass to the umbilicus. The **inferior epigastric arteries** and **veins** raise ridges of peritoneum as they pass toward the rectus abdominis, and their position immediately medial to the deep inguinal ring aids in distinguishing direct from indirect inguinal hernias.

Arteries and Nerves

The **inferior epigastric artery,** a branch of the external iliac, pierces the transversalis fascia to ascend behind the rectus abdominis, but within the rectus sheath, to anastomose with the **superior epigastric artery** from the internal thoracic. Branches of the superior and inferior epigastric arteries include muscular branches to the rectus muscle and cutaneous branches to overlying skin. Additional branches of the inferior epigastric artery include the **external spermatic,** to the cremaster muscle or fascia, which passes through the deep inguinal ring into the inguinal canal, and **pubic branches** ramifying on the pubic bone. The **deep iliac circumflex artery,** a second branch of the external iliac, passes laterally to ramify on and supply the iliacus muscle in the iliac fossa.

Innervation of muscles and skin of the anterolateral abdominal wall is derived from the anterior primary rami of spinal nerves from the seventh thoracic to the fourth lumbar, as thoracoabdominal, subcostal, iliohypogastric, and ilioinguinal nerves. The **thoracoabdominal** (lower intercostals) and **subcostal nerves** pass deep to costal cartilages and descend medially between the transversus abdominis and the internal abdominal oblique muscles to supply abdominal muscles and terminate as lateral and anterior cutaneous branches in line with the more superior intercostal nerves.

The **iliohypogastric nerve** (T_{12} and L_1) emerges at the upper lateral border of the psoas major, crosses the quadratus lumborum to the crest of the ilium, where it pierces the transversus abdominis muscle. It gives **lateral cutaneous branches,** which supply the skin immediately above the iliac crest and the gluteal region, and **anterior cutaneous branches,** which pierce the aponeurosis of the external abdominal oblique an inch above the subcutaneous inguinal ring to innervate the skin of the hypogastric region. The **ilioinguinal nerve** (L_1) follows a course parallel but inferior to the iliohypogastric nerve, piercing the internal abdominal oblique and accompanying the spermatic cord through the superficial inguinal ring. It supplies skin over the upper medial part of the thigh and root of the penis and scrotum or mons pubic and labia majora.

LUMBAR PLEXUS (FIG. 26)

The **lumbar plexus** is formed by the anterior primary rami of the first four lumbar spinal nerves with a contribution from the twelfth thoracic nerve. Part of the fourth lumbar nerve joins with the fifth lumbar nerve to form the lumbosacral trunk, which contributes to the formation of the sacral plexus. The

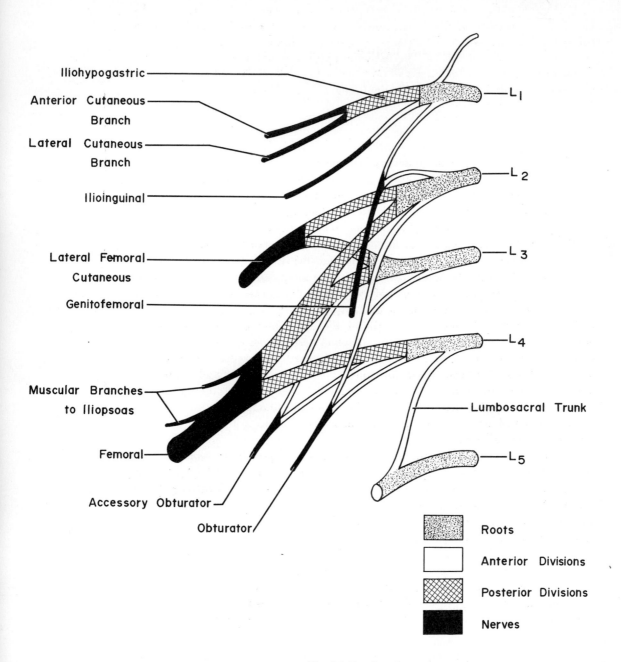

Iliohypogastric

Anterior Cutaneous
Branch

Lateral Cutaneous
Branch

Ilioinguinal

Lateral Femoral
Cutaneous

Genitofemoral

Muscular Branches
to Iliopsoas

Femoral

Accessory Obturator

Obturator

L₁

L₂

L₃

L₄

Lumbosacral Trunk

L₅

Roots

Anterior Divisions

Posterior Divisions

Nerves

Fig. 26. Lumbar plexus.

lumbar plexus differs from the brachial plexus in that no intricate interlacing of fibers occurs. From intervertebral foramina, the nerves pass obliquely outward behind the psoas major and anterior to the quadratus lumborum muscles to form their several branches.

The **iliohypogastric** and **ilioinguinal nerves** described above are the first two branches of the lumbar plexus. **Muscular branches** arising segmentally as independent twigs pass from all four lumbar spinal nerves to the quatratus lumborum, and from the second and third lumbar nerves to the psoas major and minor muscles. The **genitofemoral nerve** (L_1 and L_2) passes through the substance of the psoas major, emerges from its medial border close to the lower lumbar vertebrae, and descends on the anterior surface of this muscle. This nerve divides into two branches, an **external spermatic** and a **lumboinguinal.** The former pierces the transversalis fascia to pass through the inguinal canal behind the spermatic cord and to supply the cremaster muscle and the skin of the scrotum. The lumboinguinal branch descends on the external iliac artery to enter the femoral sheath and to supply skin of the upper and medial regions of the thigh. The **lateral femoral cutaneous nerve** (L_2 and L_3) emerges at the middle of the lateral border of the psoas major to cross the iliacus muscle obliquely toward the anterior superior iliac spine. It courses deep to the inguinal ligament to be distributed to the skin of the lateral aspect of the thigh. The **obturator nerve** (L_2, L_3, and L_4) descends through the substance of the psoas major to emerge from the medial border of this muscle near the brim of the pelvis. It passes behind the common iliac vessels, along the lateral wall of the pelvis superoanterior to the obturator vessels, to leave the pelvis through the obturator canal. Its distribution will be considered with the inferior extremity.

The **femoral nerve** (L_2, L_3, and L_4), the largest branch of the lumbar plexus, descends through the fibers of the psoas major to emerge from its lateral border, gives a few filaments to the iliacus and psoas major and minor, then continues inferiorly passing deep to the inguinal ligament to enter the thigh. The anterior primary ramus of the fourth lumbar nerve divides into an upper and lower division. The upper division contributes to the lumbar plexus, the lower division joins the fifth lumbar to form the **lumbosacral trunk** passing to the sacral plexus.

DIAPHRAGM (FIG. 27)

The **diaphragm,** a movable musculotendinous partition between the cavities of the thorax and the abdomen, forms the concave roof of the abdominal cavity and the convex floor of the thoracic cavity. The diaphragm rises higher on the right side than on the left owing to the larger right lobe of the liver. The central portion is aponeurotic and forms the strong **central tendon,** which is indistinctly divided into three leaflets. The muscle fibers of the diaphragm originate at the margins of the thoracic outlet and insert into the central tendon. The short and narrow **sternal portion** arises as small slips from the back of the xiphoid process; the extensive **costal portion,** from the inner surface of the lower six costal cartilages; and the **vertebral portion,** from the arcuate ligaments and

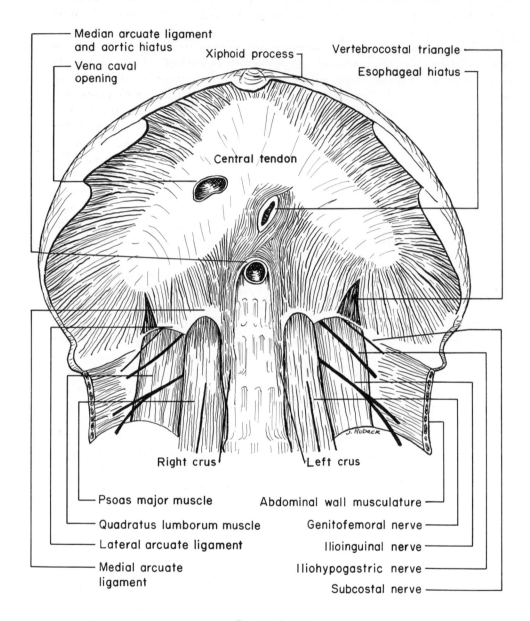

Median arcuate ligament and aortic hiatus

Vena caval opening

Xiphoid process

Vertebrocostal triangle

Esophageal hiatus

Central tendon

Right crus

Left crus

J. Ruback

Psoas major muscle

Quadratus lumborum muscle

Lateral arcuate ligament

Medial arcuate ligament

Abdominal wall musculature

Genitofemoral nerve

Ilioinguinal nerve

Iliohypogastric nerve

Subcostal nerve

Fig. 27. Diaphragm.

the upper lumbar vertebrae as a pair of muscular crura. Each crus is a thick, fleshy bundle which tapers inferiorly and becomes tendinous. The **left crus** attaches to the upper two lumbar vertebrae and the intervening vertebral disc; the **right crus,** to the upper three lumbar vertebrae and intervening discs. Fibers of each crus spread out and ascend to attach to the central tendon, with the right crus encircling the esophagus. The medial, lateral, and midline median arcuate ligaments give partial origin to the diaphragm. The unpaired **median arcuate ligament,** opposite the twelfth thoracic vertebra, arches between the right and left crura and crosses the aorta as it enters the abdomen. The paired **medial arcuate ligaments** are highly arched and pass laterally from the tendinous part of each crus to curve across the psoas and attach to the tip of the transverse process of the first or second lumbar vertebra. The paired **lateral arcuate ligaments** stretch across the quadratus lumborum from the tip of the transverse process of the first or second lumbar vertebra to the tip and lower margin of the twelfth rib. That portion of the diaphragm attaching to the lateral arcuate ligament is thin and sometimes devoid of muscular fibers, with only connective tissue separating the pleura from the renal fat. Through this weakened area, the **vertebrocostal triangle,** abdominal contents may herniate into the thorax.

The continuity of the diaphragm is interrupted by three large, and several small, apertures. Between the crura the **aortic hiatus,** at the level of the twelfth thoracic vertebra, is bridged anteriorly by the median arcuate ligament. This aperture transmits the aorta, the azygos vein, and the thoracic duct. At the level of the tenth thoracic vertebra the oval **esophageal hiatus** is situated obliquely behind the central tendon an inch to the left of the midline and is surrounded by the right crus of the diaphragm. It transmits the esophagus, gastric nerves (vagi), and esophageal branches of the left gastric vessels. At the level of the eighth thoracic vertebra the wide **caval opening** is located within the central tendon of the diaphragm an inch to the right of the median plane. It transmits the inferior vena cava, terminal branches of the right phrenic nerve, and lymph vessels. Additional structures passing between the thorax and the abdomen include the superior epigastirc vessels, musculophrenic vessels, the lower five thoracoabdominal nerves, and the subcostal vessels and nerve. The sympathetic trunk lies behind the medial arcuate ligament, and the three splanchnic nerves pierce the crus on their side of origin to enter the abdomen.

Innervation to the diaphragm is derived from the **phrenic nerve** and from twigs of the **lower intercostal nerves.** The **inferior phrenic artery,** a branch of the abdominal aorta, is the chief arterial supply to the diaphragm; additional blood is supplied from the **pericardiophrenic branch** of the internal thoracic artery, from irregular twigs of the thoracic aorta, and peripherally via branches from the **musculophrenic artery.**

ABDOMINAL CAVITY

The **abdominal cavity,** the largest cavity in the body, is bounded anteriorly by the rectus abdominis; laterally by the external, internal, and transverse abdominal and iliacus muscles; and posteriorly by the vertebral column and the psoas major and minor and quadratus lumborum muscles. Superficially it is subdivided for descriptive purposes into nine regions by two horizontal and three vertical arbitrary lines (or planes). The horizontal lines are the **transpyloric,** at the level of the pylorus of the stomach, and the **intertubercular,** at the level of the iliac tubercles. One of the vertical lines is the midline; the two lateral lines bisect the clavicles. The resulting **subdivisions of the abdomen** are from superior to inferior, **right** and **left hypochondriac** and **middle epigastric, right** and **left lumbar** and **middle umbilical,** and **right** and **left inguinal** and **middle hypogastric.**

Peritoneal Cavity (Fig. 28)

A serous membrane, the **peritoneum,** lines the walls of the abdominal cavity. Developmentally, abdominal and pelvic viscera invaginate into the abdominal cavity carrying peritoneum before them. This results in a covering of **visceral peritoneum** continuous with the **parietal peritoneum** lining the abdominal walls. The layers of apposing peritoneum between viscera and body wall or between two organs form the **mesenteries,** or **ligaments,** of the abdominal cavity. The disappearance, fusion, shifting, shortening, or redundant growth of these peritoneal folds during development divides the peritoneal cavity into two distinct parts, the greater and lesser sac. The **lesser sac** (omental bursa) is situated posterior to the lesser omentum, stomach, and gastrocolic ligament. It is limited inferiorly by the transverse colon with its mesocolon and bounded on the left by the gastrolienal and lienorenal ligaments. To its right, the omental bursa communicates via the **epiploic foramen** (of Winslow) with the **greater sac,** i.e., the remainder of the peritoneal cavity. In the male, the peritoneum forms a closed cavity, while in the female, it communicates with the exterior through the openings of the fallopian tubes. Structures within the abdominal cavity not suspended from the body wall by a mesentery or from other viscera by a visceral ligament, are considered to be **retroperitoneal.**

Nerves

Parasympathetic innervation of the abdominal viscera is derived from vagal and sacral nerves. The **left** and **right vagus nerves** form a plexus around the esophagus and, upon passing through the diaphragm, are reconstituted as the anterior and posterior gastric nerves, respectively. The **anterior gastric nerve** innervates the liver, gallbladder, bile ducts, pylorus of the stomach, duodenum, and pancreas. The **posterior gastric nerve** supplies the rest of the stomach and then joins the celiac plexus. Here it intermingles with sympathetic filaments and is distributed, with branches of the celiac and its subsidiary plexuses, to the kidney, small intestine, and ascending and transverse colon. The distal portion of the large intestine beyond the splenic flexure is innervated by **sacral parasympathetic nerves.** Postganglionic parasympathetic cell bodies are usually located within the substance of the organ they supply.

The principal sources of sympathetic innervation to abdominal viscera are the **greater** (T_5 to T_9), **lesser** (T_{10} and T_{11}), and **least** (T_{12}) **splanchnic**

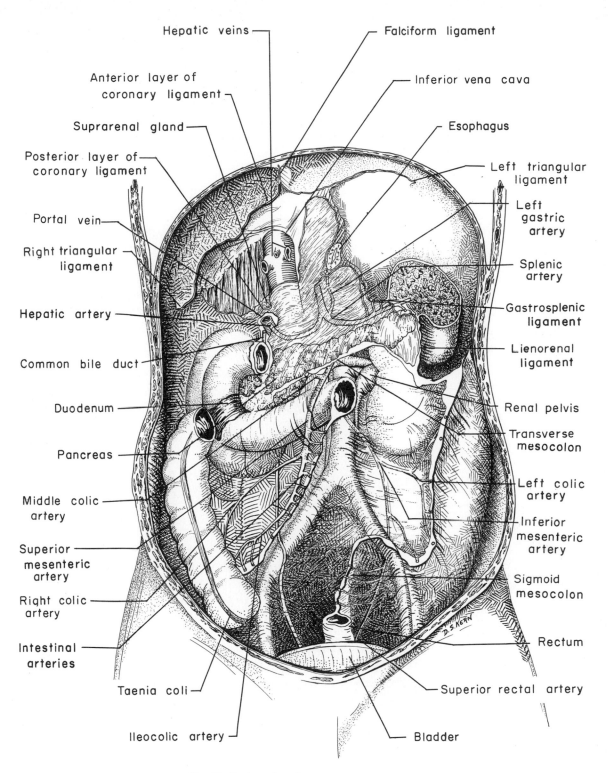

Hepatic veins — Falciform ligament

Anterior layer of coronary ligament — Inferior vena cava

Suprarenal gland — Esophagus

Posterior layer of coronary ligament — Left triangular ligament

Portal vein — Left gastric artery

Right triangular ligament — Splenic artery

Hepatic artery — Gastrosplenic ligament

Common bile duct — Lienorenal ligament

Duodenum — Renal pelvis

Pancreas — Transverse mesocolon

Middle colic artery — Left colic artery

Superior mesenteric artery — Inferior mesenteric artery

Right colic artery — Sigmoid mesocolon

Intestinal arteries — Rectum

Taenia coli — Superior rectal artery

Ileocolic artery — Bladder

Fig. 28. Peritoneal cavity.

nerves. Additional sympathetic fibers, the **lumbar splanchnic nerves,** arise directly from the lumbar vertebral chain. The sympathetic nerves form plexuses around the main branches of the abdominal aorta. The large **celiac ganglia** and **plexus** lie adjacent to the celiac artery; smaller plexuses surround the phrenic, hepatic, renal, splenic, superior and inferior mesenteric, gastric, suprarenal, and gonadal arteries. Ganglia associated with these plexuses contain postganglionic sympathetic cell bodies, but fibers distributed by the plexus consist of both sympathetic and parasympathetic components.

GASTROINTESTINAL TRACT

STOMACH (FIG. 29)

The **stomach,** a very distensible organ, is the first abdominal subdivision of the alimentary canal. Its size, position, and configuration are determined by its physiological state, the impingement of other abdominal viscera, and general body build. Classically it is described as pear-shaped, with its blunt upper end related to the diaphragm to the left of the median plane. The upper and lower

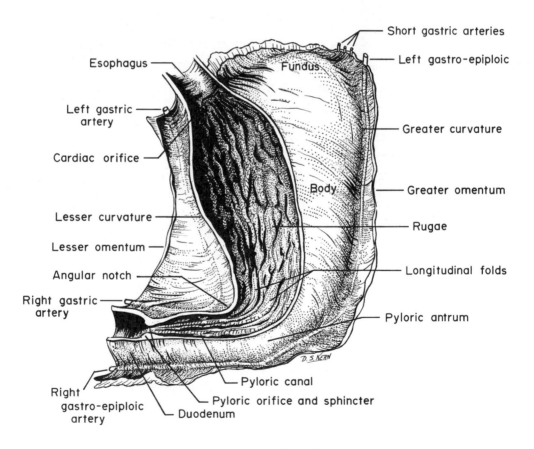

Fig. 29. Stomach.

ends of the stomach are relatively fixed, and its midportion moves as the position of the other viscera or its contents may require. It is subdivided into the cardiac portion, the fundus, the body, and the pyloric portion, with anterior and posterior surfaces, and greater and lesser curvatures. The esophagus joins the stomach at the **cardiac orifice,** with the limited **cardiac portion** located adjacent to this opening. The **fundus** is the full-rounded uppermost part above the level of the esophageal junction, while the main part of the stomach, the **body,** lies below the fundus. The **pyloric region** includes the dilated antrum, the pyloric canal, and the pyloric orifice, which is surrounded by a thickened muscular coat, the **pyloric sphincter.** The anterior surface of the stomach is closely related to the diaphragm, the left lobe of the liver, and the left rectus abdominis muscle. The posterior surface is related to many structures, which collectively make up the "bed of the stomach." These include the body of the pancreas, the splenic artery, the medial border of the left kidney, the left suprarenal gland, the spleen, the diaphragm, the transverse colon, and the transverse mesocolon.

The **lesser curvature** of the stomach is concave and affords attachment for the **lesser omentum** (gastrohepatic and hepatoduodenal ligaments), a double layer of peritoneum extending between the stomach and the liver. At the lesser curvature the peritoneum separates to cover the anterior and posterior surfaces of the stomach and fuses at the **greater curvature,** where it continues as the greater omentum. From the convex greater curvature of the stomach, the **greater omentum** passes inferiorly to cover most of the abdominal contents. Inferiorly it reflects back on itself as four fused layers of peritoneum and passes over the transverse colon to attach to the posterior body wall. That portion of the greater omentum between the transverse colon and the greater curvature is referred to as the **gastrocolic ligament.** Between the transverse colon and the body wall, the greater omentum fuses with the transverse mesocolon.

Blood Vessels and Nerves

The stomach receives a rich blood supply from all branches of the **celiac artery.** This vessel originates from the anterior aspect of the uppermost part of the abdominal aorta as a short trunk and gives rise to splenic, hepatic, and left gastric arteries. The **left gastric,** the smallest of the three branches, ascends behind the lesser sac toward the esophagus to pass forward and then descend between the layers of the lesser omentum. This artery parallels and supplies the lesser curvature of the stomach, gives branches to the lower esophagus, and terminates by anastomosing with the **right gastric artery.** The latter vessel, arising as a branch of the hepatic artery, enters the lesser omentum from its retroperitoneal position and passes to the left, between the layers of the lesser omentum along the lesser curvature, to supply the stomach. The splenic artery sends **short gastric branches** and the **left gastroepiploic branch** to the stomach. The former pass through the gastrolienal ligament to the upper part of the greater curvature of the stomach. The **left gastroepiploic,** a long branch passing first through the gastrolienal ligament and continuing between the layers of the greater omentum, supplies the greater curvature of the stomach and the greater omentum and anastomoses with the **right gastroepiploic artery.** The latter vessel, a branch of the gastroduodenal from the hepatic artery, passes to the left between the layers of the greater omentum also to supply the greater curvature of the stomach. Veins draining the stomach correspond in position to the arteries and are named similarly, except for the **pyloric vein,** which is the companion of the right gastric artery, and the **coronary vein,** the companion of the left gastric artery.

The plexiform arrangement of the left and right vagi around the esophagus is reconstituted as anterior and posterior gastric nerves as the esophagus enters the abdomen. They are distributed with the **celiac plexus** and provide **parasympathetic** innervation to the abdominal viscera. The stomach receives its **sympathetic** nerve supply from the celiac plexus.

SMALL INTESTINE (FIG. 30)

The **small intestine,** a convoluted tube continuing from the pylorus to the ileocecal valve, is subdivided into the duodenum, the jejunum, and the ileum. It gradually diminishes in diameter and is encircled laterally and superiorly by the large intestine. Anteriorly, it is related to the greater omentum and the anterior abdominal wall, and posteriorly, to the posterior abdominal wall, the pancreas, the kidney, and occasionally the rectum.

The **duodenum,** the first segment (ten inches) of the small intestine, has the widest lumen and the thickest wall of any region of the intestine. It follows a C-shaped course and is divided into four portions. The first (superior) portion, arising from the pylorus of the stomach, passes posteriorly and superiorly, and at the neck of the gallbladder makes a sharp inferior bend to become the second (descending) part. It is connected by the **heptoduodenal ligament** to the porta hepatis. The second segment passes inferiorly, and opposite the disc between the third and fourth lumbar vertebrae bends to the left to become the third (horizontal) part. The bile and the pancreatic ducts penetrate the posteromedial surface of the second part to form the **hepatopancreatic ampulla** (of Vater). The third portion passes horizontally across the vertebral column, the crura of the diaphragm, the inferior vena cava, and the aorta to become the fourth (ascending) part. The fourth and terminal part of the duodenum passes upward to the left side of the aorta and head of the pancreas to bend sharply at the duodenojejunal flexure, where it becomes the jejunum. Except for about an inch at its origin and termination, the duodenum is entirely retroperitoneal. A fibromuscular band, the **ligament of Trietz,** attaches the small intestine to the posterior abdominal wall at the duodenojejunal flexure. The internal structure of the duodenum presents rather short broad villi and the **duodenal papilla** at the entrances of the common bile duct and the pancreatic duct.

The junctional area between the jejunum and the ileum has no gross morphological points of distinction. The gross division is arbitrary; however, histological characteristics change so that sections taken from the two areas can be distinguished. The **jejunum** is wider and has thicker walls and prominent circular folds (plicae circulares); the **ileum** has fewer circular folds, has aggregates of lymph nodules (Peyer's patches), and terminates by joining the medial aspect of the cecum at the **ileocecal valve.** The jejunum and ileum are attached

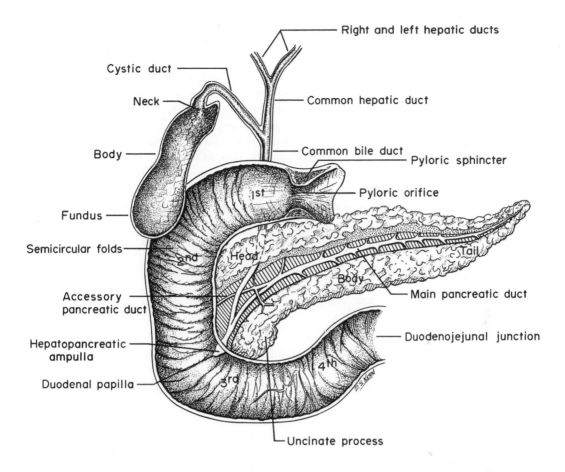

Fig. 30. Duodenum, pancreas, and gallbladder.

to the posterior abdominal wall by an extensive fold of peritoneum, the fan-shaped **mesentery,** which projects eight to ten inches into the abdominal cavity. The **root of the mesentery,** six to seven inches long, is attached obliquely along the posterior abdominal wall and crosses successively the horizontal part of the duodenum, the aorta, the inferior vena cava, the right ureter, and the right psoas major and minor muscles.

Arteries

The duodenum receives its blood supply from the **superior pancreatico-duodenal branch** of the gastroduodenal artery, which passes between the head of the pancreas and the duodenum to its distribution, and the **inferior pancreaticoduodenal branch** of the superior mesenteric artery, which follows a similar course to give twigs to the duodenum. **Intestinal arteries,** twelve to fifteen branches of the superior mesenteric artery, lie parallel to each other between the layers of the mesentery before forming a series of two to five loops (or arcades) from which arteries arise and encircle and supply the intestine.

LARGE INTESTINE

The **large intestine,** extending from the ileum to the anus, is about four to five feet in length and diminishes in diameter from its origin toward its termination. It differs from the small intestine in its greater luminal size; more fixed position; the presence of **sacculations,** or haustra; the presence of fat tabs on its external coat, the **appendices epiploicae;** and the disposition of its external longitudinal muscular coat into three longitudinal bands, the **taenia coli.**

The **cecum,** the beginning of the large intestine, is a large blind pouch two to three inches long. The ileum opens into it medially via a longitudinal slit, the **ileocecal orifice,** guarded by upper and lower thin protruding lips, the **ileocecal valve.** Below the orifice, the vermiform appendix opens into the cecum and usually lies in the right iliac fossa immediately above the left half of the inguinal ligament.

The **vermiform appendix,** a blind tube about a quarter of an inch thick and four inches long, is suspended by a mesentery which is continuous with, or attached to, the mesentery of the small intestine. The appendix has no fixed position, but commonly moves with the cecum and is most usually below and behind it.

The **ascending colon** passes superiorly on the posterior abdominal wall from the right iliac fossa to become the transverse colon as it bends to the left at the **hepatic flexure.** This first portion normally is retroperitoneal, but it may possess a limited mesentery. The **transverse colon** extends to the left from the hepatic flexure. It passes transversely across the superior region of the abdominal cavity to the spleen, where it makes a sharp inferior bend at the **splenic flexure** to become the descending colon. It is always suspended from the posterior abdominal wall by the **transverse mesocolon,** which varies in length and thereby permits the location of the transverse colon to vary in position from just inferior to the liver down to the level of the iliac fossae. From the splenic flexure the **descending colon** passes inferiorly along the lateral border of the left kidney in the angle between the psoas major muscle and the quadratus lumborum, to become the **sigmoid colon** at the level of the iliac crest. This portion, usually situated within the pelvis, may be displaced into the abdominal cavity owing to its long mesentery. Being fixed in position only at its junctions with the descending colon and the rectum, the sigmoid colon curves on itself, resulting in an S-shaped configuration. From the sigmoid colon, the **rectum** continues inferiorly to follow the sacral curvature to the pelvic diaphragm, where it makes a ninety-degree bend to become the **anal canal.** Externally the rectum has no sacculation; the taenia coli spread out to form a uniform outer muscular coat, and the peritoneum covers only its anterior and lateral aspects. From the rectum, the peritoneum reflects onto the bladder in the male to form the **rectovesical pouch,** and onto the uterus in the female as the **rectouterine pouch.**

The **anal canal** is surrounded by the levator ani and external anal sphincter muscles as it passes through the pelvic diaphragm posterior to the perineal body. The **external anal sphincter** is disposed into a **subcutaneous portion** just deep to the skin, a **superficial part** attaching to the tip of the coccyx and perineal body, and a **deep portion** associated with the puborectalis muscle (a portion of the levator ani), which also attaches anteriorly to the perineal body. Internally the mucosa of the upper half of the anal canal forms five to ten vertical folds designated as the **anal,** or **rectal, columns.** Each fold contains small veins which, if they become overdistended, result in internal hemorrhoids. The lower ends of these columns are joined by small crescentic folds of mucosa, the **anal valves** (anal sinuses), with the scalloped **pectinate line** present at their lower limit. In this region, the anal mucosa merges with the skin of the anus as the **mucocutaneous line.** Venous varicosities in the area below the pectinate line result in external hemorrhoids.

Arteries

The blood supply to the large intestine is from branches of the superior and inferior mesenteric and internal iliac arteries. The **middle colic branch** of the superior mesenteric artery passes between the layers of the transverse mesocolon to divide into right and left branches supplying the transverse colon. Arising at about the middle of the superior mesenteric artery, the **right colic branch** courses to the right behind the peritoneum toward the middle of the ascending colon to divide into ascending and descending branches. They supply the ascending colon and then anastomose, respectively, with the middle colic and ileocolic arteries. The **ileocolic artery,** the terminal branch of the superior mesenteric, sends a colic branch to supply the cecum and the appendix and small ileal branches to the distal portion of the ileum. The inferior mesenteric artery arises from the anterior aspect of the aorta one to two inches above its bifurcation. Coursing inferiorly in a retroperitoneal position, the inferior mesenteric artery gives origin to the **left colic artery,** which passes to the left and divides into ascending and descending branches to supply the left half of the transverse colon and the descending colon, respectively. Three or four **sigmoid branches** of the inferior mesenteric artery pass within the sigmoid mesocolon to supply the lower part of the descending and sigmoid colon. The inferior mesenteric then terminates as the **superior rectal artery,** which continues inferiorly between the layers of the sigmoid mesocolon to ramify on the upper part of the rectum. Additional blood to the rectum is derived from the **middle rectal branch** of the internal iliac and the **inferior rectal branch** of the internal pudendal arteries.

LIVER (FIG. 31)

The **liver,** the largest gland in the body, is roughly wedge-shaped, with the base of the wedge directed to the right. The **superior** convex **surface** continues undemarcated into the posteroinferior surface. The **anterior surface** of the liver is triangular, slightly convex, and related to the anterior body wall, the diaphragm, and the ribs. The **posterior surface** is roughly triangular and markedly concave from left to right as it passes in front of the vertebral column. The oblong **inferior (visceral) surface** is very uneven and, when hardened in situ, bears the impressions of structures in contact with it. Anteriorly the inferior surface is separated from the anterior surface by a sharp border.

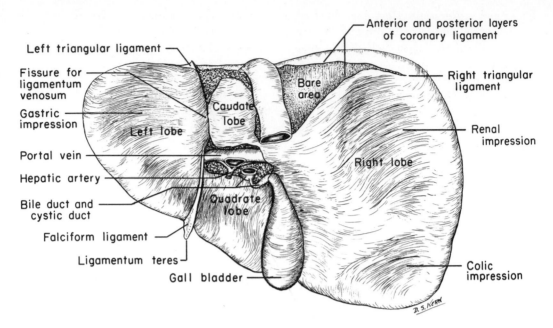

Left triangular ligament

Fissure for
ligamentum
venosum

Gastric
impression

Portal vein

Hepatic artery

Bile duct and
cystic duct

Falciform ligament

Ligamentum teres

Gall bladder

Anterior and posterior layers
of coronary ligament

Bare area

Caudate Lobe

Left lobe

Quadrate Lobe

Right lobe

Right triangular
ligament

Renal
impression

Colic
impression

D. S. KERN

Fig. 31. Visceral surface of the liver.

The **porta hepatis** is a relatively deep and wide area, approximately two inches long, through which the portal vein, the hepatic artery, bile ducts, nerves, and lymphatics pass. The porta hepatis separates the quadrate lobe inferiorly from the caudate lobe superiorly, and its boundaries serve as the site of attachment of the **hepatoduodenal ligament.** The **fissure for the ligamentum venosum** extends superiorly from the left end of the porta hepatis. It holds the ligamentum venosum and the remnant of the fetal ductus venosus, and affords attachment for the **gastrohepatic ligament,** which, with the hepatoduodenal ligament, forms the **lesser omentum.** The liver is partially divided by the fissures for the ligamentum venosum and ligamentum teres into a large **right** and a small **left lobe.** Two circumscribed areas on the medial aspect of the right lobe are further demarcated by the **fossae for the gallbladder** and the **interior vena cava** and are separated by the porta hepatis into the caudate and quadrate lobes. The larger right lobe rises higher than the left, pushing the right dome of the diaphragm upward and thus partially displacing the right lung.

Structures on the posterior surface of the liver include the fissure for the ligamentum venosum, the fossa for the inferior vena cava, and the caudate lobe, which projects into the lesser peritoneal sac. Between the layers of the coronary ligament, the posterior surface is not covered by peritoneum and is in direct contact with the diaphragm as the "bare area" of the liver. On the inferior surface the left lobe presents the gastric impression for the stomach and the tuber omentale, a bulging prominence above the lesser curvature of the stomach. The fossa for the gallbladder, impressions of the duodenum, right colic flexure, and right kidney are associated with the inferior surface of the right lobe.

Ligaments

The **falciform ligament** is a thin, sickle-shaped, anteroposterior fold consisting of two apposing layers of peritoneum. One of its three borders is attached to, and reflected over, the anterior surface of the liver; another is attached to, and reflected over, the diaphragm and the anterior abdominal wall to the level of the umbilicus; while the third inferior free border encloses the **ligamentum teres.** At the upper extent of the border of the falciform ligament attaching to the anterior surface of the liver, the peritoneal layers diverge laterally and reflect onto the diaphragm. The right reflection forms the **anterior layer of the coronary ligament,** which passes laterally to bend sharply at the **right triangular ligament,** where it becomes the **posterior layer of the coronary ligament.** The peritoneum forming the coronary ligament reflects from the liver onto the diaphragm, to enclose an area devoid of peritoneum in direct contact with the diaphragm. The left divergence of the falciform ligament, the **left triangular ligament,** reflects on the left lobe corresponding to, and continuous posteriorly with, the posterior layer of the coronary ligament. The two folds of peritoneum composing this left divergence are not widely separated.

Gallbladder and Biliary Tree (Fig. 30)

The **gallbladder,** a small piriform sac, is the reservoir for bile. It holds two to five ounces of fluid; lies in a small fossa on the visceral (inferior) surface of the liver; and is divided into the fundus, body, and neck. The inferior extremity of the sac, the **fundus,** is wide, usually protrudes beyond the inferior margin of the liver, and is covered by peritoneum. It is in contact with the transverse colon, the anterior body wall, and the ninth costal cartilage at the point the latter is crossed by the linea semilunaris. The anterior surface of the **body** of the gallbladder is in direct contact with the liver, and the posterior surface and sides of the body are covered by peritoneum. Posteriorly the body is related to the transverse colon and the second part of the duodenum. The narrow **neck** of the gallbladder is continuous with the cystic duct, both structures being closely applied to the liver, and is related inferiorly to the first part of the duodenum. The inch-long **cystic duct** enters the gastroduodenal ligament at the right end of the porta hepatis and runs a short distance with, and then joins, the common hepatic duct to form the common bile duct.

Bile secreted by the liver cells is carried away from the liver lobules via **bile canaliculi** to **intralobular ductules.** These unite to become **interlobar ducts,** which in turn join to form **right** and **left hepatic ducts,** whose junction results in the formation of the **common hepatic duct** at the porta hepatis. This latter duct, joined by the cystic duct, forms the **common bile duct,** which descends in the free margin of the lesser omentum anterior to the portal vein and lateral to the hepatic artery. The common bile duct continues inferiorly between the duodenum and the head of the pancreas, and as it terminates may unite with the pancreatic duct before penetrating the second part of the duodenum. The musculature in the wall of the common bile duct thickens to form a **sphincter** at its junction with the pancreatic duct. Within the wall of the duodenum it expands slightly as the **hepatopancreatic ampulla** (of Vater), which bulges the mucous membrane of the gut inward to form the **duodenal papilla** with the duct opening at the summit.

Arteries

Blood is supplied to the liver by the hepatic branch of the celiac trunk. The **hepatic artery** runs inferiorly to the right to course retroperitoneally behind the lesser sac to the first part of the duodenum. Here it continues below the epiploic foramen to gain a position between the layers of the hepatoduodenal ligament and pass to the porta hepatis. Within the hepatoduodenal ligament it divides into the **left** and **right hepatic branches,** which supply their respective hepatic lobes, and gives a third branch, the **cystic artery,** to the cystic duct and the gallbladder. The cystic artery may arise from the right hepatic vessel.

Portal Circulation

The **portal vein,** originating behind the neck of the pancreas by the union of the **splenic** and **superior mesenteric veins,** ascends behind the first part of the duodenum to pass in the free margin of the lesser omentum and divide into right and left branches to their respective lobes of the liver. These branches further subdivide eventually to gain a position at the margin of the liver lobule, where they course with the branches of the hepatic artery and the bile duct. The portal vein drains the spleen, pancreas, gallbladder, and all of the alimentary canal from the stomach distally, except for the lower rectum and anal canal. Tributaries of the portal system in addition to the splenic and superior mesenteric veins include the **short gastric, right** and **left gastroepiploic,** and **coronary veins** draining the stomach; small **pancreatic veins** from the pancreas; and the **inferior mesenteric vein** draining blood from the upper rectum and the distal half of the colon. The **hepatic veins** draining the liver to the heart begin as **central veins** of the liver lobules. These small vessels drain into **sublobular veins,** as tributaries of the hepatic veins, which empty into the inferior vena cava before it passes through the diaphragm.

PANCREAS (FIG. 30)

The **pancreas,** an elongated endocrine and exocrine gland, lies obliquely on the upper part of the posterior abdominal wall, extending from the concavity of the duodenum to the spleen. It is soft and pliable, contains a minimum of connective tissue, and is subdivided into a head, neck, body, and tail. The flattened, expanded **head** occupies the concavity of the duodenum. Posteriorly it is related to the aorta and inferior vena cava, with the common bile duct embedded in its lateral margin. It is related anteriorly to the superior mesenteric vessels and is in contact with the transverse colon. The **uncinate process** is an extension of the head, and the latter is continuous with the **neck** (isthmus) of the pancreas. Laterally, the anterior surface of the **body** forms part of the stomach bed and bulges slightly in the median plane as the **tuber omentale** immediately inferior to the celiac artery. The splenic artery courses along the superior border of the pancreas, and the transverse mesocolon reflects from the posterior abdominal wall at its inferior border. Posteriorly the body of the pancreas rests on the aorta, the superior mesenteric artery, the left crus of the diaphragm, the left psoas muscles, and the left kidney. The **tail** is thick and blunt and related to the hilus of the spleen.

Two ducts drain the pancreas. The **main pancreatic duct** courses along the entire length of the gland, emerging to join the common bile duct and pierce the duodenal wall three to four inches beyond the pylorus, as the duodenal papilla. The much smaller **accessory pancreatic duct** commonly appears in the neck as an offshoot from the main pancreatic duct and usually opens independently into the duodenum an inch above the duodenal papilla.

Arteries and Nerves

The pancreas receives blood from small twigs of the **splenic artery** as it courses along the superior border of the pancreas; from the **superior pancreaticoduodenal branch** of the gastroduodenal artery and from the **inferior pancreaticoduodenal branch** of the superior mesenteric artery. Innervation to the gland is derived from an extension of the **celiac plexus** surrounding its arterial supply.

SPLEEN

The **spleen** (lien), an oblong, flattened, highly vascularized organ, is located behind the stomach and inferior to the diaphragm in the left hypochondriac region. It is described as having diaphragmatic and visceral surfaces; superior and inferior extremities; and anterior, posterior, and inferior borders. The convex **diaphragmatic surface** is molded to fit the diaphragm. The **visceral surface** is divided by a ridge into an anterior (gastric) portion and an inferior (renal) portion. A fissure for the passage of vessels and nerves, the **hilus,** separates the gastric from the renal portions. The gastric portion is concave and in contact with the posterior wall of the stomach, while the renal portion, somewhat flattened, is related to the left kidney and left suprarenal gland. The **superior extremity** is directed toward the vertebral column at the level of the eleventh thoracic vertebra. The flat, triangular **inferior extremity** (colic surface) rests on the left colic flexure in contact with the tail of the pancreas. The notched **anterior border** is free and sharp, and separates diaphragmatic and gastric surfaces. The rounded blunt **posterior border** demarcates diaphragmatic from renal surfaces, while the **interior border** divides diaphragmatic from colic surfaces.

The spleen is almost entirely surrounded by peritoneum and held in position by two peritoneal ligaments. The short **lienorenal ligament** extends from the upper half of the left kidney to the hilus and contains the splenic artery and vein, sympathetic nerves, and lymphatics. The **gastrolienal ligament,** transmitting the gastroepiploic and the short gastric artery and vein, nerve filaments, and lymphatics to the stomach, passes forward from the hilus to become continuous with the greater omentum.

Arteries

The **splenic artery,** the largest branch of the celiac trunk, follows a tortuous course along the superior border of the pancreas behind the posterior wall of the lesser sac to terminate in five or six branches which pass through the lienorenal ligament to supply the spleen. The artery gives pancreatic branches in its retroperitoneal position and sends the left gastroepiploic and short gastric branches through the gastrolienal ligament to supply the stomach.

KIDNEY

The **kidney,** a retroperitoneal structure embedded in fascia and fat, is ovoid in outline, with the medial border markedly concave. It lies obliquely in the upper part of the posterior abdominal wall; the left kidney is opposite the twelfth thoracic and upper three lumbar vertebrae, and the right is slightly lower. The middle of the hilus is approximately two inches from the median plane, with the upper pole of the kidney closer to the midline than the lower. The kidney presents anterior and posterior surfaces, medial and lateral borders, and upper and lower poles.

Relations of the **anterior surface** vary on each side. On the right the anterior surface is related to the liver, duodenum, right colic flexure, and small intestine. On the left side the surface is related to the spleen, splenic vessels, left colic flexure, and small intestine. The portions of the kidney in contact with the suprarenal gland, pancreas, colon, and duodenum are devoid of peritoneum, while the remainder of the anterior surface is covered by peritoneum. The **posterior surface** of each kidney has similar relations, being embedded in areolar and fatty tissue, entirely devoid of peritoneum, and lying on the lower part of the diaphragm, lumbocostal arches, psoas major, quadratus lumborum, and transversus abdominis muscles, one or two lumbar arteries, and subcostal, ilioinguinal, and iliohypogastric nerves.

Adipose tissue completely surrounds the kidney and is separated by a thin membranous sheet into **perirenal fat** adjacent to the kidney and **pararenal fat** external to this membrane. From the lateral border of the kidney this membrane splits to pass anterior and posterior to the kidney as the **renal fascia.** Traced medially, the anterior layer of renal fascia passes anterior to the renal vessels, over the aorta, and becomes continuous with the same layer of the opposite side. Superiorly it passes over the suprarenal gland to become continuous with the posterior layer, which is the thicker of the two, and passes medially behind the aorta and the vena cava to unite with connective tissue over the vertebral column. Inferiorly the renal fascia fuses with the extraperitoneal connective tissue and loses its identity. Thus in emaciation a loss of the fat surrounding the kidney may be accompanied by a downward displacement (ptosis) of the kidney because of the nonclosure of this fascia inferiorly.

Internal Anatomy (Fig. 32)

On sagittal section the internal anatomy of the kidney presents a fibrous tunic **(capsule)** adjacent to the cortex and an inner medulla. The **cortex** consists of granular appearing tissue containing glomeruli and elements of the nephron. At intervals extensions of cortical tissue project centrally between the pyramids of the medulla as the **renal columns.** The **medulla** is composed of a series of eight to sixteen conical masses, the renal or medullary **pyramids,** containing the collecting tubules. The bases of the pyramids are directed toward the cortex and their apices converge at the **renal sinus,** forming within the sinus the prominent **renal papillae.** Four to thirteen cup-shaped, sleeve-like projections of the renal pelvis surround one or more renal papillae as the **minor calyces.** They join to form two or three **major calyces,** which empty into, and are continuous with, the funnel-shaped **renal pelvis,** which is also the proximal dilatation of the ureter.

Blood Vessels and Nerves

Arising from the aorta at the upper border of the second lumbar vertebra a half inch below the origin of the superior mesenteric artery, the **renal artery** passes transversely to the hilus of the kidney. The right renal artery, longer and lower than the left, passes behind the inferior vena cava, the head of the pancreas, and the second part of the duodenum to reach the kidney. The left vessel passes

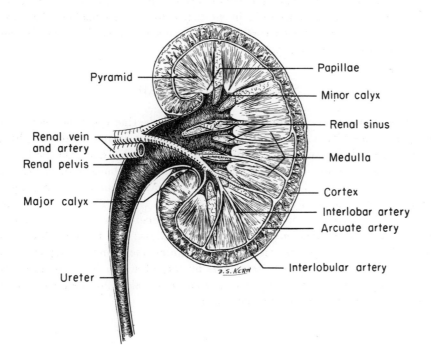

Fig. 32. Sagittal section of the kidney.

behind the renal vein, the pancreas, and the splenic vein to enter the kidney. Each gives an **inferior suprarenal branch** as it enters the hilus; then divides into interlobar branches traversing the renal sinus. The **interlobar branches** course in the renal columns to reach the cortex of the kidney, where adjacent interlobar arteries anastomose to form **arcades.** From the arcades **interlobular arteries** pass peripherally into the cortex giving a series of **afferent arterioles** to the glomeruli. The large **renal veins,** disposed anterior to the renal arteries, empty into the inferior vena cava after receiving suprarenal, left gonadal, and left phrenic tributaries. Innervation to the kidney is derived from the **renal autonomic plexus,** whose fibers accompany the renal artery into the substance of the organ.

URETER

The **ureter** carries urine from the renal pelvis to the urinary bladder. It is a thick-walled, muscular tube with a narrow lumen, approximately ten inches long, and situated half in the abdominal and half in the pelvic cavities. Descending retroperitoneally on the psoas major muscle, it passes anterior to the bifurcation of the iliac artery and posterior to the gonadal and right or left colic arteries. The ureter then turns anteriorly at the level of the ischial spine to reach the posterior aspect of the urinary bladder. In the male the ureter is crossed on its medial side by the ductus deferens and, as it approaches the bladder, lies anterior to the upper end of the seminal vesicle. In the female it is related to the posterior border of the ovary, and along the lateral pelvic wall it turns anteromedially to pass close to the vagina and cervix in its course toward the bladder. The ureter receives its **vascular** and **nervous supply** regionally from the renal, gonadal, and vesicular arteries and nerves.

SUPRARENAL GLAND

The **suprarenal (adrenal) gland** is an endocrine organ adjacent to the upper pole of the kidney. On the right side the gland is related to the diaphragm anteriorly, the inferior vena cava medially, and the liver laterally. On the left side it rests on the left crus of the diaphragm anteriorly, the stomach superiorly, and the pancreas inferiorly. The two glands are separated from each other by the celiac axis and plexus and are enclosed in the renal fascia. The suprarenal gland is supplied by the six to eight small **superior suprarenal** twigs from the phrenic artery; the **middle suprarenal,** a branch of the aorta; and the **inferior suprarenal,** a branch of the renal artery. Veins draining the gland correspond to the arteries; however, the principal drainage is by way of a prominent single **central vein** which emerges from the hilus to empty on the left side into the renal vein, and on the right side into the inferior vena cava.

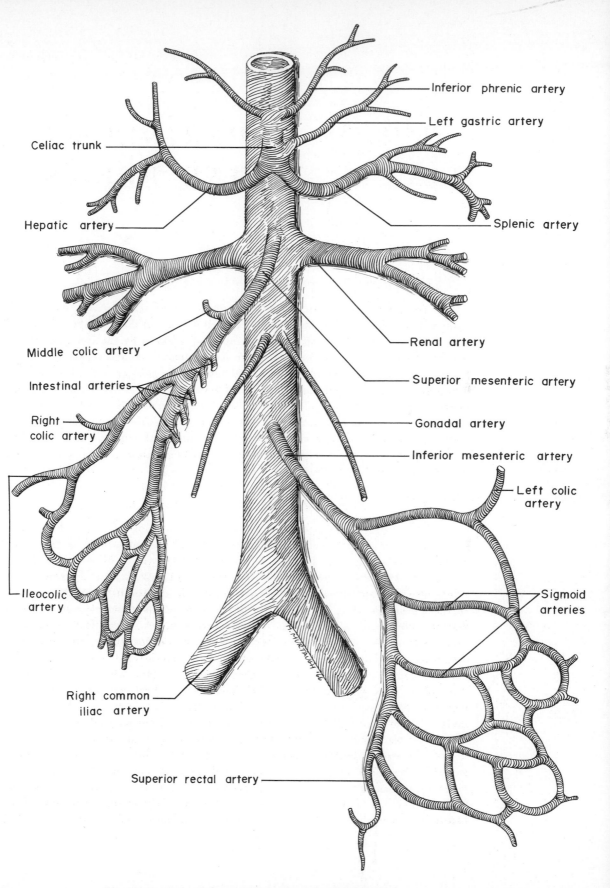

Inferior phrenic artery

Left gastric artery

Celiac trunk

Splenic artery

Hepatic artery

Renal artery

Middle colic artery

Superior mesenteric artery

Intestinal arteries

Gonadal artery

Right colic artery

Inferior mesenteric artery

Left colic artery

Ileocolic artery

Sigmoid arteries

Right common iliac artery

Superior rectal artery

Fig. 33. Summary of the arterial supply of the abdomen.

PERINEUM
AND PELVIS

PERINEUM

SURFACE ANATOMY (FIG. 34)

The **perineum,** conforming to the deeply lying outlet of the pelvis, is a diamond-shaped area at the lower end of the trunk between the thighs and buttocks. It is bounded anteriorly by the pubic symphysis, laterally by the ischial tuberosities, and posteriorly by the coccyx. A line passing transversely through the central point of the perineum, between the ischial tuberosities, divides it into an anterior **urogential triangle** and a posterior **anal triangle.** The **central point of the perineum,** located between the anus and the urethral bulb in the male, and between the anus and the vestibule in the female, overlies the deeply lying perineal body. In the male a slight median ridge, the **perineal raphe,** passes forward from the anus to become continuous with the **median raphe** of the scrotum and the **ventral raphe** of the penis.

FASCIAE AND SUPERFICIAL PERINEAL SPACE (FIG. 35)

The **superficial fascia** of the perineum, consisting of a superficial fatty and a deeper membranous layer, is continuous with the superficial fascia of the abdominal wall, thigh, and buttock. In the male the fatty layer of superficial fascia is lost as it is prolonged over the scrotum, where both superficial and membranous layers fuse and gain smooth muscle fibers to form the **dartos tunic** of the scrotum. In the female the fat in the superficial layer increases as it passes over the labia majora and the mons pubis. The **membranous layer** (superficial perineal or Colles' fascia) is attached posteriorly to the posterior margin of the urogenital diaphragm and laterally to the ischiopubic rami; anteriorly it is continuous with the dartos tunic and, at the superior extent of the scrotum, with the membranous layer of the superficial fascia of the abdomen. In urethral rupture fascial attachments of the membranous layer prevent urine from passing beyond the posterior margin of the urogenital diaphragm or into the thigh, but may allow it to spread a considerable distance into the subcutaneous tissue over the abdomen.

The **superficial perineal space,** between the superficial perineal fascia and the superficial layer of the urogenital diaphragm, contains the crura of the penis or clitoris, the bulb of the penis or vestibule, the superficial transverse perineal muscles, and perineal vessels and nerves. **External perineal (Gallaudet's) fascia** covers the ischiocavernosus, bulbocavernosus, and superficial

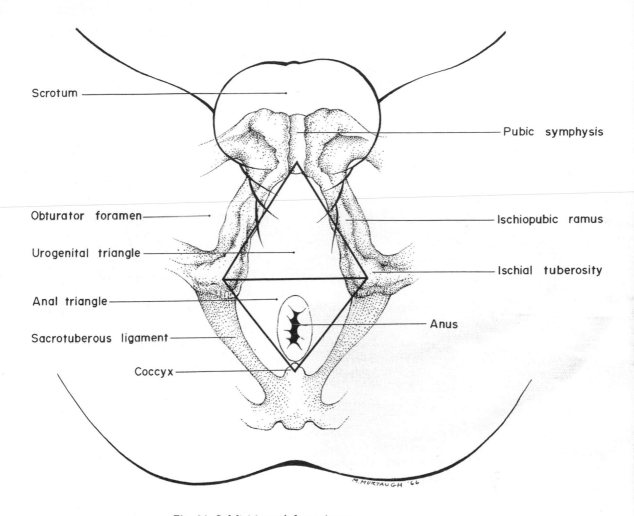

Scrotum

Pubic symphysis

Obturator foramen

Ischiopubic ramus

Urogenital triangle

Ischial tuberosity

Anal triangle

Anus

Sacrotuberous ligament

Coccyx

M.MURTAUGH '66

Fig. 34. Subdivisions of the perineum.

transverse perineal muscles and is firmly adherent to the inferior layer of the urogenital diaphragm. Within the superficial perineal space the root of the penis, consisting of two crura and the bulb, is composed mostly of erectile tissue. The crura of the penis are attached to the inferior aspect of the ischiopubic rami and the inferior layer of the urogenital diaphragm and are covered by the ischio-cavernosus muscles. Anteriorly they converge toward each other to form the two corpora cavernosa of the penis. The bulb of the penis (urethral bulb) is attached to the inferior layer of the urogenital diaphragm and surrounds the urethra. It is covered by the bulbocavernosus muscle and passes forward to lie inferior to the corpora cavernosa of the penis as the corpus spongiosum penis.

The **perineal body** (tendinous center of the perineum) is a fibromuscular mass located in the median plane between the anal canal and the urogenital diaphragm, with which it is fused. Several muscles attach, at least in part, to it,

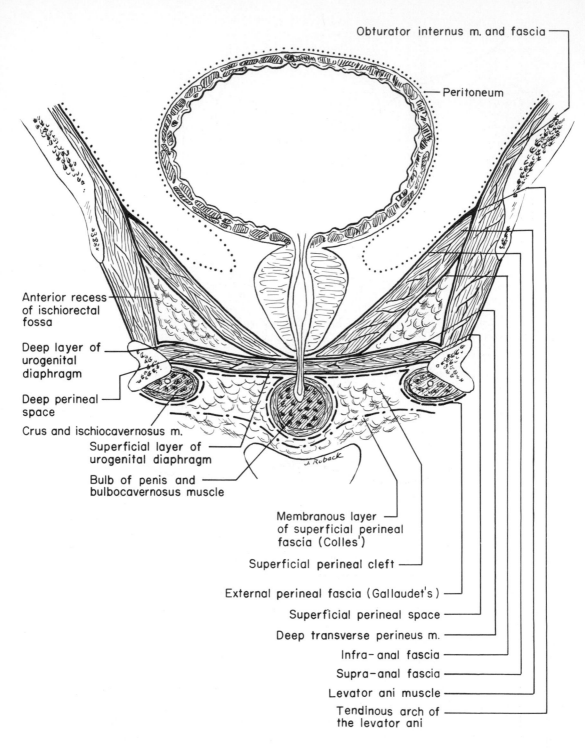

Obturator internus m. and fascia

Peritoneum

Anterior recess
of ischiorectal
fossa

Deep layer of
urogenital
diaphragm

Deep perineal
space

Crus and ischiocavernosus m.

Superficial layer of
urogenital diaphragm

Bulb of penis and
bulbocavernosus muscle

Membranous layer
of superficial perineal
fascia (Colles')

Superficial perineal cleft

External perineal fascia (Gallaudet's)

Superficial perineal space

Deep transverse perineus m.

Infra-anal fascia

Supra-anal fascia

Levator ani muscle

Tendinous arch of
the levator ani

J. Ruback

Fig. 35. Perineal spaces and fasciae.

including the superficial and deep transverse perinei, the bulbocavernosus, the central portion of the levator ani, the external anal sphincter, and smooth muscle from the longitudinal coat of the rectum. The perineal body is of special importance in the female, as it may be torn or damaged during parturition.

UROGENITAL DIAPHRAGM AND DEEP PERINEAL SPACE (FIG. 35)

The **urogenital diaphragm** is situated within the infrapubic angle between the ischiopubic rami. It is formed by connective tissue membranes spanning this area as the superficial and deep layers of the urogenital diaphragm and by structures between them. The **superficial layer of the urogenital diaphragm** (inferior perineal membrane) is composed of strong bands of fibrous connective tissue which pass between ischiopubic rami and separate the deep perineal space from the external genitalia. A similar structure, the **deep layer of the urogenital diaphragm** (superior perineal membrane), also passes between the ischiopubic rami and separates the deep perineal space from the anterior recess of the ischiorectal fossa. Anteriorly these membranes fuse to form the **transverse ligament of the pelvis,** and posteriorly they fuse at the posterior extent of the deep transverse perineus muscle.

The **deep perineal space** or pouch is the area between the superficial and deep layers of the urogenital diaphragm. It contains the deep transverse perineus and external urethral sphincter muscles, the internal pudendal vessels and pudendal nerve, the urethra, in the male the bulbourethral (Cowper's) glands, and in the female a small segment of the vagina.

MUSCLES (TABLE IX, FIG. 36)

Muscles of the perineum include the external anal sphincter, the structures within the deep perineal space, and muscles covering the crura and bulb of the penis or clitoris and vestibule.

The **external anal sphincter** is disposed into subcutaneous, superficial, and deep portions. The **subcutaneous part** surrounds the lowermost part of the anal canal, where its fibers decussate anteriorly and posteriorly and attach to the skin of the anus. The **superficial segment** is attached to the tip of the coccyx and the perineal body, and the **deep portion,** associated with the puborectalis muscle, attaches anteriorly to the perineal body and fuses with the wall of the anal canal as it surrounds this structure.

Within the superficial perineal space, thin sheet-like muscles, the median bulbocavernosus and two ischiocavernosi, cover, respectively, the bulb and crura of the penis. At the posterior extent of the urogenital diaphragm the superficial transverse perinei pass from the ischial tuberosities to the central tendon of the diaphragm.

The **bulbocavernosus** originates at the central tendon of the perineum and the median raphe on the superficial (ventral) aspect of the bulb. Its fibers spread over the bulb and the corpus spongiosum to insert into the superficial perineal membrane. They then encircle the corpus spongiosum to interdigitate with those of the opposite side, and the most distal fibers spread over and attach to the corpus cavernosum penis. In the female the counterparts of the bulbocavernosus are separate muscles which cover the bulb of the vestibule and may act as a weak sphincter of the vagina. Originating from the central tendon, their fibers pass anteriorly to insert into the body of the clitoris.

The **ischiocavernosus** originates from the tuberosity and ramus of the ischium and pubis surrounding and inserting into the crus of the penis.

The **superficial transverse perineus,** a narrow muscular slip, passes from its origin on the inner surface of the ischial tuberosity to insert medially into the central tendon of the perineum.

TABLE IX. MUSCLES OF THE PERINEUM

Muscle	Origin	Insertion	Action	Nerve
External anal sphincter	Skin and fascia surrounding and tip of coccyx	Central tendon of perineum	Closes anus	Inferior rectal
Bulbocavernosus	*Male:* median raphe, ventral surface of bulb, and central tendon of perineum *Female:* central tendon of perineum	*Male:* corpus cavernosum, subpubic triangle, and root of penis *Female:* dorsum of clitoris and superficial layer of urogenital diaphragm between crura of clitoris	*Male:* compresses bulb and bulbous portion of urethra; anterior fibers believed to act in erection *Female:* compresses vaginal orifice	Perineal branch of pudendal
Ischiocavernosus	Pelvic surface of inferior ramus of ischium surrounding crus	Crus near pubic symphysis	Maintains erection of penis or clitoris by compression of crus	Perineal branch of pudendal
Superficial transverse perineus	Ramus of ischium near tuberosity	Central body of perineum	Supports central body of perineum	Perineal branch of pudendal
Deep transverse perineus	Internal aspect of inferior ramus of ischium	Median raphe, central tendon of perineum, and external anal sphincter	Fixes central body of perineum	Perineal branch of pudendal
External urethral sphincter	Inferior ramus of ischium	Fibers interdigitate around urethra	Closes and compresses urethra	Perineal branch of pudendal

In the female, the muscles of the deep perineal space are specialized as the transversus and constrictor vaginae and act to compress the vagina and greater vestibular glands.

Two muscles are located within the deep perineal space. Centrally the **external urethral sphincter** surrounds the membranous portion of the urethra, and in the same plane, peripherally, the **deep transverse perineus** passes from the ischiopubic rami to interdigitate with its opposite member and insert into a fibrous raphe.

ISCHIORECTAL FOSSAE

Each of the paired **ischiorectal fossae** (the area between the perineum and the pelvis) is bounded anterolaterally by the fascia of the obturator internus, the ischial tuberosity, and the ischiopubic ramus; medially by the inferior layer of fascia covering the levator ani; and posterolaterally by the fascia of the gluteus maximus. Each continues anteriorly toward the body of the pubis as the **anterior recess,** situated between the ischiopubic rami, the levator ani, and the deep layer of the urogenital diaphragm. Anterosuperiorly the anterior recess is limited at the point of origin of the levator ani. The **posterior recess** of each fossa extends posteriorly between the coccygeus medially and the gluteus maximus and sacro-tuberous ligament posterolaterally.

Each fossa is filled by an **ischiorectal fat pad,** composed of adipose tissue traversed by irregular connective tissue septa, which are continuous with the subcutaneous fatty layer of the perineum. The **pudendal (Alcock's) canal,** a fascial tunnel located on the medial aspect of the ischial tuberosity internal to the obturator internus muscle, is formed by a splitting of the obturator fascia. The pudendal canal transmits the pudendal nerves and internal pudendal vessels which supply structures in the urogenital triangle. The **inferior hemorrhoidal vessels** and **nerves,** arising from nerves and vessels noted above, pass from the canal across the ischiorectal fossa to supply the lower rectum and anal canal.

EXTERNAL MALE GENITALIA

Penis (Fig. 36)

The **penis,** formed by two corpora cavernosa and the corpus spongiosum, is covered by skin and fascia. The thin elastic skin is loosely connected to the deeper parts and extends over the distal end of the penis for a variable distance, as the **prepuce.** A narrow median fold extends from the inferior aspect of the glans to the prepuce, as the **frenulum.** The **superficial fascia** is directly continuous with dartos tunic of the scrotum, and the **deep (Buck's) fascia** forms a tubular investment of the shaft of the penis to the corona, surrounding the corpora with a strong capsule. The **suspensory ligament,** a strong, fibroelastic triangular band of deep fascia, extends from the anterior border of the pubic symphysis to the penis, where it divides into right and left lamellae. The latter fuse to the deep fascia at the sides of the shaft of the penis, allowing vessels and nerves to pass to the dorsum of the penis.

The **corpora cavernosa penis** are a pair of elongated bodies extending from the perineum to the corona. They consist of **erectile tissue** (dilated vascular spaces) filled with blood, and each is surrounded by a dense white fibrous capsule,

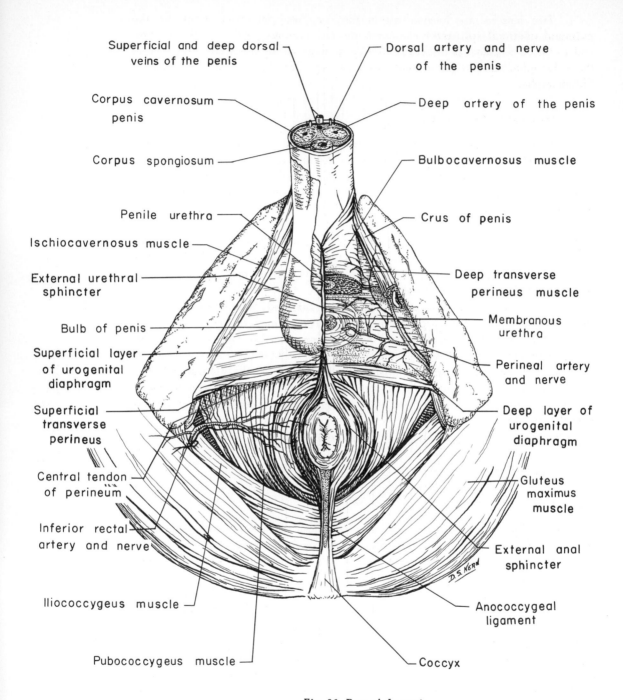

Superficial and deep dorsal veins of the penis

Dorsal artery and nerve of the penis

Corpus cavernosum penis

Deep artery of the penis

Corpus spongiosum

Bulbocavernosus muscle

Penile urethra

Crus of penis

Ischiocavernosus muscle

External urethral sphincter

Deep transverse perineus muscle

Bulb of penis

Membranous urethra

Superficial layer of urogenital diaphragm

Perineal artery and nerve

Superficial transverse perineus

Deep layer of urogenital diaphragm

Central tendon of perineum

Gluteus maximus muscle

Inferior rectal artery and nerve

External anal sphincter

Iliococcygeus muscle

Anococcygeal ligament

Pubococcygeus muscle

Coccyx

D.S. KERN

Fig. 36. Root of the penis.

the **tunica albuginea.** The apposing sides of this capsule are imperfectly fused to form the **septum.** The **deep arteries of the penis** are terminal branches of the internal pudendal arteries located in the center of each corpus cavernosum penis. The **corpus spongiosum penis,** a structure similar to the corpus caver-nosum penis, has a thinner, less dense capsule, lies in a groove on the under surface of the corpora cavernosa penis, and contains centrally the penile portion of the **urethra.** The anterior extremity of the corpus spongiosum is expanded to form the **glans,** and the area of junction between the glans and the shaft of the penis is the **corona.**

The **superficial dorsal vein** of the penis lies in the superficial fascia in the median plane and drains into either the right or the left external pudendal vein. The **deep dorsal vein,** also in the median plane but deep to the deep fascia, passes between the lamellae of the suspensory ligament below the infrapubic liga-ment to drain into the pudendal and prostatic plexuses. Two **dorsal arteries,** ter-minal branches of the internal pudendal vessels, course lateral to the deep dorsal vein and end as branches to the glans and skin. The dorsal arteries are accompanied by two **dorsal nerves,** the terminal branches of the pudendal nerve, which course lateral to the dorsal arteries and supply twigs to the skin and glans.

Scrotum

The **scrotum,** a pendulous purse-like sac of skin and fascia, contains the testis, the epididymis, and the spermatic cord. The skin is rugose, contains smooth muscle fibers and sebaceous glands, and is covered with sparse hair. **Dartos tunic** forming part of the wall of the scrotum is a continuation of the two layers of the superficial fascia of the abdomen (Camper's and Scarpa's layers) which fuse into a single layer. It is devoid of fat, highly vascular, and interspersed with smooth muscle fibers. The **septum** (a midline extension of deep fascia), incomplete su-periorly, passes into the interior of the scrotum to divide it into two chambers.

Spermatic Cord

The **spermatic cord** is formed at the deep inguinal ring and passes through the inguinal canal to exit at the superficial ring and enter the scrotum, where it is attached to the testis. It contains the vas deferens, a hard cord-like tube which transmits spermatozoa from the epididymis to the urethra, the testicular artery from the aorta, and the artery of the vas deferens. Other structures within the spermatic cord include the pampiniform plexus of veins, which drain on the right side into the inferior vena cava and on the left side to the renal vein (via internal spermatic veins), lymph vessels draining to nodes at the aortic bifurcation, sym-pathetic nerves from the renal and aortic plexuses, and the remnant of the processus vaginalis.

The **coverings of the spermatic cord** are continuous with aponeuroses and fasciae of the abdominal wall. The **external spermatic fascia,** attached to the crura of the inguinal ligament, is continuous above with the fascia of the external oblique muscle. The **cremasteric fascia,** with interspersed skeletal mus-cle fibers, is an extension of the internal oblique and its fascia. The **internal**

spermatic fascia is continuous with the transversalis fascia of the abdominal cavity, and the **subserous fascia** is continuous with the extraperitoneal connective tissue.

Testis (Fig. 37)

The **testis,** a flattened oval body, lies free in the scrotum except for its attachment to the epididymis. In longitudinal section the testis presents the **tunica albuginea,** a dense, tough, fibrous outer coat, and the **mediastinum** of the testis, a longitudinal thickened ridge along the posterior edge of the testis traversed by nerves, arteries, veins, lymph channels, and a network of channels, the **rete testis.** Radiating fibrous septa passing from the mediastinum to the tunica albuginea separate the testis into about 250 **lobules** which contain the **seminiferous tubules.** The seminiferous tubules unite to form **straight tubules** passing to the rete testis within the mediastinum. The rete testis continues as **efferent ducts** to the head of the epididymis.

In early intrauterine life the retroperitoneal testis is high in the abdominal cavity. It is attached to the posterior body wall by the **suspensory ligament** and

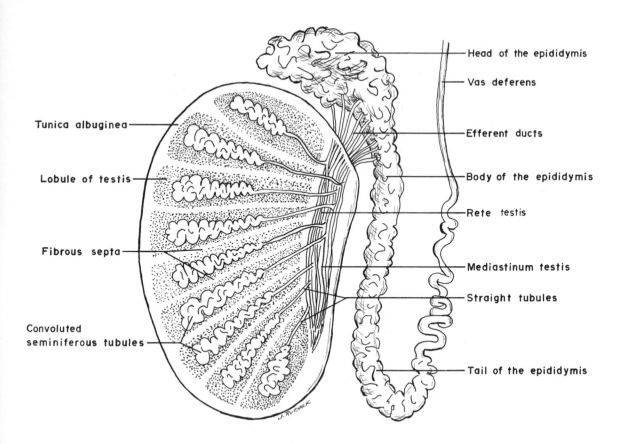

Fig. 37. Testis and epididymis.

to the developing scrotum by the **gubernaculum testis.** Differential growth rate results in a retroperitoneal descent of the testis into the scrotum preceded by a pouch of peritoneum, the **processus vaginalis.** This sac of peritoneum traverses the inguinal canal and forms a serous cavity within the scrotum. As the testis descends into the scrotum, the processus vaginalis within the inguinal canal is usually obliterated. The testis invaginates into the **serous cavity** within the scrotum to form a **parietal layer** lining the inner surface of the internal spermatic fascia and a **visceral layer** applied to the front and sides of the testis and covering the epididymis. The posterolateral aspect of the visceral layer is tucked between the body of the epididymis and testis to form a slit-like recess, the **sinus of the epididymis.**

Epididymis (Fig. 37)

The comma-shaped **epididymis** is composed of a **head,** which receives fifteen to twenty efferent ducts from the rete testis; a **body,** separated from the posterior aspect of the testis by the sinus of the epididymis; and a **tail,** which is continuous with the ductus deferens. The spirally coiled efferent ducts form a series of small masses, the **lobules** of the epididymis.

EXTERNAL FEMALE GENITALIA (FIG. 38)

Subcutaneous fat anterior to the pubic symphysis forms a rounded median eminence, the **mons pubis** (mons veneris). The **pudendal cleft,** a midline fissure in the urogenital triangle, is enclosed by the **labia majora,** two elongated swellings at the lateral boundary of the vulva. The labia majora converge anteriorly at the mons pubis to unite at the lower border of the symphysis pubis as the **anterior commissure.** Posteriorly the labia majora do not unite; however, the forward projection of the perineal body gives the appearance of a posterior commissure which lies between the vagina and the anus.

The **labia minora** are two thin folds of skin devoid of hair and subcutaneous fat but richly supplied with blood vessels and nerve endings. They flank the vaginal orifice and diverge posteriorly to blend with the labia majora. A transverse fold of skin, the **fourchette,** passes between the posterior terminations of the labia minora. Anteriorly each labium minus divides into two small folds which extend above and below the distal extremity of the clitoris to unite with similar folds of the opposite side to form dorsally the **prepuce** and ventrally the **frenulum of the clitoris.**

The cleft between the labia minora, the **vestibule,** receives the openings of the vagina, the urethra, and the ducts of the greater vestibular glands. The **external urethral orifice,** a median slit-like aperture, opens posterior to the glans clitoris. The urethral margins are slightly everted, and minute **paraurethral ducts (of Skene)** open into the pudendal cleft.

The **vaginal opening** is located posterior to the urethral orifice and is narrowed in the virgin by a crescent-shaped, fibrovascular membrane, the **hymen.** The **fossa navicularis** is that portion of the floor of the vestibule between the vaginal orifice and the fourchette. **Greater vestibular glands (of Bartholin)** are located bilaterally between the labia minora and the vaginal opening and

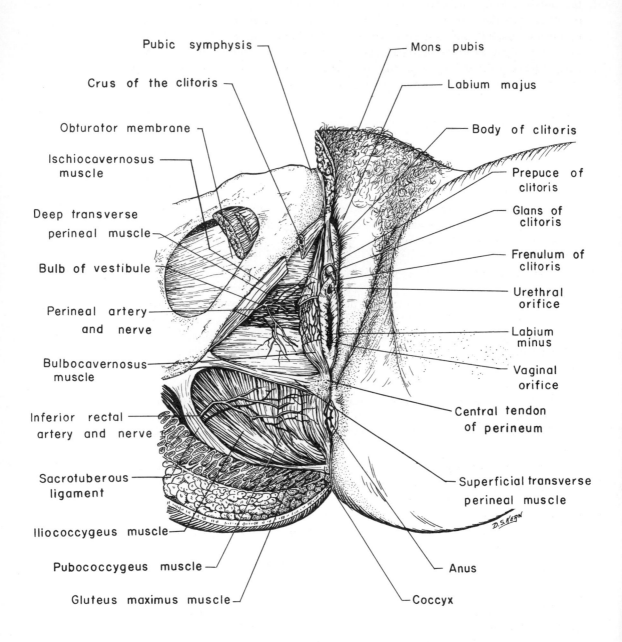

Pubic symphysis

Crus of the clitoris

Obturator membrane

Ischiocavernosus
muscle

Deep transverse
perineal muscle

Bulb of vestibule

Perineal artery
and nerve

Bulbocavernosus
muscle

Inferior rectal
artery and nerve

Sacrotuberous
ligament

Iliococcygeus muscle

Pubococcygeus muscle

Gluteus maximus muscle

Mons pubis

Labium majus

Body of clitoris

Prepuce of
clitoris

Glans of
clitoris

Frenulum of
clitoris

Urethral
orifice

Labium
minus

Vaginal
orifice

Central tendon
of perineum

Superficial transverse
perineal muscle

D. S. KERN

Anus

Coccyx

Fig. 38. Vulva.

during coitus are compressed to release a mucus-like secretion to lubricate the lower end of the vagina.

Paired elongated masses of erectile tissue forming the **bulbs of the vesti-bule** are located at the sides of the vaginal orifice, attached to the superficial layer of the urogential diaphragm; they are covered by the bulbocavernosus muscle.

The **clitoris,** an erectile organ corresponding anatomically to the male penis, is composed of a body, two crura, and a glans. It differs from the penis in its smaller size and not being tranversed by the urethra. The **body,** formed by the union of the crura, is entirely embedded in the tissues of the vulva and sus-pended from the pubic symphysis by the **suspensory ligament.** The **crura** of the clitoris are attached to the perineal surface of the ischial rami just anterior to the ischial tuberosities, to the inferior layer of the urogenital diaphragm, and are covered by the ischiocavernosus muscles. The **glans,** like the crura, is composed of erectile tissue but also contains abundant sensory nerve endings. It is a small, rounded elevation at the free end of the body.

PELVIS

The funnel-shaped **pelvis,** that portion of the trunk inferoposterior to the abdominal cavity, is limited by the innominate, sacral, and coccygeal bones. The **pelvis minor,** or true pelvic cavity, is below the brim of the pelvis, while the **pelvis major,** or false pelvic cavity, is located between the iliac fossae and is a part of the abdominal cavity. The pelvis contains the lower part of the alimentary canal, the distal end of the ureter, the urinary bladder, and most of the internal reproductive system. The abdominal peritoneal cavity extends into the pelvic cavity.

For descriptive purposes the pelvic boundaries can be divided into the lateral and posterior walls and the floor. The **bony framework** of the true pelvis is formed by that portion of the paired innominate bones below the arcuate line, the sacrum, and the coccyx. Most of the pelvic surface of the innominate bone is covered by the obturator internus muscle and its fascia. The gap between each innominate bone and the sacrum is partially filled by the **sacrotuberous** and **sacrospinous ligaments.** The former attaches superiorly to the posterior iliac spines, the lower sacrum, and the upper coccyx, while inferiorly its fibers converge to attach to the ischial tuberosity. An extension of this ligament, the **falciform process,** passes to the lower margin of the ramus of the ischium. The triangular **sacrospinous ligament** lies anterior to the sacrotuberous ligament, with its base attached to the lower sacrum and the upper coccyx and its apex attached to the ischial spine. The sacrotuberous and sacrospinous ligaments convert the sciatic notches into foramina, with the sacrospinous ligament demarcating the **lesser** from the **greater sciatic foramen.** The latter transmits the piriformis muscle; the superior and inferior gluteal vessels and nerves; the internal pudendal vessels; and the pudendal, sciatic, and posterior femoral cutaneous nerves. The lesser sciatic foramen is traversed by the tendon of the obturator internus, the internal pudendal vessels and the pudendal nerve, and nerves to the obturator internus.

The curved **posterior wall** of the pelvis faces anteroinferiorly, is composed of the sacrum and coccyx, and is covered laterally by the piriformis and coccygeus muscles and their fasciae. The **floor** of the pelvis includes all structures giving support to pelvic viscera: the peritoneum, the pelvic and urogenital diaphragms, and structures associated with them. The rectum passes through the pelvic floor posteriorly; the urethra in the male, and the urethra and vagina in the female, penetrate the floor anteriorly. The **peritoneum** covers pelvic viscera to a variable extent, reflecting from the rectum onto the urinary bladder to form the **rectovesical pouch** in the male, and onto the uterus in the female to form the **rectouterine pouch.** Anterior to the rectouterine pouch, the peritoneum reflects onto the bladder and forms the **uterovesical pouch.** Subserous connective tissue between the peritoneum and the pelvic diaphragm varies in thickness and contains blood vessels and nerve plexuses to pelvic viscera, the lower part of the ureter, and the terminal part of the ductus deferens. Localized connective tissue thickenings form ligaments which aid in the support of various organs.

MUSCLES

The levator ani and coccygei muscles and fasciae covering the upper and lower surfaces of these muscles form the **pelvic diaphragm.** The **levator ani** is a wide, thin, curved sheet of muscle, variable in thickness, which forms the muscular floor of the true pelvis and separates the pelvis from the ischiorectal fossae. A narrow midline gap permits passage of the vagina in the female and the urethra and rectum in both sexes. The levator ani is subdivided into three parts, the pubococcygeus, puborectalis, and iliococcygeus muscles, which may be differentiated by the position, direction, and attachment of their fibers.

The **pubococcygeus** forms the main part of the levator ani and originates from the posterior aspect of the body of the pubis and tendinous arch of the levator ani. Its more lateral fibers insert into the perineal body, the wall of the anal canal, and the anococcygeal body. In the male its most medial fibers insert into the prostate as the **levator prostatae muscle,** while in the female these fibers insert into the urethra and vagina as the **pubovaginalis muscle.** Fasciculi of the latter encircle the urethra and vagina and interdigitate with the opposite muscle to form the **sphincter vaginae.**

The most conspicuous portion of the levator ani, the **puborectalis muscle,** passes posteriorly from the pubis and unites with fibers from the opposite side to form a muscular sling behind the rectum near its anorectal junction.

The **iliococcygeus,** although extending over a relatively large area, is often the most poorly developed portion of the levator ani. It originates from the tendinous arch and the ischial spine and passes obliquely inferiorly to insert into the sides of the coccyx and the anococcygeal body.

Located posterior to the levator ani, the **coccygeus** (ischiococcygeus), may be present only as tendinous strands. It arises from the pelvic aspect of the ischial spine, and its fibers spread out to insert into the lateral and lower margins of the sacrum and the upper part of the coccyx.

FASCIAE

The **pelvic fascia** is a continuation of the transversalis fascia which passes onto the lateral pelvic wall as the iliac fascia to become the **obturator fascia** at the brim of the pelvis. The latter, the most definite layer of fascia in the pelvis, lines the internal surface of the obturator internus and at the margins of this muscle fuses with the periosteum. Inferiorly it joins the falciform process of the sacrotuberous ligament and at the anterior margin of the obturator foramen fuses with the obturator membrane to form the floor of the obturator canal. The obturator fascia gives origin to most of the levator ani and, below the origin of this muscle, forms the lateral walls of the ischiorectal fossae, where it splits, near the ischial tuberosity, to form the pudendal canal.

The thin **obturator membrane** closes the obturator foramen except anterosuperiorly where a gap, the **obturator canal,** transmits the obturator nerve and vessels to the adductor region of the thigh. The obturator membrane also gives partial origin to the obturator internus and externus muscles.

The **supra-anal fascia,** attaching at the tendinous arch of the levator ani, covers the pelvic surface of the levator ani and coccygeus muscles. **Infra-anal fascia,** thinner than the above, covers the lower surface of the levator ani and coccygeus muscles. Anteriorly a midline thickening of these fasciae forms the **puboprostatic (pubovesical** in the female) **ligament;** posteriorly the fasciae thin out to cover the coccygeus and fuse with the sacrospinous ligament.

NERVES

Innervation to pelvic structures is from the **sacral** and **coccygeal spinal nerves** and the **sacral portion of the autonomic nervous system.** Each of the five sacral and the coccygeal nerves divides into anterior and posterior primary rami within the sacral canal. Posterior primary rami of the first through fourth sacral nerves pass through the posterior sacral foramina and divide into a medial muscular branch to the erector spinae muscles and a lateral cutaneous branch which forms a series of loops to give perforating branches to the skin over the buttocks. Posterior primary rami of the fifth sacral and coccygeal nerves pass through the sacral hiatus to supply the skin over the coccyx and around the anus. The anterior primary rami of the first four sacral nerves pass through sacral foramina into the pelvis, while the ramus of the fifth sacral nerve passes between the coccyx and the sacrum. The anterior primary rami of the first and second sacral nerves are the largest components of this plexus, and thereafter the anterior primary rami decrease in size. The anterior primary ramus of the coccygeal nerve passes below the rudimentary transverse process of the coccyx to form, with the fourth and fifth sacral nerves, the small coccygeal plexus. The second, third, and fourth sacral nerves give off **pelvic splanchnic nerves,** which transmit parasympathetic preganglionic fibers to the pelvic autonomic plexuses and supply the large intestine below the level of the splenic flexure as well as the pelvic viscera.

Sacral Plexus (Fig. 39)

The **sacral plexus,** situated largely anterior to the piriformis muscle, is formed by the anterior primary rami of the fourth and fifth lumbar nerves and the first four sacral nerves. The anterior primary ramus of the fourth lumbar nerve divides into an upper and lower segment. The latter joins with the anterior primary ramus of the fifth lumbar to form the **lumbosacral trunk,** which descends to join the sacral plexus. Twelve named nerves are described as arising from the

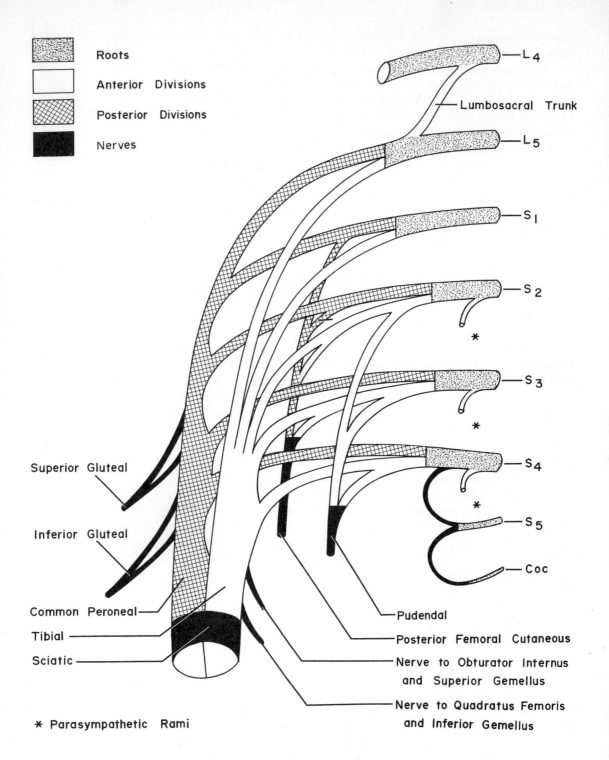

Roots

Anterior Divisions

Posterior Divisions

Nerves

L₄

Lumbosacral Trunk

L₅

S₁

S₂

*

S₃

*

S₄

*

S₅

Coc

Superior Gluteal

Inferior Gluteal

Common Peroneal

Tibial

Sciatic

Pudendal

Posterior Femoral Cutaneous

Nerve to Obturator Internus
and Superior Gemellus

Nerve to Quadratus Femoris
and Inferior Gemellus

∗ Parasympathetic Rami

Fig. 39. Sacral plexus.

sacral plexus: Seven are directed to the buttock and lower limb, and five supply pelvic structures.

The **superior gluteal nerve** (L_4, L_5, and S_1) passes posteriorly through the greater sciatic foramen above the level of the piriformis muscle. It is accompanied in its course by the superior gluteal artery and vein. It innervates the gluteus medius and minimus muscles and terminates in the tensor fascia lata muscle. The **inferior gluteal nerve** (L_5, S_1, and S_2) passes posteriorly through the greater sciatic foramen below the level of the piriformis muscle to supply the gluteus maximus.

The nerve to the quadratus femoris and inferior gemellus muscles (L_4, L_5, and S_1) leaves the pelvis through the greater sciatic foramen inferior to the piriformis muscle. The nerve to the obturator internus (L_5, S_1, and S_2) leaves via the same foramen and, after giving a branch to the superior gemellus, re-enters the pelvis through the lesser sciatic foramen to supply the obturator internus.

The **posterior femoral cutaneous nerve** (S_1, S_2, and S_3) also leaves the pelvis through the greater sciatic foramen, passing inferior to the piriformis muscle. It accompanies the inferior gluteal vessels to the inferior border of the gluteus maximus, where it courses down the thigh superficial to the biceps femoris and deep to the fascia lata. It innervates skin over the posterior aspect of the thigh and leg.

Inferior cluneal (perforating cutaneous) **nerves** (S_2 and S_3) pierce the gluteus maximus and deep fascia midway between the coccyx and the ischial tuberosity to supply skin of the lower gluteal region.

The largest nerve in the body, the **sciatic** (L_4, L_5, S_1, S_2, and S_3), enters the gluteal region through the lower part of the greater sciatic foramen. It traverses the gluteal region in the interval between the greater trochanter of the femur and the ischial tuberosity and passes under cover of the gluteus maximus. It is related anteriorly, in sequence from superior to inferior, to the nerve to the quadratus femoris, the tendon of the obturator internus, the two gemelli, and the quadratus femoris muscles. As it enters the posterior compartment of the thigh, it descends on the posterior aspect of the adductor magnus muscle to divide into the **tibial (medial popliteal)** and **common peroneal (lateral popliteal) nerves.** Its distribution will be considered with the inferior extremity.

The **nerve to the piriformis** (S_1 and S_2) enters the anterior aspect of this muscle directly from the sacral plexus, while the **nerve to the levator ani and coccygeus** (S_3 and S_4) descends on the deep aspect of these muscles to innervate them. The **nerve to the external anal sphincter** (S_4) passes either through the coccygeus or between this muscle and the levator ani to continue forward in the ischiorectal fossa to supply the external anal sphincter and the skin surrounding the anus.

The **pudendal nerve** (S_2, S_3, and S_4) supplies most of the perineum. It emerges from the pelvis through the greater sciatic foramen inferior to the piriformis muscle, crosses the posterior aspect of the ischial spine medial to the internal pudendal artery, then passes through the lesser sciatic foramen to enter the pudendal canal. Its branches include several inferior hemorrhoidal nerves to the rectum and the anal canal which pass across the ischiorectal fossa, the perineal nerves giving cutaneous innervation to the perineum, muscular branches to muscles in the urogenital triangle, and its terminal branch, the dorsal nerve of the penis or clitoris. The inferior **hemorrhoidal nerve** may arise anywhere along the course of the pudendal nerve, but it usually pierces the fascia forming the pudendal canal to cross the ischiorectal fossa and supply the external anal sphincter, the overlying skin, and the lining of the anal canal below the pectinate line. The **perineal nerve** divides into a **superficial** and a **deep branch** within the pudendal canal. The former supplies **posterior scrotal** or **labial nerves,** which are distributed to the posterior aspect of the scrotum or the labium majus and to the skin of the perineum. The **deep branch** pierces the medial wall of the pudendal canal to supply twigs to the levator ani and the external anal sphincter and sends branches to structures in the superficial perineal space, namely, the bulbocavernosus, ischiocavernosus, and superficial transverse perineus muscles and the bulb of the penis. The **dorsal nerve to the penis** pierces the posterior margin of the urogenital diaphragm to supply the deep transverse perineus muscle, the sphincter urethra, and the corpus cavernosum penis. It then continues anteriorly to pass between the lamellae of the suspensory ligament of the penis and runs forward on the dorsum of the penis supplying the skin, prepuce, and glans of that organ.

Coccygeal Plexus

The **coccygeal plexus** is formed by the lower division of the fourth sacral nerve, the anterior primary ramus of the fifth sacral, and the coccygeal nerve. It supplies twigs to the sacrococcygeal joint and the skin over the coccyx.

Autonomic Nerves

The **pelvic splanchnic nerves (nervi erigentes)** are slender filaments passing from the second, third, and fourth sacral nerves. They transmit **preganglionic parasympathetic fibers** to the pelvic plexuses and have their cell bodies at the above-named levels of the spinal cord. They also supply parasympathetic innervation to the large intestine distal to the splenic flexure.

Pelvic autonomic plexuses receive their **sympathetic contribution** from either the inferior extension of the vertebral trunk or the downward continuation of the preaortic plexus. The sacral portion of the sympathetic trunk consists of three or four ganglia lying on the anterior aspect of the sacrum just medial to the sacral foramina. It ends in a fusion of the two trunks in the midline to form the **ganglion impar.** Gray rami communicantes pass to sacral and coccygeal spinal nerves and are distributed via those nerves to the inferior extremity and perineum as well as to the pelvis.

The **superior hypogastric autonomic plexus** is located between the common iliac arteries and receives its component fibers from the lower lumbar splanchnic nerves and descending fibers of the inferior mesenteric plexus. It continues inferiorly, divides, and passes to either side of the rectum as the **inferior hypogastric plexus.** Further subdivisions are designated according to the vessels they follow or the organs they supply, as, the middle rectal, prostatic, vesical, uterovaginal, and cavernous nerves of the penis or clitoris. These plexuses contain postganglionic sympathetic fibers, postganglionic parasympathetic cell bodies and fibers, and visceral afferent (sensory) fibers.

ARTERIES (FIG. 40)

The **internal iliac (hypogastric),** the smaller of the two terminal branches of the common iliac artery, arises at the level of the lumbosacral articulation. It usually divides into an **anterior** and **posterior trunk** before giving origin to its several named branches. Branches from the trunks are not constant, but usually all visceral branches (the vesicular, uterine, vaginal, and rectal) arise from the anterior trunk, as do the obturator, inferior gluteal, and internal pudendal arteries.

In the male the **superior vesical (umbilical) artery** gives off a branch close to its origin, the **artery to the ductus deferens,** before it continues along the lateral pelvic wall to the apex of the bladder. This small artery supplies the lower end of the ureter, the ductus deferens, the seminal vesicle, and part of the bladder. The superior vesical artery gives one or more twigs to the bladder before becoming a solid cord, the obliterated umbilical artery, which is embedded in a fold of peritoneum on the internal aspect of the anterior abdominal wall as it passes to the umbilicus.

The **obturator artery** passes along the lateral pelvic wall on the surface of the obturator internus to supply the muscle. With the obturator nerve and vein it passes through the obturator canal to be distributed to the muscles in the adductor compartment of the thigh. The **uterine artery** passes inferiorly along the lateral pelvic wall and turns medially at the base of the broad ligament to pass to the cervicouterine junction. Here it gives rise to one or more **vaginal branches,** ascends on the uterus, which it supplies, and terminates as twigs to the uterine tube. The **middle rectal (hemorrhoidal) artery,** variable in both origin and size, passes to the rectum just superior to the pelvic diaphragm.

The **inferior gluteal artery** enters the gluteal region below the piriformis muscle at the lateral edge of the sacrotuberous ligament and supplies the gluteus maximus and other muscles in this area. It gives a named branch, the **artery to the sciatic nerve,** which passes inferiorly on or into that nerve. The **internal pudendal artery** emerges from the pelvic cavity in company with the inferior gluteal artery and the pudendal nerve, then winds around the ischial spine to re-enter the pelvic cavity through the lesser sciatic notch. With the nerve and a corresponding vein it courses in the pudendal canal and is distributed to the perineum.

The posterior trunk of the internal iliac artery gives rise to three branches. One of these, the **iliolumbar artery,** divides near its origin into an iliac and a lumbar branch. The **iliac branch** crosses the pelvic brim and passes deep to the common or external iliac artery and the psoas major muscle to supply structures in the iliac fossa. The **lumbar branch** parallels the lumbosacral trunk, supplies the psoas muscles, and then gives twigs to the structures within the vertebral canal. Usually two **lateral sacral arteries** pass into the vertebral canal to supply the cord, meninges, and spinal nerves.

The **superior gluteal artery,** the largest branch of the internal iliac, leaves the pelvic cavity through the greater sciatic foramen above the level of the piriformis muscle to enter the gluteal region. It usually courses between the two elements of the lumbosacral trunk, or between the lumbosacral trunk and the first

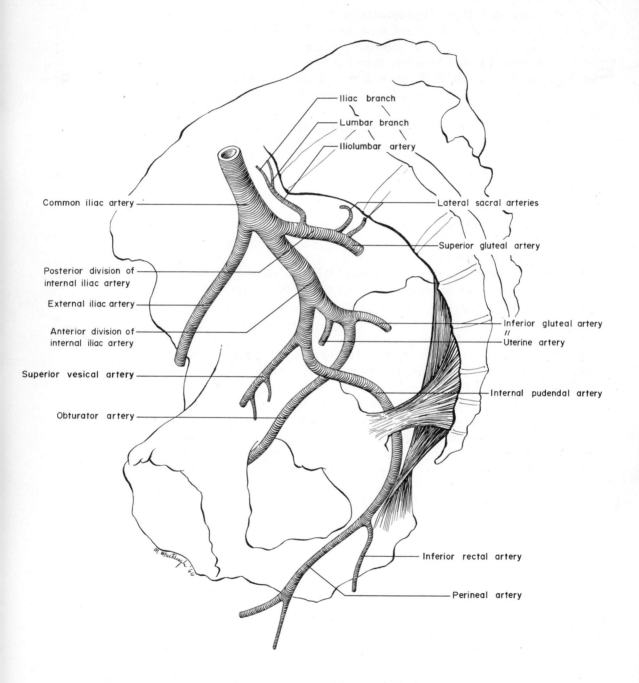

Iliac branch

Lumbar branch

Iliolumbar artery

Common iliac artery

Lateral sacral arteries

Superior gluteal artery

Posterior division of
internal iliac artery

External iliac artery

Anterior division of
internal iliac artery

Inferior gluteal artery

Uterine artery

Superior vesical artery

Internal pudendal artery

Obturator artery

Inferior rectal artery

Perineal artery

Fig. 40. Arterial supply of the pelvis.

sacral nerve. Passing between the gluteus maximus and medius muscles it divides into a superficial and a deep branch. The former supplies the gluteus maximus and the latter further divides into superior and inferior branches to supply the gluteus medius and minimus.

MALE PELVIC ORGANS

Urinary Bladder (Fig. 41)

The size, shape, and position of the **urinary bladder** vary with its contents. The distended bladder is spherical, rises into the abdomen, and has an average capacity in the adult of about 500 milliliters. The empty bladder lies on the pubis and adjacent pelvic floor at the level of the pelvic inlet, slightly lower in position in the female than in the male. The flattened posterior surface forms the **base (fundus)** of the bladder. The apical superior surface is covered with peritoneum and is convex when filled, but concave and resting on the other bladder surfaces when empty. The inferolateral surfaces rest on the pelvic diaphragm and are continuous with the superior surface at the **apex,** from which the **urachus** (medial umbilical ligament) extends to the umbilicus. The **body** of the bladder lies between the apex and the fundus, while the neck surrounds the internal urethral orifice.

The **anterior surface** of the bladder has no peritoneal covering and faces anteroinferiorly toward the pubic symphysis, from which it is separated by the prevesical space (of Retzius). The **inferolateral surface** is separated from the levator ani and the obturator internus muscles by extraperitoneal tissue enclosing the vesicular vessels. In the male, it is related posteriorly to the ductus deferens, and its **posterior surface** is in direct contact with the anterior wall of the rectum, the ampulla of the ductus deferens, and the seminal vesicle. The neck is related inferiorly to the prostate and, in the female, adherent to the cervix of the uterus and the upper portion of the anterior wall of the vagina.

The **neck** is the least movable portion of the bladder. It is firmly anchored to the pelvic diaphragm and is continuous in the male with the prostate, where an external groove demarcates the separation of the two organs. The **medial puboprostatic (pubovesicular) ligament** passes from the body of the pubis to the anterior aspect of the prostate in the male, or the neck of the bladder in the female. The **lateral puboprostatic (pubovesicular) ligament** extends from the tendinous arch of the levator ani to the capsule of the prostate or the neck of the bladder. Lateral ligaments (condensations of subserous fascia) from the base of the bladder pass lateroposteriorly and posteriorly to continue as the **rectovesical folds** in the male and the **rectouterine folds** in the female.

In the empty bladder the internal surface is thrown into folds and modified at the posterior aspect to form a smooth triangular area, the **trigone.** The apices of the trigone are marked by the orifices of the two ureters and the urethra. Between the ureteric orifices a transverse ridge, the **interureteric fold** (plica interureterica), is formed by the underlying musculature. Later extensions of this fold, **plicae uretericae,** are formed by the passage of the ureters through the wall of the bladder. The **uvula,** a medial longitudinal ridge above and behind the internal urethral orifice, is formed by the underlying median lobe of the prostate. The **internal urethral orifice,** situated at the lowest point of the bladder, is encircled by a thickening of the smooth muscle of the wall of the bladder, the **urethral annulus.**

Prostate (Fig. 41)

The **prostate,** situated behind the pubic symphysis and below the urinary bladder, is formed by smooth muscle and collagenous fibers, in which is embedded secretory glandular tissue. The **apex** is the lowermost part of the prostate, and the **base,** penetrated by the internal urethral orifice, lies horizontally and fuses with the wall of the more superiorly located bladder. Peripherally a narrow groove separates the two organs. The convex **inferolateral surfaces** are surrounded by

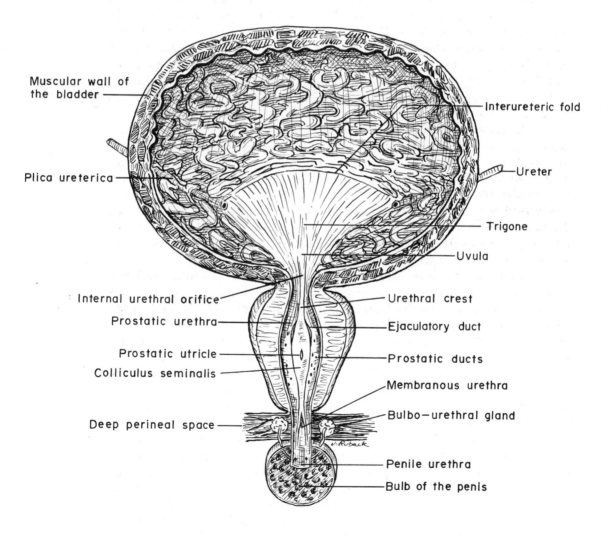

Fig. 41. Bladder and prostate.

the prostatic plexus of veins, while the narrow **anterior surface** is separated from the pubis by the retropubic fat pad. The flattened triangular **posterior surface,** which may have a more or less prominent median groove, can be palpated rectally. The prostate consists of two lateral and a median lobe. No superficial demarcation is present between the **lateral lobes,** which are connected by the isthmus anterior to the urethra. The **median lobe,** responsible for the formation of the uvula, is variable in size and projects inwardly from the upper part of the posterior surface between the ejaculatory ducts and the urethra. The enlargement of the median lobe may block urinary flow.

Ductus Deferens

The **ductus deferens** begins as a continuation of the ductus epididymis and passes as a component of the spermatic cord to the deep inguinal ring. From the deep ring it ascends anterior to the external iliac artery, then turns posteriorly to enter the pelvic cavity. It passes onto the lateral pelvic wall, medial to the umbilical artery and obturator vessels, crosses the ureter and continues medially to reach the posterior aspect of the bladder. Near the base of the prostate it enlarges and becomes tortuous, as the **ampulla,** and then is joined by the duct of the seminal vesicle to form the **ejaculatory duct.** The latter penetrates the base of the prostate and passes anteroinferiorly to enter the prostatic portion of the urethra just lateral to the colliculus seminalis.

Seminal Vesicle

The **seminal vesicles,** two large sacculated pouches, approximately two inches in length, consist of blind coiled tubes with several diverticula which secrete the seminal fluid. When the bladder is empty, the seminal vesicles lie horizontally; when the bladder is distended, they are nearly vertical in position. The upper parts of the seminal vesicles are separated from the rectum by the rectovesical pouch, with the terminal parts of the ureters and ampullae of the ductus deferens located medially and the prostatic and vesical venous plexuses laterally.

Urethra

The **urethra** in the male extends from the bladder to the external urethral orifice in the glans penis. It serves as a passage for both urine and semen and consists of the prostatic, membranous, and penile portions. The **prostatic portion** passes through the substance of the prostate where the posterior wall presents a large fold, the **urethral crest,** which is elevated at its midpoint into an enlargement, the **colliculus seminalis.** A small depression at the center, the **prostatic utricle,** corresponds developmentally to the uterus and the vagina of the female. The ejaculatory ducts open at either side of the colliculus, and more distally, small openings are present for the ducts of the prostate.

The **membranous portion** penetrates the urogenital diaphragm, where it is surrounded by the **external urethral sphincter muscle** located in the deep perineal space. Ducts of two small **bulbourethral glands** lie at either side of the urethra in the deep pouch and pierce the inferior layer of the urogenital diaphragm to enter the penile urethra.

The **penile portion** of the urethra is surrounded by the corpus spongiosum penis and, at the glans, flattens laterally to form the **fossa navicularis.** Numerous minute urethral glands (**of Littré**) open into this portion, with the largest of their orifices forming the **urethral lacunae** (of Morgagni).

The **female urethra,** approximately an inch and a half long, extends inferiorly and slightly forward from the neck of the bladder to the external urethral orifice. It passes through the pelvic and urogenital diaphragms and opens between the labia minora, anterosuperior to the vaginal orifice and posteroinferior to the glans clitoris. The urethra is closed except during the passage of urine and is marked internally by longitudinal folds, the most prominent of which is located on the posterior aspect as the **urethral crest.** The female urethra is fused with the anterior wall of the vagina and fixed to the pubis by the **pubovesical ligament.**

FEMALE REPRODUCTIVE ORGANS (FIG. 42)

Ovary

The **ovary** is located within a depression, the **ovarian fossa,** on the lateral pelvic wall at the level of the anterior superior iliac spine. It is about the size and shape of an almond and presents medial and lateral surfaces, anterior and posterior borders, and tubal and uterine poles. The **lateral surface** is in contact with parietal peritoneum; the **medial surface,** adjacent to the uterine tube, is in contact with the coils of the ileum.

A ligament, the mesovarium, attaches to the **anterior border** at the hilus, and the major ovarian vessels and nerve enter the gland at this border. The **posterior free border** is related anteriorly to the uterine tube and posteriorly to the ureter.

The suspensory ligament of the ovary is attached to the **upper (tubal) extremity** with the opening of the fallopian tube in close proximity. The **lower (uterine) pole,** directed toward the uterus, affords attachment for the ovarian ligament.

The **mesovarium** is a short, two-layered mesenteric reflection of the posterior layer of the broad ligament which encloses the ovary. Between the broad ligament and the anterior border of the ovary the layers of the mesovarium are in apposition to each other. The **suspensory (infundibulopelvic) ligament** is a connective tissue condensation from the lateral pelvic wall to the superior pole of the ovary and surrounds the ovarian vessels and nerve. The **ligament of the ovary** is a rounded cord containing some smooth muscle fibers which passes from the ovary to the uterus where it attaches between the uterine tube and the round ligament of the uterus.

Uterine Tube

The **uterine (fallopian) tubes** convey ova from the ovaries to the uterine cavity and transmit spermatozoa in the opposite direction. Each tube is approximately four inches long and is located between the layers of the upper margin of the broad ligament. The uterine tube courses laterally from the uterus to the uterine end of the ovary to arch over and terminate close to the upper pole of the ovary. The fallopian tube is divided into four segments: the infundibulum, the ampulla, the isthmus, and the uterine portion. The **infundibulum** is somewhat funnel-shaped, with the abdominal or pelvic opening located at the outlet of the funnel, and has a number of irregular processes, the **fimbriae** projecting from its margins. The slightly tortuous **ampulla** is the longest portion and has rela-tively thin walls. The narrow and thicked-walled **isthmus** is adjacent to the uterus, and the **uterine (intramural) portion** is embedded in the wall of, and opens into, the uterine cavity.

Uterus

The **uterus** is a somewhat pear-shaped organ lying entirely within the pelvic cavity, with its narrow end directed inferoposteriorly. It is composed of the fundus, the body, the isthmus, and the cervix. The **fundus** is the rounded upper portion above the level of the openings of the uterine tubes. The **body** is the main portion of the uterus which constricts at the **isthmus** to become the **cervix.** The latter pierces the anterior wall of the vagina, entering it at the deepest aspect of the vagina. The entire organ forms an angle slightly greater than ninety degrees with the vagina and usually inclines toward the right and is slightly twisted.

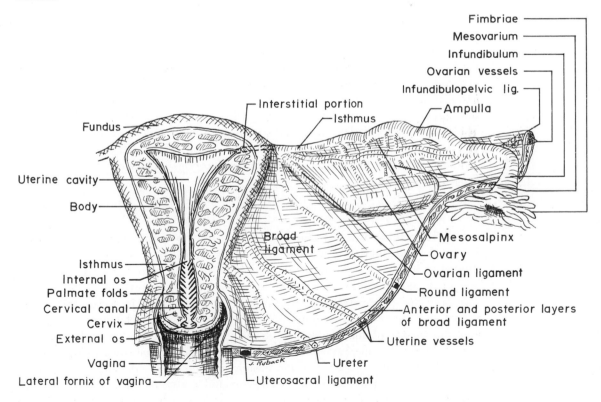

Fig. 42. Female reproductive organs with associated ligaments.

The anterior surface of the uterus is separated from the urinary bladder by the **uterovesical pouch** and the posterior surface from the rectum by the **rectouterine pouch.** The right and left margins of the uterus are related to the **broad ligament** with its enclosed structures. The uterine cavity is widest at the entry of the uterine tubes and narrows at the isthmus. The **cervical canal,** wider above than below, is an extension of the uterine cavity below the **internal ostium (os)** and opens into the vagina at the **external ostium (os).** Vertical folds are present on the anterior and posterior walls of the cervical canal, with **palmate folds** passing obliquely from the vertical folds.

The uterus derives much of its support from direct attachment to the surrounding organs, the vagina, the rectum, and the bladder, with additional support from peritoneal reflections. The **peritoneum** passes from the posterior surface of the bladder onto the isthmus of the uterus; continues over its anterior surface, fundus, and posterior surface; then passes onto the rectum to form the **uterovesical** and **rectouterine pouches** between these reflections. Laterally the peritoneum comes into apposition at the lateral border of the uterus and passes as the **broad ligament** to the pelvic wall, where it becomes parietal peritoneum. Superiorly the broad ligament encloses the uterine tubes and the ovaries.

That portion of the broad ligament between the level of the mesovarium and the uterine tubes is designated the **mesosalpinx.** The **mesovarium** is an extension of the posterior layer of the broad ligament which encloses the ovary. The **mesometrium** is the remainder of the broad ligament below the level of the mesovarium.

The **round ligament** of the uterus is a narrow band of fibrous connective tissue between the layers of the broad ligament attaching to the uterus just inferior and anterior to the entrance of the uterine tube. It passes laterally toward the anterior abdominal wall, hooks around the inferior epigastric vessels, traverses the inguinal canal, and blends with the subcutaneous tissue of the labium majus. The **transverse cervical** (cardinal or Mackenrodt's) **ligament** is a thickening of fascia and connective tissue together with smooth muscle fibers at the junction of the cervix and the vagina. The transverse cervical ligament gives the major support to the uterus.

Vagina

The **vagina** is a cylindrical musculomembranous tube, three to four inches in length, extending from the vestibule to the uterus. It is constricted inferiorly, dilated at its middle, and narrowed superiorly as it surrounds and attaches to the periphery of the cervix of the uterus. Its posterior wall is longer than the anterior wall, and the space between the cervix and the vaginal wall is designated the **anterior** and **posterior fornices.** Anteriorly the vagina is related to the urethra and the fundus of the bladder; posteriorly it is separated superiorly from the rectum by the rectouterine pouch and inferiorly from the anal canal by the perineal body; laterally it is attached to the levator ani and its fascia. The mucous membrane of the internal wall presents anterior and posterior longitudinal folds, the **vaginal columns,** and numerous transverse ridges, the **rugae vaginalis.** The entire structure forms an angle slightly greater than ninety degrees with the uterus.

INFERIOR EXTREMITY

Surface Anatomy

The inferior extremity is subdivided into the hip, thigh, knee, leg, ankle, and foot. It is limited superiorly by the iliac crest, inguinal ligament, symphysis pubis, ischiopubic ramus, sacrotuberous ligament, and coccyx. The **iliac crest,** palpable in its entirety, extends superiorly as high as the level of the fourth lumbar vertebra. Anteriorly the **anterior superior iliac spine** is palpable and affords the lateral attachment for the **inguinal ligament,** whose position is marked by the inguinal fold (groin). Posteriorly the **gluteal fold** delineates the inferior border of the gluteus maximus muscle. The **ischial tuberosities** are easily felt when the thighs are flexed, as are also the **ischiopubic rami** on the medial aspect of the thighs. Just lateral to the midline the **pubic tubercles** are readily palpable, especially in the thin individual. The **greater trochanter** of the femur, approximately a hand's breadth below the crest of the ilium, can be palpated about two inches posterior to the anterior superior iliac spine.

The massive **quadriceps femoris muscle** tapers inferiorly over the front of the thigh to terminate in the **suprapatellar tendon,** which inserts into the margins of the subcutaneous **patella** and continues as the **infrapatellar tendon** to insert into the **tibial tuberosity.** Laterally the tendons of the **biceps femoris** can be palpated and, with the medially situated tendons of the **semimembranosus** and **semitendinosus,** form prominent cords at the posterior aspect of the knee. With the thigh flexed, abducted, and laterally rotated, the outline of the **sartorius muscle** is visible anteriorly as it crosses the thigh obliquely.

The subcutaneous lateral portions of the **condyles of the femur** give width to the knee, and inferiorly the **head of the fibula** is easily felt at the lateral side of the knee. The **anterior border** and **medial surface of the tibia** are subcutaneous throughout its length and are continuous proximally with the medial condyle of the tibia. The **malleoli,** formed laterally by the fibula and medially by the tibia, are readily recognized at the ankle. Posteriorly the prominent **calcaneal tendon** serves as the insertion of the soleus and gastrocnemius muscles into the tuberosity of the calcaneus (heel bone).

Fasciae

The **superficial fascia** has special features only in the thigh and on the sole of the foot. In the thigh it contains considerable adipose tissue and varies in thickness, being relatively thick in the inguinal region. Here it is disposed into a

superficial fatty and a **deeper membranous layer,** with superficial lymph nodes, the great saphenous vein, and smaller blood vessels lying between them. The deeper layer is rather prominent on the medial side, where it blends with the deep fascia and covers the saphenous opening as the **cribriform fascia.** The superficial fascia fuses with the femoral sheath and lacunar ligament superiorly and with the deep fascia laterally. In the sole of the foot the superficial fascia is greatly thickened by fatty tissue and disposed into pockets extending inwardly from the skin. These **fibrous fat pads** are especially thick at weight-bearing sites, such as on the heel, ball of the foot, and pads of the toes, where they protect deeply lying structures.

The **deep fascia** in the thigh, the **fascia lata,** varies considerably in thickness and strength. It attaches superiorly to the inguinal ligament, the body of the pubis, the pubic arch, and the ischial tuberosity; laterally to the iliac crest; medially to the sacrotuberous ligament; and posteriorly to the sacrum and the coccyx. The oval **saphenous opening** at the upper medial portion of the thigh presents a medial crescentic border and is roofed by the cribriform fascia derived from the deep layer of the superficial fascia which, in turn, is perforated by the long saphenous vein and other smaller vessels. At the medial side of the thigh the deep fascia is relatively thin, but it thickens laterally as the **iliotibial tract,** a wide, strong band extending from the iliac crest to the lateral condyle of the tibia, the capsule of the knee joint, and the patellar ligament. The iliotibial tract affords insertion for the tensor fascia lata muscle and about three-fourth of the gluteus maximus muscle. With the body erect the iliotibial tract serves as a powerful brace which helps to steady the pelvis and keep the knee joint firmly extended. Extensions of the fascia lata inwardly to the linea aspera of the femur as **lateral, medial,** and **posterior intermuscular septa,** separate the thigh into extensor, adductor, and flexor muscular compartments.

Inferiorly the deep fascia attaches to the medial and lateral margins of the patella, the tibial tuberosity, the condyles of both the tibia and the femur, and the head of the fibula. At the posterior aspect of the knee joint it forms a roof for the popliteal fossa. The deep fascia of the leg is firmly attached anteromedially to the subcutaneous shaft of the tibia and sends **intermuscular septa** deeply, which, with the interosseous membrane, divide the leg into extensor, peroneal, and flexor muscular compartments. The flexor (posterior) compartment is further subdivided by **transverse intermuscular septa** into deep, intermediate, and superficial portions. Inferiorly the deep fascia attaches at both the malleoli and continues onto the foot.

The deep fascia surrounding the ankle thickens to form bands, the extensor, flexor, and peroneal retinacula, which bind or hold the tendons of the leg muscles in place and prevent bow-stringing of these tendons during contraction of the corresponding muscles. The **extensor retinaculum** is subdivided into a superior and inferior portion. The **superior extensor retinaculum** (transverse crural ligament), a strong band an inch wide situated immediately above the ankle joint, is attached laterally to the fibula and medially to the tibia. The **inferior extensor retinaculum** (cruciate ligament) is Y- or V-shaped, with the Y lying on its side. The stem of the Y is attached laterally to the upper surface of the calcaneus and overlies the tendons of the extensor digitorum longus and peroneus tertius. The

proximal band passes to the medial malleolus at the medial side of the ankle, while
the distal band blends with the deep fascia over the dorsum of the foot. The **flexor
retinaculum** (laciniate ligament) bridges the gap between the medial malleolus
and the medial surface of the calcaneus and is firmly attached to both these structures. Septa extend from the deep surface to the underlying bone and deltoid
ligament to form osseofibrous tunnels transmitting structures from the posterior
compartment of the leg. The **peroneal retinaculum** is subdivided into superior
and inferior components and binds the peroneal tendons in place. Septa from the
deep surface pass to the **peroneal trochlea,** forming two osseofibrous tunnels
which separate the tendons of the peroneus longus muscle from the brevis. Both
the superior and inferior peroneal retinacula extend from the lateral malleolus to
the lateral surface of the calcaneus.

Cutaneous Innervation (Figs. 43 and 44)

Skin over the gluteal region is supplied by **lateral branches of the iliohypogastric** and **subcostal nerves,** derived from the lumbar plexus and twelfth
thoracic nerve. Branches from the posterior primary rami, the **superior** and **middle cluneal nerves,** supply the skin over the sacrum. The **inferior cluneal
nerves,** derived from the posterior femoral cutaneous nerve, pass superiorly over
the lower border of the gluteus maximus to supply the skin of the inferior aspect
of the buttocks.

Cutaneous innervation of the anterior surface of the thigh is supplied by
two branches of the femoral nerve, the **medial** and **intermediate femoral
cutaneous nerves.** The lateral aspect of the thigh is innervated by anterior and
posterior branches of the **lateral femoral cutaneous nerve,** a direct branch
of the lumbar plexus. The medial surface of the thigh is supplied by the medial
femoral cutaneous and **cutaneous branches from the obturator** and **perineal
nerves.** The **femoral branch of the genitofemoral** reaches a small area just
below the inguinal ligament. The **genital branch of the genitofemoral,**
together with the ilioinguinal nerve, distribute to the skin adjacent to the region
of the superficial inguinal ring, the base of the penis and scrotum in the male,
and the labia majora in the female. The posterior surface of the thigh is supplied
by the **posterior femoral cutaneous nerve** from the sacral plexus.

The femoral nerve continues into the leg as the **saphenous nerve,** passing
inferiorly to supply the anteromedial and medial surfaces of the leg, the medial
side of the foot, and a small area on the medial aspect of the sole. Its **infrapatellar
branch,** arising in the thigh, ramifies on the anterior surface of the leg immediately below the knee. The lateral surface of the upper leg receives its cutaneous
innervation from a branch of the **common peroneal.** The distal third of the
anterior surface of the leg and the dorsum of the foot are innervated by a continuation of the **superficial peroneal nerve,** except for the adjacent sides of
the great and second toe, which are supplied by a cutaneous branch of the **deep
peroneal.** The **sural nerve,** derived from both tibial and common peroneal
nerves, distributes to the posterior surface of the leg, the lateral side of the foot,
the little toe, and a small portion of the posterolateral surface of the sole.

The **calcaneal branch of the tibial nerve** supplies most of the plantar

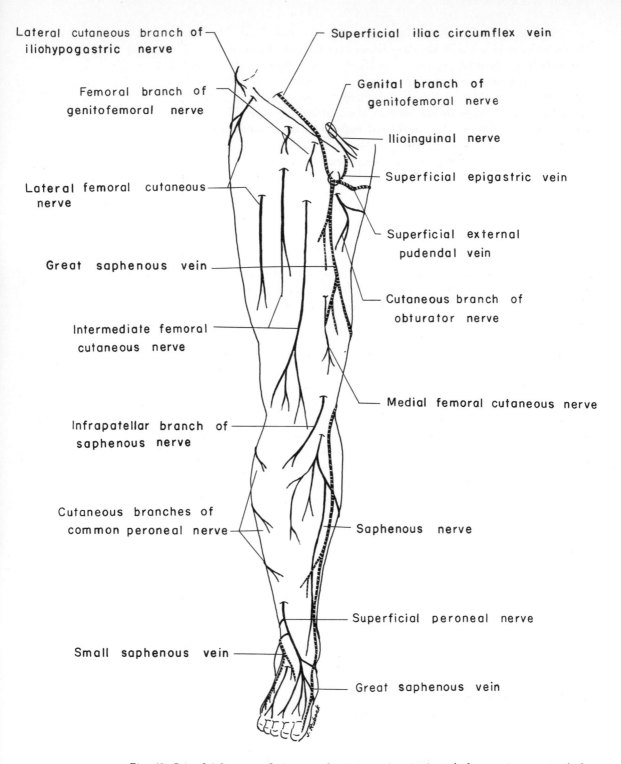

Lateral cutaneous branch of iliohypogastric nerve

Superficial iliac circumflex vein

Femoral branch of genitofemoral nerve

Genital branch of genitofemoral nerve

Ilioinguinal nerve

Lateral femoral cutaneous nerve

Superficial epigastric vein

Superficial external pudendal vein

Great saphenous vein

Cutaneous branch of obturator nerve

Intermediate femoral cutaneous nerve

Medial femoral cutaneous nerve

Infrapatellar branch of saphenous nerve

Cutaneous branches of common peroneal nerve

Saphenous nerve

Superficial peroneal nerve

Small saphenous vein

Great saphenous vein

Fig. 43. *Superficial venous drainage and cutaneous innervation of the anterior aspect of the inferior extremity.*

116

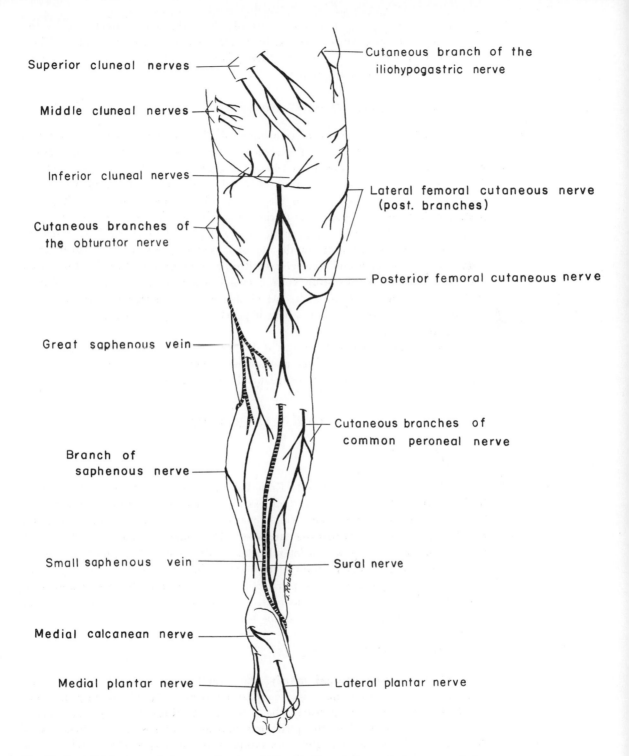

Superior cluneal nerves

Middle cluneal nerves

Inferior cluneal nerves

Cutaneous branches of
the obturator nerve

Great saphenous vein

Branch of
saphenous nerve

Small saphenous vein

Medial calcanean nerve

Medial plantar nerve

Cutaneous branch of the
iliohypogastric nerve

Lateral femoral cutaneous nerve
(post. branches)

Posterior femoral cutaneous nerve

Cutaneous branches of
common peroneal nerve

Sural nerve

Lateral plantar nerve

*Fig. 44. Superficial venous drainage and cutaneous innervation of the posterior aspect of the
inferior extremity.*

surface of the heel, while the anterior two-thirds of the sole is innervated by the **medial** and **lateral plantar nerves,** both cutaneous branches of the tibial. Their areas of distribution to the sole are divided by an anteroposterior line passing through the middle of the fourth toe.

Venous Drainage (Figs. 43 and 44)

The **superficial venous drainage** of the inferior extremity is via two major vessels, the great and small saphenous veins. The **great** (long) **saphenous vein** begins at the junction of the medial digital vein of the great toe and the dorsal venous arch of the foot. From its origin it ascends anterior to the medial malleolus and along the medial border of the tibia to the knee, where it passes posterior to the medial epicondyle of the femur. It continues on the medial aspect of the thigh to the saphenous opening, where it pierces the cribriform fascia to empty into the femoral vein. In the inguinal region it receives the **superficial epigastric,** the **superficial iliac circumflex,** and the **external pudendal veins.** The **small** (short) **saphenous vein** begins laterally at the dorsal venous arch of the foot, ascends posterior to the lateral malleolus and along the posterior aspect of the leg to the popliteal fossa, where it penetrates the deep fascia to empty into the **popliteal vein.**

The **deep venous drainage** is by way of the **vena comitantes** of the corresponding arteries. Numerous anastomoses occur between the great and small saphenous veins and between the superficial and deep venous drainage.

GLUTEAL REGION

Muscles (Table X)

The gluteal region extends from the iliac crest superiorly to the gluteal fold inferiorly. The mass of the buttocks is formed by the **gluteus maximus,** the largest muscle of the body, which overlies the more deeply placed **gluteus medius** and **gluteus minimus muscles.** The gluteus maximus is the chief extensor and the most powerful lateral rotator, while the medius and minimus act as abductors and medial rotators of the thigh. The small lateral rotator muscles of the thigh, the **piriformis, superior** and **inferior gemelli,** and **quadratus femoris,** underlie the gluteus maximus, are related to the back of the hip joint, and insert into the great trochanter of the femur.

Arteries and Nerves (Fig. 45)

The **superior gluteal artery,** the largest branch of the internal iliac, courses posteriorly from its origin to pass between the lumbosacral trunk and the first sacral nerve, then leaves the pelvic cavity through the greater sciatic foramen above the level of the piriformis muscle. It divides into a **superficial branch,** which supplies the gluteus maximus from its deep surface, and a **deep branch,** which passes between the gluteus medius and the gluteus minimus and ramifies on and supplies both muscles as well as the obturator internus, piriformis, levator ani, and coccygeus muscles and the hip joint.

The **inferior gluteal artery,** the larger of the two terminal branches of the internal iliac artery, passes posteriorly through the greater sciatic foramen below the level of the piriformis. It supplies the gluteus maximus and the lateral rotator muscles and gives a long slender branch which accompanies and supplies the sciatic nerve.

TABLE X. MUSCLES OF THE GLUTEAL REGION

Muscle	Origin	Insertion	Action	Nerve
Gluteus maximus	Upper ilium, posterior aspect of sacrum and coccyx, and sacrotuberous ligament	Gluteal tuberosity and iliotibial tract	Acts as chief extensor and powerful lateral rotator of thigh	Inferior gluteal
Gluteus medius	Ilium between middle gluteal line and iliac crest	Greater trochanter and oblique ridge of femur	Abducts and rotates thigh medially	Superior gluteal
Gluteus minimus	Ilium between middle and inferior gluteal lines	Greater trochanter and capsule of hip joint	Abducts and rotates thigh medially	Superior gluteal
Tensor fascia lata	Iliac crest and anterior border of ilium	Iliotibial tract	Tenses fascia lata; assists in flexion, abduction, and medial rotation of thigh	Superior gluteal
Piriformis	Internal aspect of sacrum, greater sciatic notch, and sacrotuberous ligament	Upper part of greater trochanter	Rotates thigh laterally	Branches from S_1 and S_2
Gemelli superior and inferior	Superior, upper margin of lesser sciatic notch; inferior, lower margin of sciatic notch	Obliquely into either border of tendon of obturator internus and greater trochanter	Rotates thigh laterally	Branches from sacral plexus
Quadratus femoris	Lateral border of ischial tuberosity	Posterior aspect of greater trochanter and adjoining shaft of femur	Rotates thigh laterally	L_4, L_5, and S_1

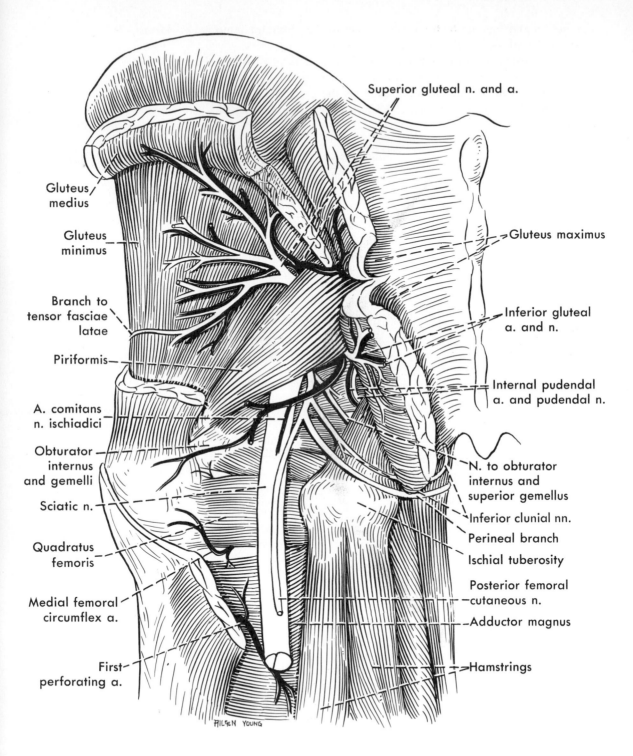

Fig. 45. Gluteal region. (From W. H. Hollinshead. Textbook of Anatomy, *ed. 2. New York, Hoeber, in press.)*

The **superior gluteal nerve** (L_4, L_5, and S_1) passes through the upper part of the greater sciatic foramen and between the gluteus medius and the gluteus minimus to supply the gluteus medius, the gluteus minimus, and the tensor fascia lata. The **inferior gluteal nerve** (L_5, S_1, and S_2) leaves the pelvis by traversing the lower part of the greater sciatic foramen to supply the gluteus maximus.

THIGH

ANTERIOR COMPARTMENT OF THE THIGH

Femoral Sheath

The **femoral sheath** is a fascial funnel formed anteriorly by the transversalis fascia and posteriorly by the iliac fascia. It encloses the upper inch and one-half of the femoral vessels and is situated deep to the inguinal ligament in a groove between the iliopsoas and the pectineus muscles. The interior of the sheath is divided by two anteroposterior septa into three compartments. The **medial compartment,** bounded medially by the crescentic base of the lacunar ligament, forms the **femoral canal** and contains only areolar connective tissue, a small lymph node, and lymphatic vessels. The **intermediate compartment** contains the **femoral vein,** and the **lateral compartment** the **femoral artery** and the **femoral branch of the genitofemoral nerve.** Structures passing deep to the inguinal ligament and lateral to the femoral sheath include the iliopsoas muscle and the femoral and lateral femoral cutaneous nerves.

Femoral Triangle (Fig. 46)

The **femoral triangle** covers the greater part of the upper third of the thigh. Its **base** is formed by the inguinal ligament superiorly and its **sides** by the medial border of the sartorius laterally and the medial border of the adductor longus medially. The above muscles meet at the **apex** inferiorly, where a narrow intermuscular cleft, the **adductor canal,** continues distally. The **roof** of the femoral triangle is formed by skin and superficial and deep fasciae, and contains superficial inguinal lymph nodes and vessels, the femoral branch of the genitofemoral nerve, superficial branches of the femoral artery, and the upper end of the great saphenous vein. The iliopsoas, adductor longus, and pectineus muscles form the **floor** of the triangle. Its **contents** include the **femoral artery** and **vein** passing from the base to the apex; the **deep external pudendal, profunda femoral,** and **lateral** and **medial femoral circumflex arteries;** the **femoral branch** of the genitofemoral, the **lateral femoral cutaneous,** and the **femoral nerves;** and several **inguinal lymph nodes.**

Adductor Canal

At the apex of the femoral triangle the femoral artery and vein continue inferiorly in the **adductor canal,** a muscular cleft between the vastus medialis and the adductors longus and magnus, which is deep to and covered by the sartorius

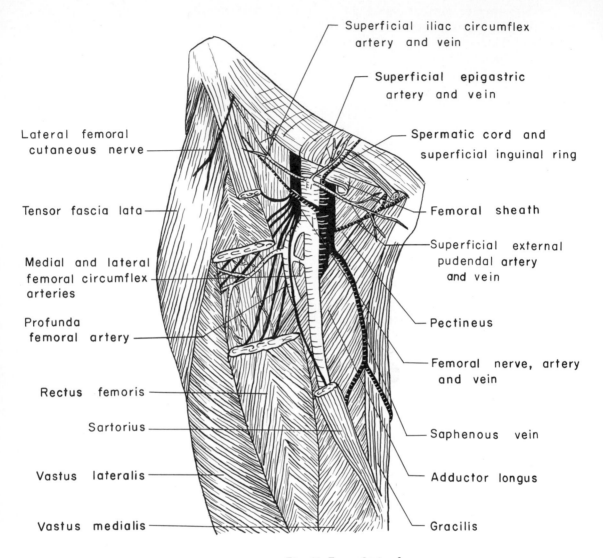

Superficial iliac circumflex
artery and vein

Superficial epigastric
artery and vein

Spermatic cord and
superficial inguinal ring

Lateral femoral
cutaneous nerve

Femoral sheath

Tensor fascia lata

Superficial external
pudendal artery
and vein

Medial and lateral
femoral circumflex
arteries

Pectineus

Profunda
femoral artery

Femoral nerve, artery
and vein

Rectus femoris

Sartorius

Saphenous vein

Vastus lateralis

Adductor longus

Vastus medialis

Gracilis

Fig. 46. Femoral triangle.

muscle as it crosses the thigh obliquely. At the lowermost extent of the adductor canal, the posterior wall, formed by the adductor magnus, presents a deficiency, or opening, the **adductor hiatus,** which leads into the popliteal fossa. In addition to the femoral artery and vein, the canal contains the saphenous nerve and branches of the femoral nerve to the vastus medialis muscle.

Muscles (Table XI)

The muscles of the anterior aspect of the thigh are the iliopsoas, the sartorius, and the quadriceps femoris. The latter two muscles are contained within the **extensor (anterior) compartment,** which is limited by the lateral and

TABLE XI. MUSCLES OF THE ANTERIOR COMPARTMENT OF THE THIGH

Muscle	Origin	Insertion	Action	Nerve
Iliopsoas: Compound muscle formed from iliacus and psoas major				
Iliacus	Iliac fossa and lateral portion of sacrum	Lesser trochanter of femur via iliopsoas tendon	Flexes and rotates thigh medially	Femoral
Psoas major	Lumbar vertebrae	Lesser trochanter of femur via iliopsoas tendon	Flexes and rotates thigh medially	Second and third lumbar
Sartorius	Anterior superior iliac spine	Upper part of medial surface of tibia	Acts on both hip and knee joints; mainly flexes leg	Femoral
Quadriceps: Consists of rectus femoris and vasti muscles, the four muscles combining into an aponeurotic and tendinous insertion into tibial tuberosity, with patella interposed as sesamoid bone				
Rectus femoris	Straight head from anterior inferior iliac spine; reflected head from postero-superior aspect of rim of acetabulum	Tibial tuberosity	Extends leg and flexes thigh	Femoral
Vastus lateralis	Intertrochanteric line, greater trochanter, linea aspera, and lateral intermuscular septum	Tibial tuberosity	Extends leg	Femoral
Vastus medialis	Intertrochanteric line, spiral line, and medial intermuscular septum	Tibial tuberosity	Extends leg	Femoral
Vastus intermedius	Upper two-thirds of shaft of femur and distal one-half of lateral intermuscular septum	Tibial tuberosity	Extends leg	Femoral
Articularis genu	Variable slip of muscle of deep aspect of vastus medialis which, in extension of knee, pulls synovial membrane out of the way			

medial intermuscular septa. The **sartorius** acts as a flexor of the leg and together with the rectus femoris and iliopsoas also flexes the thigh. The **iliopsoas** also acts as a medial rotator of the thigh. The bulky **quadriceps,** one of the largest and most powerful muscles in the body, consists of the **rectus femoris** and the **vasti lateralis, medialis,** and **intermedius.** As powerful extensors of the leg, the four muscles form an aponeurotic and tendinous insertion on the tibia, with the patella interposed as a sesamoid bone. Muscles in the extensor compartment are innervated by the femoral nerve and receive their blood supply from the femoral artery.

Arteries and Nerves

The **femoral artery,** as a continuation of the external iliac, passes deep to the inguinal ligament to enter the femoral triangle. At the apex of the triangle is passes deep to the sartorius muscle to traverse the adductor canal and becomes the **popliteal artery** at the adductor hiatus. Branches within the femoral triangle include the **superficial epigastric artery,** which pierces the femoral sheath to ascend superficial to the inguinal ligament and courses toward the umbilicus; the **superficial circumflex iliac,** which penetrates the femoral sheath to run in the subcutaneous tissue toward the anterior superior iliac spine; the **superficial external pudendal,** which supplies skin and muscles in the inguinal region and gives anterior scrotal or labial branches to the skin of the external genitalia; and the **deep external pudendal,** which lies on and supplies the pectineus and adductor longus muscles and sends twigs to the external genitalia.

The large **profunda branch** of the femoral artery arises from its posterolateral aspect and passes inferiorly, posterior to the adductor longus. It gives rise to the medial and lateral circumflex arteries, then courses deeply to give origin to the **three perforating branches,** and terminates as the **fourth perforating artery.** These perforating vessels supply the adductor and the flexor muscle groups. The **medial femoral circumflex artery** courses between the pectineus and the iliopsoas, then around the neck of the femur, where it divides into a **superficial** and a **deep branch** to supply muscles in this region. The **lateral femoral circumflex** passes laterally deep to the sartorius and rectus femoris, where it divides into ascending, transverse, and descending branches. The **ascending branch** distributes to the gluteal region; the **transverse branch** encircles the femur to anastomose with the medial femoral circumflex; and the **descending branch** passes inferiorly to terminate in the anastomosis around the knee joint.

The **femoral nerve,** the largest branch of the lumbar plexus, emerges from the lateral side of the psoas major muscle just below the iliac crest to descend between the psoas and the iliacus muscles. It passes deep to the inguinal ligament in the lateral neuromuscular compartment to enter the thigh and divide into a number of branches in the femoral triangle. Its terminal branch, the **saphenous nerve,** passes through the adductor canal to become superficial at the adductor hiatus and course between the sartorius and gracilis muscles to supply the skin of the leg. Branches of the femoral nerve in the abdomen include the **nerve to the iliacus** and the **nerve to the pectineus;** in the thigh it gives **muscular branches** to the sartorius, rectus femoris, and vasti muscles, and twigs to the pectineus, as well as the **intermediate** and **medial femoral cutaneous branches.**

ADDUCTOR COMPARTMENT OF THE THIGH

Muscles (Table XII)

The adductor muscles, arranged in three layers, occupy the medial (adductor) compartment, which is limited by the medial and posterior intermuscular septa. The **pectineus** and **adductor longus** are the most superficial; the **adductor brevis** lies intermediate, and the **adductor magnus** occupies the deepest stratum. The **gracilis** (also an adductor) lies superficially on the medial aspect of the thigh. The two divisions of the obturator nerve are interposed between the three muscular layers and supply the muscles in the adductor compartment.

TABLE XII. MUSCLES OF THE ADDUCTOR COMPARTMENT OF THE THIGH

Muscle	Origin	Insertion	Action	Nerve
Adductor longus	Body of pubis immediately below pubic crest	Linea aspera of femur	Adducts, flexes, and rotates thigh laterally	Obturator
Adductor brevis	Body of pubis below origin of adductor longus	Between lesser trochanter and linea aspera and upper part of linea aspera	Adducts, flexes, and rotates thigh laterally	Obturator
Adductor magnus	Side of pubic arch and ischial tuberosity	Extensive into linea aspera, medial supracondylar ridge, and adductor tubercle	Adducts, flexes, and rotates thigh laterally; distal fibers aid in extension and medial rotation of thigh	Obturator; distal portion by sciatic
Pectineus	Pectineal line and pectineal surface of pubis	Posterior aspect of femur between lesser trochanter and linea aspera	Adducts and assists in flexion of thigh	Obturator and femoral
Gracilis	Lower half of body of pubis	Upper part of medial surface of tibia	Adducts thigh; flexes knee joint; and rotates leg medially	Obturator
Obturator externus	Margins of obturator foramen and obturator membrane	Posterior aspect of intertrochanteric fossa of femur	Flexes and rotates thigh laterally	Obturator

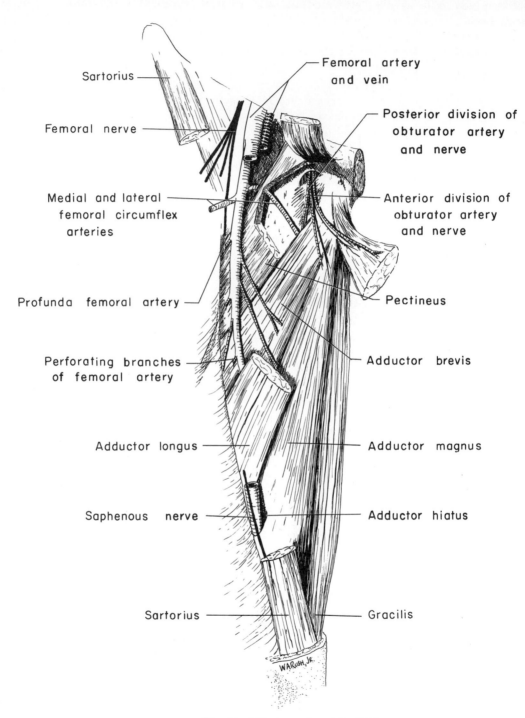

Sartorius

Femoral nerve

Medial and lateral
femoral circumflex
arteries

Profunda femoral artery

Perforating branches
of femoral artery

Adductor longus

Saphenous nerve

Sartorius

Femoral artery
and vein

Posterior division of
obturator artery
and nerve

Anterior division of
obturator artery
and nerve

Pectineus

Adductor brevis

Adductor magnus

Adductor hiatus

Gracilis

W.A.Rush, Jr.

Fig. 47. Adductor region of the thigh.

All three adductors act in adduction and lateral rotation of the thigh. The pectineus and gracilis, in addition to adduction, act as flexors; the pectineus aids in flexion of the thigh, and the gracilis in flexion of both the thigh and the knee. The gracilis also assists in medial rotation of the thigh.

Arteries and Nerves (Fig. 47)

The **obturator artery,** a branch of the internal iliac, arises in the pelvis and accompanies the obturator nerve through the obturator canal to divide into anterior and posterior branches which follow the margins of the obturator foramen deep to the obturator externus. The **anterior branch** supplies the obturator externus, the pectineus, the adductors, and the gracilis; the **posterior branch** is distributed to muscles attaching to the ischial tuberosity and gives a branch, which passes deep to the transverse acetabular ligament, to supply the head of the femur.

The **obturator nerve** originates in the abdomen as a branch of the lumbar plexus in the substance of the psoas major muscle. Emerging from the medial surface of this muscle, it passes on the lateral wall of the pelvic cavity, through the obturator canal, and divides into anterior and posterior divisions as it enters the thigh. The divisions pass to either side of the adductor brevis muscle, where the **anterior division** lies between the adductors longus and brevis and supplies these muscles and sends branches to the gracilis and pectineus muscles. The **posterior division** passes between the adductors brevis and magnus, supplying these muscles as well as the obturator externus. The pectineus and the adductor magnus each has dual innervations, with the pectineus receiving additional innervation from the **femoral nerve** and the adductor magnus from the **tibial division** of the sciatic nerve.

POSTERIOR COMPARTMENT OF THE THIGH

Muscles (Table XIII)

The posterior compartment of the thigh is located between the posterior and lateral intermuscular septa and contains the flexor, or hamstring, muscles. All the flexors are innervated by the sciatic nerve, with the short head of the biceps receiving its nerve supply from the common peroneal division and the remaining muscles from the tibial division. The **biceps** arises by a long and short head; the **semimembranosus** has a long membranous origin; and the **semitendinosus** a long tendinous insertion. The long head of the biceps, the semimembranosus, and the semitendinosus span both hip and knee joint, and all act as flexors of the leg and extensors of the thigh. They also act in rotation of the leg and thigh, with the biceps rotating laterally and the semimembranosus and semitendinosus rotating medially.

Arteries and Nerves (Fig. 48)

No major artery courses through the posterior compartment. The blood supply is derived from the previously described **perforating branches** of the profunda femoris branch of the femoral artery.

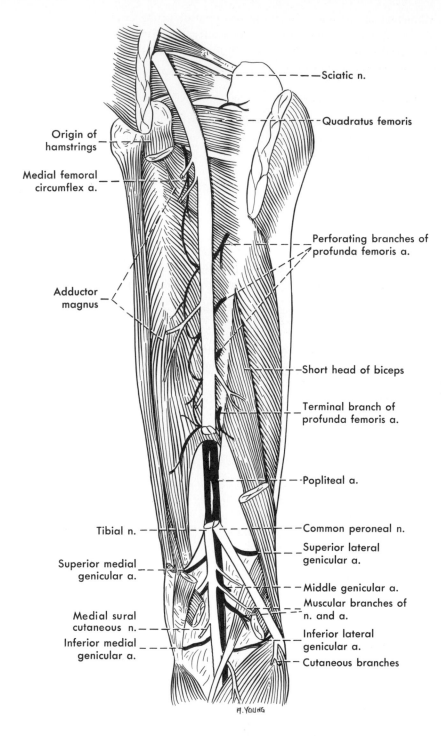

Origin of hamstrings

Medial femoral circumflex a.

Adductor magnus

Tibial n.

Superior medial genicular a.

Medial sural cutaneous n.

Inferior medial genicular a.

Sciatic n.

Quadratus femoris

Perforating branches of profunda femoris a.

Short head of biceps

Terminal branch of profunda femoris a.

Popliteal a.

Common peroneal n.

Superior lateral genicular a.

Middle genicular a.

Muscular branches of n. and a.

Inferior lateral genicular a.

Cutaneous branches

A. YOUNG

Fig. 48. Posterior region of the thigh. (From W. H. Hollinshead. Textbook of Anatomy, *ed. 2. New York, Hoeber, in press.)*

TABLE XIII. MUSCLES OF THE POSTERIOR COMPARTMENT OF THE THIGH

Muscle	Origin	Insertion	Action	Nerve
Biceps femoris	Long head, common tendon with semi-tendinosus from ischial tuberosity; short head, linea aspera and upper half of supracondylar ridge of femur	Common tendon into head of fibula	Flexes knee; rotates leg laterally; long head extends hip	Long head by tibial portion, short head by peroneal portion, of sciatic
Semitendinosus	In common with long head of biceps from ischial tuberosity	Upper part of medial surface of tibia	Flexes knee; rotates leg medially; extends hip joint	Tibial portion of sciatic
Semi-membranosus	Ischial tuberosity	Medial condyle of tibia	Extends hip joint; flexes knee; rotates leg medially	Tibial portion of sciatic

The **sciatic nerve,** a branch of the sacral plexus, is the largest nerve of the body. It enters the thigh inferior to the piriformis muscle, passing through the greater sciatic foramen, to descend deep to the gluteus maximus muscle lying on the gemelli muscles, the obturator internus tendon, and the quadratus femoris muscle. As it continues distally through the thigh, it lies on the adductor magnus and is crossed obliquely by the long head of the biceps femoris. It terminates by dividing into **tibial** and **common peroneal nerves.** This division may occur anywhere from its origin in the pelvis to the popliteal fossa, but usually takes place as the sciatic nerve enters the popliteal fossa. Branches from the common peroneal division supply the short head of the biceps; from the tibial division branches supply the long head of the biceps, the semimembranosus, the semitendinosus, and the adductor magnus muscles.

POPLITEAL FOSSA (FIG. 49)

The **popliteal fossa** is a diamond-shaped area on the posterior aspect of the knee joint extending from the lower third of the femur to the upper part of the tibia. With the knee flexed this area presents a depression, but with the joint fully extended forms a slight posterior bulge. The fossa is **bounded** superiorly and laterally by the biceps femoris; superiorly and medially by the semitendinosus, semimembranosus, gracilis, sartorius, and adductor magnus; and inferiorly by the converging heads of the gastrocnemius and the laterally placed plantaris muscle.

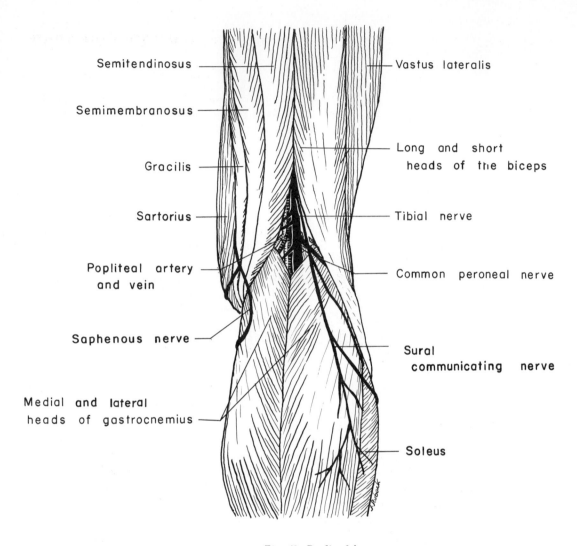

Semitendinosus ——— Vastus lateralis

Semimembranosus ———

Gracilis ——— Long and short heads of the biceps

Sartorius ——— Tibial nerve

Popliteal artery and vein ——— Common peroneal nerve

Saphenous nerve ———

Medial and lateral heads of gastrocnemius ——— Sural communicating nerve

Soleus

Fig. 49. Popliteal fossa.

The **floor** is formed above downward by the popliteal surface of the femur, the oblique popliteal ligament, the popliteus muscle, and the upper part of the tibia. The fossa **contains** the common peroneal and tibial nerves, the popliteal artery and vein, the posterior femoral cutaneous nerve, the small saphenous vein, lymph nodes, and numerous synovial bursae.

The **popliteal artery,** the direct continuation of the femoral at the adductor hiatus, descends mediolaterally through the popliteal fossa to terminate at the lower border of the popliteus muscle by dividing into the **anterior** and **posterior tibial arteries.** Branches of the popliteal artery within the fossa consist of several **genicular branches** which join in the anastomosis around the knee joint.

LEG

In the leg, as in the thigh, the muscles are located in fascial compartments. The **lateral (peroneal) compartment** is limited by the **anterior** and **posterior intermuscular septa;** the **anterior (extensor) compartment** is between the **anterior intermuscular septum** and the **tibia;** and the **posterior (flexor) compartment** is bounded by the **tibia** and the **posterior intermuscular septum.** Passing between the tibia and the fibula, the deeply lying **interosseous membrane** separates the extensor from the flexor compartments. The latter is further divided by two **transverse intermuscular septa** into a deep subdivision containing the tibialis posterior muscle, a superficial subdivision containing the gastrocnemius and soleus muscles, and an intermediate compartment containing the remaining muscles, the posterior tibial artery, and the tibial nerve. Each of the three major compartments transmits a major nerve which supplies muscles within the compartment, but, as in the thigh, one compartment, the lateral, has no major artery coursing through it.

ANTERIOR COMPARTMENT OF THE LEG (FIG. 50)

Muscles (Table XIV)

Within the anterior compartment the superficially located **tibialis anterior muscle** lies along the lateral side of the tibia, adjacent to the interosseous membrane. It acts in dorsiflexion and inversion of the foot and, with the peroneus longus,

TABLE XIV. MUSCLES OF THE ANTERIOR COMPARTMENT OF THE LEG

Muscle	Origin	Insertion	Action	Nerve
Tibialis anterior	Lateral condyle of upper two-thirds of tibia and interosseous membrane	First cuneiform and first metatarsal	Dorsiflexes and inverts foot	Deep peroneal
Extensor digitorum longus	Lateral condyle of tibia, upper three-fourths of fibula, and interosseous membrane	By four tendons; forms membranous expansion over metatarsophalangeal joints of second to fifth toes	Extends toes; continued action dorsiflexes and everts foot	Deep peroneal
Peroneus tertius	Distal one-fourth of fibula and interosseous membrane	Fifth metatarsal or deep fascia of foot	Dorsiflexes and everts foot	Deep peroneal
Extensor hallucis longus	Middle half of fibula and interosseous membrane	Base of distal phalanx of great toe	Extends great toe; aids in dorsiflexion and inversion of foot	Deep peroneal

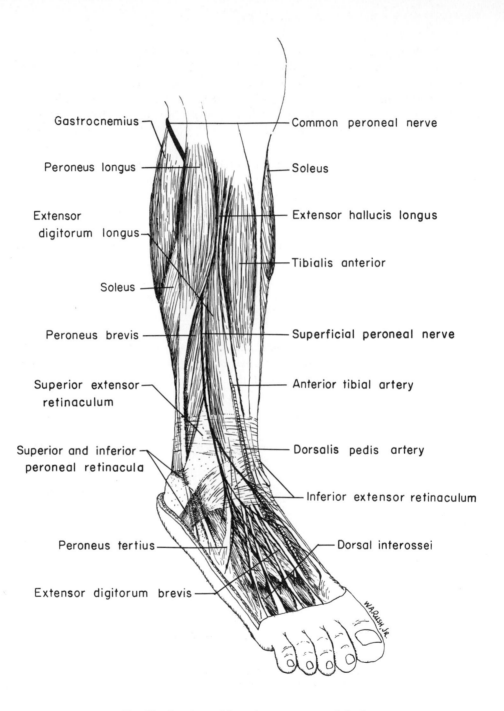

Gastrocnemius

Peroneus longus

Extensor
digitorum longus

Soleus

Peroneus brevis

Superior extensor
retinaculum

Superior and inferior
peroneal retinacula

Peroneus tertius

Extensor digitorum brevis

Common peroneal nerve

Soleus

Extensor hallucis longus

Tibialis anterior

Superficial peroneal nerve

Anterior tibial artery

Dorsalis pedis artery

Inferior extensor retinaculum

Dorsal interossei

W.A.Rush, Jr.

Fig. 50. Anterior and lateral compartments of the leg.

functions to maintain the longitudinal arch of the foot. The long, thin **extensor digitorum longus** is situated along the fibula and acts to extend the toes and secondarily to dorsiflex and evert the foot. Usually the **peroneus tertius** can be distinguished from the extensor digitorum longus only by its insertion into deep fascia of the foot or to the bases of the fourth and fifth metatarsals. The **extensor hallucis longus,** deeply located between the tibialis anterior and the extensor digitorum longus, extends the great toe and aids in dorsiflexion of the foot. Muscles in the anterior compartment are innervated by the deep peroneal (anterior tibial) nerve and receive their blood supply from the anterior tibial artery. The tibialis anterior usually receives additional innervation directly from the common peroneal.

Arteries and Nerves

At the bifurcation of the popliteal artery its **anterior tibial branch** passes distally between the heads of origin of the tibialis posterior muscle. It then pierces the proximal portion of the interosseous membrane to course inferiorly on the anterior surface of the membrane passing between the tibialis anterior and the extensor digitorum longus proximally, and the tibialis anterior and the extensor hallucis longus distally. The anterior tibial artery terminates under the cruciate ligament as the **dorsalis pedis artery.** In addition to supplying the muscles of the anterior compartment, its branches include the **posterior tibial recurrent,** which passes superiorly between the popliteal ligament and the popliteus muscle to join the genicular anastomosis, and the **anterior tibial recurrent,** which crosses the interosseous membrane to pass superiorly and join the genicular anastomosis. At the ankle the **medial anterior malleolar branch** passes deep to the tendon of the tibialis anterior to anastomose with branches of the posterior tibial artery, whereas the **lateral anterior malleolar** winds around the lateral malleolus deep to the extensor digitorum longus and peroneus tendons to join the malleolar branches of the posterior tibial and dorsalis pedis arteries.

The **deep peroneal** (anterior tibial) **nerve,** a branch of the common peroneal, courses around the head of the fibular to pass deep to the peroneus longus muscle, pierces the extensor digitorum longus, and descends in the anterior compartment on the interosseous membrane. It terminates under the extensor retinaculum as **medial** and **lateral digital branches.** It gives twigs to the peroneus longus, supplies muscles in the anterior compartment and the extensor digitorum brevis on the dorsum of the foot, and its most distal branch supplies the skin of the contiguous sides of the great and second toe.

LATERAL COMPARTMENT OF THE LEG (FIG. 50)

Muscles (Table XV)

Two muscles, the **peroneus longus** and the **peroneus brevis,** are located in the lateral compartment of the leg. Both are supplied by the superficial peroneal nerve, with the peroneus longus frequently receiving additional innervation from the common peroneal. Both muscles act as everters and aid in plantar flexion of the foot. The peroneus longus and the tibialis anterior form a sling by their manner of insertion and give support for the longitudinal arch of the foot.

TABLE XV. MUSCLES OF THE LATERAL COMPARTMENT OF THE LEG

Muscle	Origin	Insertion	Action	Nerve
Peroneus longus	Lateral condyle of tibia, head and upper two-thirds of fibula	First metatarsal and first cuneiform	Everts and aids in plantar flexion of foot	Superficial peroneal
Peroneus brevis	Lower two-thirds of fibula	Base of fifth metatarsal	Everts and aids in plantar flexion of foot	Superficial peroneal

Arteries and Nerves

No major artery courses in the lateral compartment of the leg. The muscles are supplied by perforating twigs of the **peroneal branch** of the posterior tibial artery located within the posterior compartment.

The **superficial peroneal** (musculocutaneous) **nerve,** a branch of the common peroneal, passes between the extensor digitorum longus and the peronei muscles to descend in the lateral compartment and supply the peroneus longus and peroneus brevis muscles. In the distal third of the leg it becomes superficial to supply skin on the anterior surface of the leg and the dorsum of the foot.

POSTERIOR COMPARTMENT OF THE LEG (FIG. 51)

Muscles (Table XVI)

The deeply placed **tibialis posterior muscle,** the principal inverter of the foot, is separated from the **flexor digitorum longus** and the **flexor hallucis longus muscles** by the deeper of two transverse intermuscular septa. The tibialis posterior aids in plantar flexion of the foot, and both flexors assist in inversion of the foot. The **gastrocnemius** and the **soleus** are separated from the intermediate flexor muscles by the more superficial transverse intermuscular septum. Inserting by the common **calcaneal tendon** (tendon of Achilles) into the calcaneus, the gastrocnemius and the soleus are the strongest of the plantar flexors or the foot. Two small muscles within the popliteal region complete the flexor group of muscles, namely, the **popliteus,** which performs the important initial "unlocking action" in flexion of the knee, and the relatively unimportant **plantaris,** which sends its long slender tendon to insert into the medial side of the calcaneal tendon.

Arteries and Nerves

The **posterior tibial artery,** the larger terminal branch of the popliteal, passes distally in the intermediate portion of the posterior compartment of the leg on the superficial aspect of the flexor digitorum longus. At the ankle it passes deep to the laciniate ligament, where it divides into the **lateral** and **medial plantar arteries.** At the knee it gives off the **fibular branch,** which passes laterally toward the head of the fibula giving twigs to the peroneus longus and peroneus

TABLE XVI. MUSCLES OF THE POSTERIOR COMPARTMENT OF THE LEG

Muscle	Origin	Insertion	Action	Nerve
Gastrocnemius	Lateral head, lateral condyle of femur; medial head, popliteal surface and medial condyle of femur	With soleus via calcaneal tendon into posterior surface of calcaneus	Plantar flexes foot and flexes knee	Tibial
Soleus	Upper one-third of fibula, soleal line on tibia	With gastrocnemius via calcaneal tendon into posterior surface of calcaneus	Plantar flexes foot	Tibial
Plantaris	Popliteal surface of femur above lateral head of gastrocnemius	Into medial side of calcaneal tendon	Plantar flexes foot	Tibial
Popliteus	Popliteal groove, lateral condyle of femur	Tibia above soleal line	With knee fully extended rotates femur laterally	Tibial
Flexor digitorum longus	Middle one-half of tibia below soleal line	Tendon divides into four tendons, which insert into distal phalanges of four lateral toes	Flexes phalanges of four lateral toes; continued action plantar flexes and inverts foot	Tibial
Flexor hallucis longus	Lower two-thirds of fibula and intermuscular septa	Base of distal phalanx of great toe	Flexes great toe; continued action plantar flexes and inverts foot	Tibial
Tibialis posterior	Interosseous membrane and adjoining tibia and fibula	Into tuberosity of navicular with slips to cuneiforms, cuboid, and bases of second, third and fourth metatarsals	Acts as principal inverter of foot; plantar flexes foot	Tibial

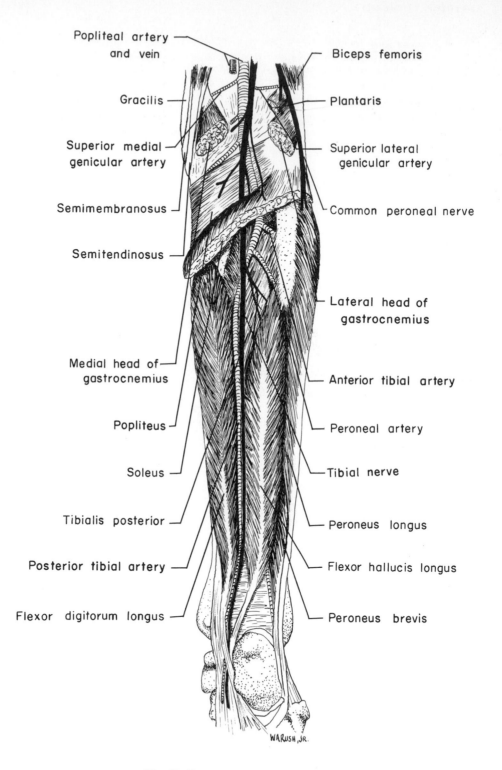

Popliteal artery and vein

Gracilis

Superior medial genicular artery

Semimembranosus

Semitendinosus

Medial head of gastrocnemius

Popliteus

Soleus

Tibialis posterior

Posterior tibial artery

Flexor digitorum longus

Biceps femoris

Plantaris

Superior lateral genicular artery

Common peroneal nerve

Lateral head of gastrocnemius

Anterior tibial artery

Peroneal artery

Tibial nerve

Peroneus longus

Flexor hallucis longus

Peroneus brevis

W.A.RUSH, JR.

Fig. 51. Posterior compartment of the leg.

brevis muscles as it ascends to join the genicular anastomosis. The large **peroneal branch** courses laterally between the flexor hallucis longus and the fibula to give a nutrient branch to the fibula, a communicating branch to the posterior tibial, and perforating branches to the peroneal compartment. Its **nutrient tibial branch** is the largest nutrient artery in the body. At the ankle joint **medial** and **posterior malleolar** and **medial calcaneal branches** join, respectively, the malleolar and calcaneal anastomoses.

From the popliteal fossa the **tibial** (posterior tibial) **nerve** passes over the tendinous arch of the soleus to descend in the intermediate division of the posterior compartment of the leg. It lies initially on the tibialis posterior, then on the flexor digitorum longus as it descends to divide under the flexor retinaculum to become the **medial** and **lateral plantar nerves.** It gives **muscular branches** to all the muscles of the posterior compartment as well as a **communicating branch to the sural nerve.**

FOOT (FIG. 52)

Plantar Aponeurosis

A sheet of deep fascia of great strength and importance, the **plantar aponeurosis,** is divided into medial, intermediate, and lateral portions differentiated by their density and demarcated superficially by two shallow grooves which traverse the foot longitudinally. At the divisional lines septa pass from the deep aspect of the plantar aponeurosis to the deeper structures of the foot. The posterior end of the intermediate portion is narrow and attaches to the medial tubercle of the calcaneus. It widens as it extends forward and, near the heads of the metatarsals, divides into five slips which pass to each of the five toes. This portion forms a strong tie, especially for the great toe, between the calcaneus and each proximal phalanx.

Muscles (Table XVII)

The muscles within the sole of the foot function basically as a group and are important in posture, locomotion, and support of the arches of the foot. The **plantar muscles** are described in **four layers** and arranged in **three groups,** a medial group for the great toe, a lateral group for the small toe, and an intermediate group for the remainder of the digits.

The **superficial layer** includes the **abductor hallucis, abductor digiti minimi,** and the **flexor digtorum brevis** muscles. The **second layer** consists of both muscles and tendons. The **tendon of the flexor hallucis longus** grooves the under surface of the talus bone (sustentaculum tali) to pass medially under the tendons of the flexor digitorum longus and insert into the base of the terminal phalanx of the great toe. The **tendons of the flexor digitorum longus** enter the flexor fibrous sheaths at the middle of the foot, perforate the tendons of the flexor digitorum brevis, and insert into the bases of the terminal phalanges. In addition to the tendons noted above, the **quadratus plantae** and **lumbricales muscles** are components of this layer.

The **third layer** is made up of the **flexor hallucis brevis,** the **adductor hallucis,** and the **flexor digiti minimi.** The flexor hallucis brevis lies on the first metatarsal along the lateral side of the abductor hallucis and is grooved by the tendon of the flexor hallucis longus to form two partially separated bellies. The adductor hallucis has two separate heads, the oblique and transverse, which may act as two distinct muscles.

TABLE XVII.   MUSCLES OF THE FOOT

Muscle	*Origin*	*Insertion*	*Action*	*Nerve*
Extensor digitorum brevis (only muscle on dorsum of foot)	Dorsal surface of calcaneus	Divides into four tendons which insert into tendons of extensor digitorum longus	Dorsiflexes toes	Deep peroneal
Abductor hallucis	Medial tubercle of calcaneus	With medial belly of flexor hallucis brevis into proximal phalanx of great toe	Abducts and aids in flexion of great toe	Medial plantar
Flexor digitorum brevis	Medial tubercle of calcaneus and plantar fascia	Divides into four tendons which enter flexor sheath and separate to admit passage of long flexor tendon before inserting into middle phalanx of lateral four toes	Flexes lateral four toes	Medial plantar
Abductor digiti minimi	Medial and lateral tubercles of calcaneus	Lateral side of proximal phalanx of little toe	Abducts little toe	Lateral plantar
Quadratus plantae	Medial head, medial side of calcaneus and plantar fascia; lateral head, lateral margin of calcaneus and plantar fascia	Tendons of flexor digitorum longus	Assists flexor digitorum longus	Lateral plantar
Lumbricales (4)	Tendons of flexor digitorum longus	Medial side of base of proximal phalanx of lateral four toes and extensor expansion	Aid interossei in flexion of metatarsophalangeal joints; extend distal two phalanges	First by medial plantar; lateral three by lateral plantar

continued

Both muscles and tendons are present in the **fourth** and **deepest layer.** The **tendon of the peroneus longus** crosses the sole of the foot obliquely from the lateral to the medial side, and slips of the **tendon of the tibialis posterior** cross the sole in the opposite direction. These tendons form a sling for the foot to help maintain both the longitudinal and transverse arches. The muscles in this layer, the **three plantar** and **four dorsal interossei,** are thin and flattened,

TABLE XVII. MUSCLES OF THE FOOT *continued*

Muscle	Origin	Insertion	Action	Nerve
Flexor hallucis brevis	Cuboid and third cuneiform	Divides into two tendons: medial, into base of proximal phalanx of great toe with abductor hallucis; lateral, with adductor hallucis	Flexes great toe	Medial and sometimes twigs from lateral plantar
Adductor hallucis Oblique head	Anterior end of plantar ligament and sheath of peroneus longus	With lateral belly of flexor hallucis brevis into proximal phalanx of great toe	Adducts and flexes great toe	Lateral plantar
Transverse head	Capsule of lateral four metatarsophalangeal joints	Joins oblique head to insert as above	Acts as tie for heads of metatarsals; adducts great toe	Lateral plantar
Flexor digiti minimi	Base of fifth metatarsal and plantar fascia	Lateral side of base of proximal phalanx of little toe	Flexes small toe	Lateral plantar
Plantar interossei (3)	Medial side of third, fourth, and fifth metatarsals	Medial side of base of proximal phalanges of third, fourth, and fifth toes	Adduct lateral three toes toward second toe; flex proximal, and possibly extend distal, phalanges	Lateral plantar
Dorsal interossei (4)	Lie in intermetatarsal space and arise from adjacent bones	Tendons pass forward as above and insert into proximal phalanges on either side of second toe and into lateral side of third and fourth toes	Abduct second, third, and fourth toes from midline of second toe; flex proximal, and possibly extend distal, phalanges	Lateral plantar

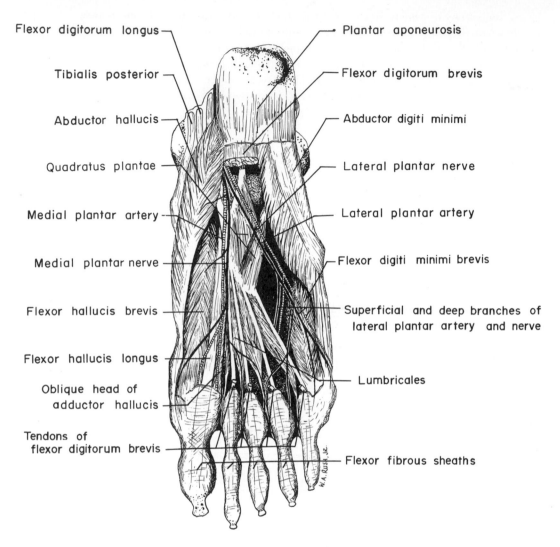

Flexor digitorum longus

Tibialis posterior

Abductor hallucis

Quadratus plantae

Medial plantar artery

Medial plantar nerve

Flexor hallucis brevis

Flexor hallucis longus

Oblique head of
adductor hallucis

Tendons of
flexor digitorum brevis

Plantar aponeurosis

Flexor digitorum brevis

Abductor digiti minimi

Lateral plantar nerve

Lateral plantar artery

Flexor digiti minimi brevis

Superficial and deep branches of
lateral plantar artery and nerve

Lumbricales

Flexor fibrous sheaths

Fig. 52. Foot.

with the medial muscles more deeply situated. Both groups are more easily seen from the plantar than from the dorsal surface and lie between, and arise from, the metatarsal bones. The line of reference for the action of abduction and adduction for these muscles passes through the center of the second toe.

Arteries and Nerves

The **dorsalis pedis,** the continuation of the anterior tibial artery as it courses under the extensor retinaculum, continues on the dorsum of the foot to the base of the first interosseous space, where it terminates by dividing into the **deep plantar** and the **first dorsal metatarsal arteries.** In its course it gives rise to **lateral** and **medial tarsal branches** supplying the extensor digitorum brevis, cutaneous and osseous twigs in the ankle region, and the **arcuate artery** near its termination. The latter passes laterally across the bases of the metatarsal bones and gives rise to the second, third, and fourth **dorsal metatarsal arteries,** each of which subsequently divides into two **dorsal digital branches** to the sides of the toes. The deep plantar branch passes deeply through the first inter-osseous space to join with the lateral plantar artery to form the **deep plantar arch.**

The smaller of two terminal branches of the posterior tibial, the **medial plantar artery,** arises under cover of the flexor retinaculum. It courses deep to the abductor hallucis, then between the abductor hallucis and the flexor digitorum brevis to supply branches to the medial side of the great toe and gives muscular, cutaneous, and articular twigs along its course. The larger of the two terminal branches of the posterior tibial, the **lateral plantar,** passes forward between the first and second layers of muscles in the sole giving calcaneal, cutaneous, muscular, and articular branches as it continues toward the base of the fifth metatarsal. Here it passes medially to join the deep plantar branch of the dorsalis pedis and form the deep plantar arch.

The **deep plantar arch** runs across the bases of the metatarsals to give a **plantar metatarsal artery** to each interosseous space, which subsequently divides into **plantar digital branches** to the adjacent sides of each toe. Separate branches supply the medial side of the great and the lateral side of the little toe. Perforating branches pass deeply in the interosseous space to join corresponding dorsal metatarsal vessels from the arcuate artery.

The **medial plantar nerve,** larger of the two terminal branches of the tibial nerve, arises under the cover of the flexor retinaculum to pass forward between the abductor hallucis and the flexor digitorum brevis lateral to the medial plantar artery. It supplies the above muscles and sends **cutaneous branches** to the medial side of the sole. It terminates in four **digitial nerves** that supply muscular branches to the flexor hallucis brevis and the first lumbricalis and cutaneous branches to the adjacent sides of the four medial toes and the medial side of the foot.

The **lateral plantar nerve** passes laterally in the foot to course anteriorly medial to the lateral plantar artery. It gives **muscular branches** to the quadratus plantae and abductor digiti minimi and cutaneous branches to the lateral aspect of the sole; it terminates in superficial and deep branches. The **superficial branch** passes forward to supply the flexor digiti minimi, the interossei of the fourth intermetatarsal space, and skin on the lateral side of the sole, the fifth toe, and the lateral side of the fourth toe. The **deep branch** accompanies the lateral plantar artery and supplies the adductor hallucis, the remaining interossei, and the three lateral lumbricales muscles.

JOINTS OF THE INFERIOR EXTREMITY

HIP JOINT

The hip joint is the best example of an **enarthrodial** (ball-and-socket) type of joint in the body. The spheroidal **head** of the femur fits into a cup-like cavity in the innominate bone, the **acetabulum.** The head of the femur is covered by articular cartilage except for a small central area, the **fovea capitis femoris,** where the ligamentum teres attaches. Articular cartilage on the acetabulum forms an incomplete horseshoe-shaped marginal ring, the **lunate surface,** with a central circular depression devoid of cartilage which, in the fresh state, is occupied by a mass of fat covered by the synovial membrane. A fibrocartilaginous rim, the **acetabular labrum,** deepens the articular cavity and is triangular in cross section, with its base attached to the margin of the acetabulum and its free apex extending into the cavity.

The extensive **synovial membrane** of the hip joint passes from the margin of the articular cartilage of the head to cover the neck of the femur internal to the articular capsule. It reflects back onto the capsule and covers the acetabular labrum and the synovial fat pad, and ensheathes the ligamentum teres. It sometimes communicates with the bursa deep to the iliopsoas tendon.

The strong, dense articular **capsule** of the hip joint is attached to the innominate bone just beyond the periphery of the acetabular labrum. Its femoral attachments are the intertrochanteric line anteriorly, the base of the neck superiorly, and just above the intertrochanteric crest posteriorly. This capsule is composed of longitudinal collagenous fibers, which are reinforced by accessory ligaments anteriorly and superiorly, and circular fibers (zona orbicularis) at the inferior and posterior aspect, where they form a sling around the neck of the femur. The **iliofemoral ligament** (Y-shaped ligament of Bigelow) is a band of great strength at the anterior aspect of the articular capsule. It is intimately associated with the capsule and is attached superiorly to the anterior inferior iliac spine; inferiorly it divides into two bands which attach to the upper and the lower parts of the intertrochanteric line. The triangular **ischiocapsular** (ischiofemoral) ligament reinforces the posterior aspect of the capsule. It attaches superiorly to the ischium below and behind the acetabulum, and inferiorly blends with the circular fibers of the capsule.

The **ligamentum capitis femoris** (round ligament of the femur) is a flattened triangular band covered by synovial membrane attached by its apex to the fovea capitis femoris, and by its base by two bands to either side of the **acetabular notch.** In the interval between the osseous attachments of the round ligament to the acetabulum, the ligament blends with the transverse acetabular ligament as the latter extends across the acetabular notch to convert it into a foramen.

KNEE JOINT

The knee joint, usually classified as a ginglymus (hinge) joint, is actually much more complex in function. It combines the actions of three diarthrodial joints namely, a **ginglymus** (hinge), a **trochoid** (pivot), and an **arthrodial** (gliding). Furthermore it may be described as three separate articulations, the **femoropatellar** and the two **tibiofemoral joints.** The articular surfaces of the medial and lateral condyles of the femur, covered by articular cartilage and separated by a groove, diverge posteriorly and articulate with the two entirely separate condyles of the tibia. Each of the condyles is deepened by a meniscus and separated by the intercondylar crest. The **medial** and **lateral menisci,** two crescentic cartilaginous lamellae, covered the peripheral two-thirds of the articular surface of the tibia, are triangular in cross section with their peripheral bases attaching to the articular capsule and the tibia by the **coronary ligaments,** and have their free apices projecting into the articular cavity.

The **synovial membrane** lining the knee joint is the largest and most extensive in the body. It begins at the superior border of the patella, sends a blind sac deep to the quadriceps femoris muscle, and frequently communicates with the large **suprapatellar bursa** between the quadriceps femoris and the femur. Inferiorly the synovial membrane lies on either side of the patella deep to the aponeurosis of the vasti muscles, and is separated from the patellar ligament by the **infrapatellar fat pad.** At the medial and lateral aspects of the patella reduplications of the synovial membrane pass into the interior of the joint as the **alar folds.** At the tibia the synovial membrane attaches to the peripheries of the menisci and reflects over and ensheathes the cruciate ligaments.

The osseous arrangement of the knee joint as a weight-bearing structure is intrinsically unstable. The stability of this joint is realized by compensating mechanisms of surrounding muscles and tendons, a strong articular capsule, strong internal and external ligaments, and modification of the joint surface by the menisci. The **patellar ligament** (ligamentum patellae), the central portion of the tendon of the quadriceps femoris, attaches superiorly to the apex and adjacent margins of the patella, and inferiorly to the tuberosity of the tibia. The posteriorly situated **oblique popliteal ligament** attaches superiorly to the femur above the condyles and to the upper margin of the intercondylar fossa; inferiorly it attaches to the posterior margin of the head of the tibia. This ligament forms part of the floor of the popliteal fossa, and the popliteal artery passes inferiorly on its surface. The **arcuate popliteal ligament** arches inferiorly from the lateral condyle of the femur to the posterior surface of the capsule, where two converging bands attach it to the styloid process of the fibula. The **tibial (medial) collateral ligament,** a broad, flat membranous band, attaches superiorly to the medial condyle of the femur immediately below the adductor tubercle and inferiorly at the medial condyle and surface of the tibia. It is crossed in its lower part by tendons of the sartorius, gracilis, and semitendinosus muscles; covers part of the semimembranosus tendon; and is intimately adherent to the medial meniscus. The **fibular (lateral) collateral ligament,** a strong rounded fibrous cord, is attached superiorly to the lateral condyle of the femur immediately above the groove for the tendon of the popliteus; inferiorly it splits the inserting tendon of the biceps femoris to attach to the head of the fibula. It has no attachment to the lateral meniscus.

Strong internal cruciate ligaments cross like the limbs on an X, are named from their position and attachment to the tibia, and are ensheathed by synovial membrane. The **anterior cruciate ligament** attaches in a depression anterior to the intercondylar eminence of the tibia and passes superiorly, posteriorly, and laterally to attach to the medial and posterior aspect of the lateral condyle of the femur. The **posterior cruciate,** stronger, shorter, and less oblique than the anterior, attaches posterior to the intercondylar eminence and to the posterior extremity of the lateral meniscus. It passes superior, anterior, and medial to the lateral and anterior parts of the medial condyle of the femur. Another internal structure, the posterior **meniscofemoral ligament** (of Wrisberg), a strong fasciculus arising from the posterior attachment of the lateral meniscus, attaches to the medial condyle of the femur immediately behind the attachment for the posterior cruciate ligament. The **transverse ligament** of the knee connects the anterior margins of the menisci.

A large number of synovial bursae surround the knee joint. Anteriorly four bursae are present: one between the patella and the skin, another between the upper part of the tibia and the patellar ligament, one between the lower part of the tuberosity of the tibia and the skin, and a large bursa between the deep surface of the quadriceps femoris and the lower part of the femur. Laterally four bursae are noted: one between the lateral head of the gastrocnemius and the articular capsule, another between the fibular collateral ligament and the biceps tendon, a third between the fibular collateral ligament and the popliteus, and the last between the tendon of the popliteus and the lateral condyle of the femur. Five bursae are medially located: the first between the medial head of the gastrocnemius and the capsule; the second superficial to, and interposed between, the tibial collateral ligament and the sartorius, gracilis, and semitendinosus tendons; the third deep to, and interposed between, the tibial collateral ligament and the semimembranosus; the fourth between the semimembranosus and the head of the tibia; and the last between the semimembranosus and the semitendinosus. Any of these bursae may communicate with the synovial cavity of the knee joint.

ANKLE JOINT

The ankle presents two joints, the tibiofibular and the talocrural, with the strength of the ankle joint largely dependent upon the integrity of the **tibiofibular syndesmosis,** a strong fibrous union between the distal ends of the tibia and the fibula. Strong interosseous ligaments connect the roughened surfaces of adjacent portions of the bones to each other and are strengthened anteriorly and posteriorly by the **anterior** and **posterior tibiofibular ligaments.** The **talocrural joint** is between the tibia, the fibula, and the trochlea of the talus. The distal ends of the tibia and fibula form a deep socket, wider anteriorly than posteriorly, to receive the upper part of the talus. It is surrounded by the joint capsule, which is greatly thickened medially and laterally. The medial reinforcement, the **deltoid ligament,** is roughly triangular in shape and attaches superiorly to the medial malleolus and inferiorly to the talus, navicular, and calcaneus bones. Laterally three discrete ligaments, often referred to as the **lateral ligament,** include the **anterior talofibular ligament** passing from the lateral malleolus to the neck of the talus, the **posterior talofibular ligament** from the malleolar fossa to the posterior tubercle of the talus, and, between the two talofibular ligaments, the **calcaneofibular ligament** passing from the lateral malleolus to the lateral surface of the calcaneus.

JOINTS OF THE FOOT

Tarsal and metatarsal bones are bound together by ligaments to form the longitudinal and transverse arches of the foot. These arches are maintained partly by the shape of the bones, partly by the tension of the ligaments and the plantar aponeurosis, but most importantly by the bracing of muscle tendons attached to the foot. The **longitudinal arch** presents a greater height and wider span on the medial side of the foot, with the talus forming the "keystone" at the summit of the arch. The short, solid **posterior pillar** is formed by the calcaneus; the much longer **anterior pillar** is supported by a medial and a lateral column. The **medial column** is formed by the navicular, three cuneiform, and three medial metatarsal bones; the **lateral column** by the cuboid and lateral two metatarsal bones. The weight of the body is transmitted to the talus at the summit. The important ligaments concerned in the prevention of flattening of the arch lie in the plantar concavity and include the **plantar calcaneonavicular (spring) ligament,** which completes the socket formed by the navicular and the calcaneus; the **long plantar ligament** attaching to most of the plantar surface of the calcaneus and passing forward to attach to the tuberosity of the cuboid; the **plantar calcaneocuboid (short plantar) ligament,** placed deep to the long plantar and consisting of a strong wide band an inch long passing from the anterior part of the plantar surface of the calcaneus to a ridge behind the groove in the cuboid; and the **plantar aponeurosis,** which passes from the anterior to the posterior pillars and acts as a tie beam.

The **talocalcaneonavicular joint** lies anterior to the tarsal canal and forms part of the **transverse tarsal joint.** The head of the talus fits into a pocket formed by the navicular above and the calcaneous below. The considerable interval between the navicular and the calcaneus is occupied by the spring ligament. The **calcaneocuboid joint** completes the transverse tarsal joint. The **bifurcate ligament** reinforces the capsule, attaches to the upper part of the calcaneus, and in the floor of the tarsal sinus divides to pass to the navicular and cuboid bones.

The **tarsometatarsal joints** are formed by the medial cuneiform and the first metatarsal, the second metatarsal fitting into a socket formed by the three lateral cuneiforms and a single joint cavity between the cuboid and the fourth and fifth metatarsals. Individually there is little movement at the above joints, but working together they give elasticity and allow for twisting of the foot.

In the **metatarsophalangeal** and **interphalangeal joints** the ligamentous arrangement is similar for each articulation. Between the heads of the metatarsal and the base of the proximal phalanx, the joint capsule is strengthened by **collateral ligaments.** The plantar portion of the capsule is thickened as the **plantar ligament** and firmly fixed to the bases of the phalanges to allow the flexor tendons to glide freely over them. Plantar ligaments are connected by strong transverse fibers of the **deep transverse metatarsal ligament.** Aided by the transverse head of the adductor hallucis, this ligament helps to hold the heads of the metatarsals together with the tendons of the interossei passing deep, and the lumbricales superficial, to this ligament.

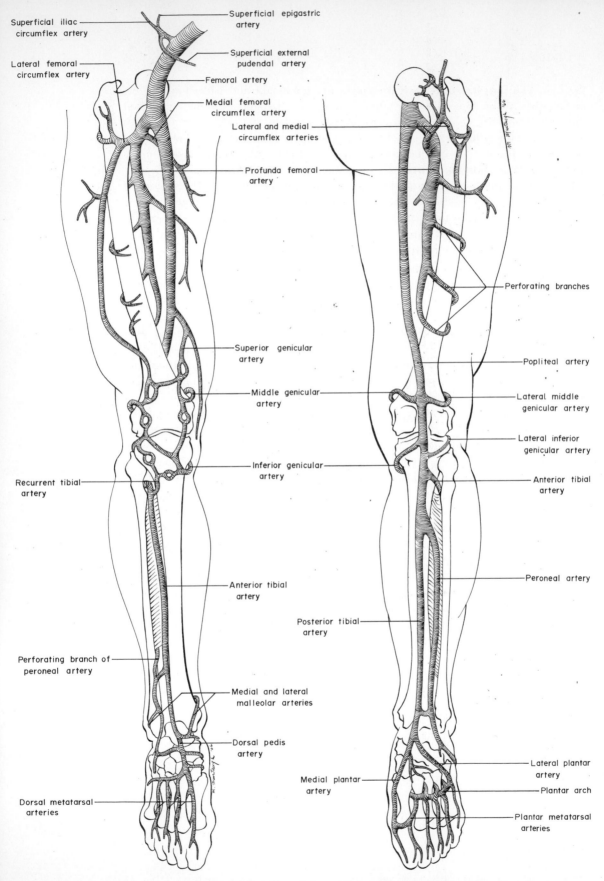

Fig. 53. Summary of the arterial supply of the inferior extremity.

HEAD
AND NECK

Surface Anatomy

At the base of the neck the superior border of the manubrium demarcates the inferior extent of the **suprasternal space** (jugular notch), which is limited laterally by the rounded tendons of the sternal heads of the sternocleidomastoideus muscles. In the midline of the neck, midway between the suprasternal space and the chin, the bulging **laryngeal prominence** (Adam's apple) is formed by the V-shaped thyroid cartilage of the larynx. At the superior border of the prominence, the **laryngeal notch** is palpable. Above the laryngeal prominence, the **hyoid bone** can be palpated.

The chin is formed by the **mental protuberance** of the mandible, while at the posterior border of the jaw the prominent **angle** is continued superiorly as the **ramus.** When the jaw is clenched, the **masseter muscle** is easily demonstrable superficial to the angle and the ramus. The bony prominence of the cheek, formed by the zygomatic bone, is continuous anteriorly and posteriorly with the zygomatic processes of the maxillary and temporal bones, respectively, and superiorly with the zygomatic process of the frontal bone. The freely movable **cartilaginous portion** of the nose can be followed superiorly to the stationary **nasal bones,** which form the bridge. At the lips, the skin of the face and the mucous membrane of the oral cavity are continuous. The **rima palpebrarum,** a slit-like orifice at the free margins of the eyelids, fuses laterally and medially as the **inner** and **outer canthi.** The skin of the lids is continuous at the free margin with the conjunctivum covering the inner surface of the eyelid. The eyelashes curve outward from the free border, while the ducts of the **tarsal (meibomian) glands** open onto the free surface of the lid. **Supraciliary** (brow) **ridges,** covered partially by the eyebrows, indicate the anterior bulging of the frontal air sinuses. The external portion of the ear, consisting of the **auricula,** or **pinna,** and the **external acoustic meatus,** will be described with the ear. The nostrils, or **external nares,** are oval, movable, and have stiff hairs (vibrissae) projecting into the **vestibule** of the nose.

Fasciae (Fig. 54)

The **superficial fascia** of the head and neck is continuous with the superficial fascia of the pectoral, deltoid, and back regions. The muscles of facial expression are embedded or inserted within this layer, and, as it sweeps off the face, it blends with the deep fascia of the neck.

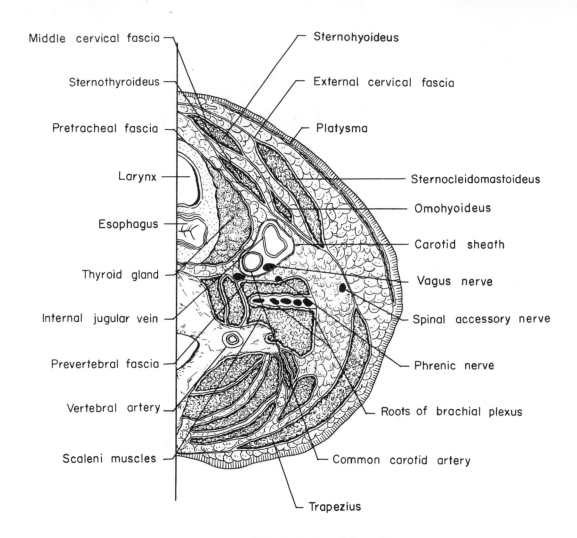

Middle cervical fascia —

Sternothyroideus —

Pretracheal fascia —

Larynx —

Esophagus —

Thyroid gland —

Internal jugular vein —

Prevertebral fascia —

Vertebral artery —

Scaleni muscles —

— Sternohyoideus

— External cervical fascia

— Platysma

— Sternocleidomastoideus

— Omohyoideus

— Carotid sheath

— Vagus nerve

— Spinal accessory nerve

— Phrenic nerve

— Roots of brachial plexus

— Common carotid artery

— Trapezius

Fig. 54. Fasciae of the neck.

The **deep fasciae** consist of the outer investing layer, the middle cervical layer, and the pretracheal and the prevertebral fasciae. The **outer investing layer (external cervical fascia)** completely invests the neck like a stocking and extends from the clavicle, over the mandible, to the zygomatic bone, where it blends with the fascia enclosing the masseter muscle. Posteriorly this layer fuses with the ligamentum nuchae and attaches superiorly to the external occipital protuberance and the superior nuchal line. In the anterior triangle this layer is bound to the hyoid bone and is subdivided into the suprahyoid and infrahyoid portions. The **suprahyoid portion** attaches to the inferior margin of the mandible, covers the submandibular gland, and sends a strong membranous process deep to the gland which attaches to the hyoid bone and angle of the mandible. This deep extension separates the submandibular and parotid glands and then splits to enclose the latter.

The **infrahyoid portion** of the outer investing layer splits inferiorly to attach to the anterior and posterior aspect of the manubrium, where it forms the **suprasternal space.** This space is limited by the sternal heads of the sternocleidomastoideus and contains the lower portion of the anterior jugular veins, their communications across the midline, and some lymph nodes. Passing laterally this fascial layer opens to invest the sternocleidomastoideus, then fuses as it crosses the posterior triangle of the neck, separates again to ensheathe the trapezius, and then fuses posteriorly in the midline with the ligamentum nuchae.

The **middle cervical fascia** is composed of two layers, with the stronger, more superficial layer enclosing the sternohyoideus and omohyoideus and fusing superficially with the outer investing layer. The delicate deeper layer encloses the thyrohyoideus and sternothyroideus, and contributes to the formation of the carotid sheath before it fuses laterally with the outer investing fascia.

The **prevertebral fascia,** covering the anterior aspect of the cervical vertebrae, passes laterally to enclose the longus colli and scaleni muscles, then continues posteriorly to surround the levator scapulae muscle. Between the anterior and middle scaleni, this layer is prolonged into the axilla as the **cervicoaxillary sheath,** which surrounds the brachial plexus and the axillary artery. The prevertebral fascia is continuous inferiorly with the endothoracic fascia of the thoracic cavity. At the cervicothoracic aperture this fascial layer expands over the apex of the lung as the **cervical diaphragm** or **Sibson's fascia.** A potential cleft between the prevertebral fascia and the fascia of the pharynx, the **retropharyngeal space,** is limited superiorly by the base of the skull and laterally by the attachment of the prevertebral fascia to the middle cervical fascia, but is continuous inferiorly with the posterior mediastinum.

The **visceral compartment** of the neck is located between the prevertebral fascia and the middle cervical fascia. It contains the major arteries and nerves within the neck, the cervical portions of the digestive and respiratory systems, and the thyroid and parathyroid glands. The **visceral (pretracheal) fascia** is a tubular prolongation into the neck of the visceral fascia of the mediastinum, where it is continuous with the fibrous pericardium. It encloses the esophagus, trachea, pharynx, and larynx, and contributes laterally to the formation of the carotid sheath. That portion covering the superior constrictor muscles is called the **buccopharyngeal fascia** and is attached superiorly to the pharyngeal tubercle at the base of the skull, and anteriorly to the pterygoid hamulus and the pterygomandibular raphe.

NECK

ANTERIOR TRIANGLE OF THE NECK (FIG. 55)

The **anterior triangle** of the neck is bounded posteriorly by the anterior border of the sternocleidomastoideus and anteriorly by the midline of the neck; the base is formed by the lower border of the mandible, and the apex is at the sternum. For descriptive purposes it is subdivided into three paired and one common triangle. The **muscular triangle,** delineated by the superior belly of the omohyoideus, the sternocleidomastoideus, and the midline, contains the infra-

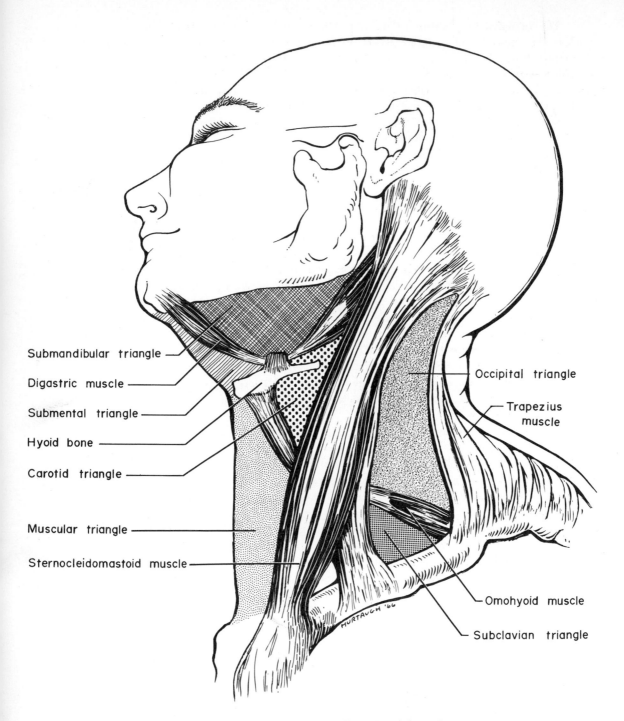

Submandibular triangle

Digastric muscle

Submental triangle

Hyoid bone

Carotid triangle

Muscular triangle

Sternocleidomastoid muscle

Occipital triangle

Trapezius muscle

Omohyoid muscle

Subclavian triangle

Fig. 55. Triangles of the neck.

hyoid muscles and the thyroid gland. The superior belly of the omohyoid, the posterior belly of the digastricus, and the sternocleidomastoideus bound the **carotid triangle,** which contains the vagus and hypoglossal cranial nerves, the common, external, and internal carotid arteries, the internal jugular vein, and the hyoid bone. The **submandibular** (digastric) **triangle** is limited by the two bellies of the digastricus muscle and the mandible, with the submandibular gland, nerves to the anterior belly of the digastricus and mylohyoideus, the hypoglossal nerve, and the lingual and facial arteries as its contents. The unpaired **submental triangle** is between the anterior bellies of the digastrici and the hyoid bone and contains superficially the anterior jugular veins.

Muscles (Table XVIII, Fig. 56)

An extensive thin sheet of muscle, the **platysma,** covers the entire anterior aspect of the neck from the lower border of the mandible to the clavicle. This superficial muscle of facial expression attaches to the skin and mandible, is innervated by the facial nerve, and acts to tense the skin over the neck. The **sternocleidomastoideus,** extending obliquely from the sternoclavicular joint to the mastoid process, divides the neck into anterior and posterior triangles. It has two origins, a **sternal head,** arising as a rounded tendon from the sternoclavicular joint, and a flattened **clavicular head,** from the superior aspect of the medial third of the clavicle. It lies superficial to the great vessels of the neck and the cervical plexus, with cutaneous branches of the latter, i.e., the lesser occipital, greater auricular, transverse cervical, and supraclavicular nerves, emerging at about the midpoint of its posterior border. This muscle is innervated by the spinal accessory nerve and twigs from the second cervical nerve.

A relatively extensive flat sheet of muscle, the two **mylohyoidei** muscles, forms the floor of the submental and part of the digastric triangles, as well as the muscular floor of the mouth. From either side of the neck, these muscles meet in the midline to insert into the median raphe. Situated deep to the mylohyoideus, the small band-like **geniohyoideus** muscle passes from the genial tubercle on the inner anterior surface of the mandible to the hyoid bone. The mylohyoideus is innervated by the mandibular division of the trigeminal nerve, and the geniohyoideus by twigs from the first loop of the cervical plexus passing with the hypoglossal nerve. Both muscles act in depressing the mandible or elevating the hyoid bone.

The **digastricus muscle,** consisting of two bellies attached to an **intermediate tendon,** demarcates the digastric subdivision of the anterior triangle. The intermediate tendon serves as a focal point in the relations of the anterior triangle and is bound by a slip of deep cervical fascia to the hyoid bone. The digastricus is innervated by two nerves, the facial to the posterior belly and the mandibular division of the trigeminal to the anterior belly, and acts to elevate the hyoid bone or assists in depressing the mandible.

The four strap-like muscles attaching to the hyoid bone or the thyroid cartilage make up the **infrahoid muscles.** The superficially placed **sternohyoideus** passes from the sternum to the hyoid bone. It lies superficial to the **thyrohyoideus,** which extends superiorly from the oblique line of the thyroid

TABLE XVIII. MUSCLES OF THE ANTERIOR TRIANGLE OF THE NECK

Muscle	Origin	Insertion	Action	Nerve
Platysma	Superficial fascia of upper pectoral and deltoid regions	Skin and facial muscles overlying mandible and border of mandible	Depresses mandible and lower lip; tenses and ridges skin of neck	Facial
Sternocleido-mastoideus	Manubrium and medial one-third of clavicle	Mastoid process and lateral one-half of superior nuchal line	Singly rotates and draws head to shoulder; together flex cervical column	Spinal accessory, C_2 and C_3
Omohyoideus	Medial lip of suprascapular notch to intermediate tendon, from which superior belly continues	Lower border of body of hyoid	Steadies hyoid; depresses and retracts hyoid and larynx	C_2 and C_3 from ansa cervicalis
Digastricus	Posterior belly from mastoid notch to intermediate tendon, and continues as anterior belly	Mandible near symphysis	Raises hyoid and base of tongue; steadies hyoid; depresses mandible	Posterior belly by facial; anterior belly by mandibular division of trigeminal
Mylohyoideus	Mylohyoid line of mandible	Median raphe and hyoid bone	Elevates hyoid and base of tongue; depresses mandible; raises floor of mouth	Mylohyoid branch of inferior alveolar
Geniohyoideus	Genial tubercle of mandible	Body of hyoid	Elevates hyoid and base of tongue	C_1 and C_2 coursing with hypoglossal nerve
Sternohyoideus	Posterior surface of manubrium and medial end of clavicle	Lower border of body of hyoid	Depresses hyoid and larynx	C_1, C_2, and C_3 from ansa cervicalis
Sterno-thyroideus	Posterior surface of manubrium	Oblique line of thyroid cartilage	Depresses thyroid cartilage	C_1, C_2, and C_3 from ansa cervicalis
Thyrohyoideus	Oblique line of thyroid cartilage	Lower portion of body and greater horn of hyoid	Depresses hyoid; elevates thyroid cartilage	C_1 and C_2 coursing with hypoglossal nerve

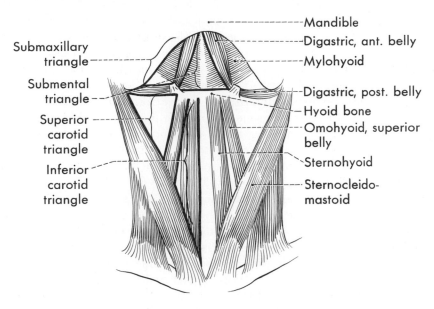

Fig. 56. *Muscles of the anterior triangle of the neck. (From W. H. Hollinshead. Textbook of Anatomy, ed. 2. New York, Hoeber, in press.)*

cartilage to the hyoid bone, as well as to the **sternothyroideus,** which passes inferiorly from the oblique line to the sternum. The **omohyoideus** consists of two bellies with an intermediate tendon. The muscle forms a wide V in passing from the notch of the scapula to the hyoid bone. The intermediate tendon attaches by deep fascia to the manubrium and the first rib or costal cartilage. All the infrahyoid muscles are innervated by the ansa cervicalis except for the thyrohyoideus, which receives a small branch from cervical components traveling with the hypoglossal nerve.

Arteries and Nerves (Fig. 57)

Arteries within the anterior triangle include the common carotid, the internal carotid, and the external carotid and its branches. The **common carotid artery** courses superiorly from behind the sternoclavicular articulation to the level of the superior border of the thyroid cartilage, where it bifurcates into the internal and external carotid arteries. The **internal carotid** has no branches in the neck but ascends within the carotid sheath with the internal jugular vein and the vagus nerve to pass into the skull via the carotid canal as the principal blood supply to the brain and orbital cavity.

Six branches arise from the **external carotid artery** in the anterior triangle; its two terminal branches, the superficial temporal and internal maxillary, originate at the angle of the mandible. The six branches in the neck radiate from the area of the intermediate tendon of the digastricus to the various structures they supply. The **superior thyroid branch** arises from the anterior aspect of the external carotid opposite the thyrohyoid membrane and arches inferiorly to supply the thyroid gland. In its course it is accompanied by the external laryngeal nerve, which innervates the cricothyroideus muscle. The **lingual artery** also arises from the anterior aspect of the external carotid opposite the greater horn of the hyoid bone and passes deep to the posterior belly of the digastricus and mylohyoideus to supply the tongue. In its course it is crossed superficially by the hypoglossal nerve. The **facial (external maxillary) artery,** also from the anterior aspect of the external carotid, follows a sigmoid course to pass deep to the posterior belly of the digastricus, grooves the inferior and posterior borders of the submandibular gland, then curves over the inferior border of the mandible onto the face. Its distribution will be considered with the discussion of the face. From the medial aspect of the external carotid the **ascending pharyngeal branch** ascends, with the internal carotid, to supply prevertebral muscles, the pharynx, and the palatine tonsil. Arising posteriorly, the **occipital branch** follows the inferior border of the posterior belly of the digastricus muscle to pass superiorly and posteriorly to the mastoid process, where it ramifies on the back of the head. The **posterior auricular branch** courses along the superior border of the posterior belly of the digastricus to pass to the notch between the external auditory meatus and the mastoid process to supply the area behind the ear. Deep to the parotid gland, the external carotid terminates by bifurcating into the **superficial temporal artery,** which ascends anterior to the ear and supplies the side of the face and head, and the **maxillary (internal maxillary) branch,** which will be described with the infratemporal fossa.

Nerves and their branches encountered in the anterior triangle of the neck include the glossopharyngeal, vagus, hypoglossal, cervical plexus, and cervical sympathetic chain.

The **vagus nerve,** the longest of the cranial nerves, leaves the skull through the jugular foramen in company with the glossopharyngeal and the spinal accessory nerves. In the neck it is enclosed within the carotid sheath and enters the thoracic cavity by passing anterior to the subclavian artery. Two **sensory ganglia,** the **superior** (jugular) at the jugular foramen and the **inferior** (nodose) an inch below, are associated with this nerve. Initial branches of the vagus include the **recurrent meningeal,** which re-enters the cranial cavity via the jugular foramen to supply dura in the posterior cranial fossa; the **auricular branch,** cutaneous to the posterior aspect of the pinna of the ear and the floor of the external auditory meatus; the **pharyngeal branches,** which join branches of the glossopharyngeal and superior cervical ganglion to form the pharyngeal plexus; and the **nerve to the carotid body.**

The **superior laryngeal branch** of the vagus arises at the nodose ganglion, passes downward deep and medial to the internal and external carotid arteries, and divides into an internal and an external branch. The **internal laryngeal nerve** with the laryngeal branch of the superior thyroid artery, pierces the thyrohyoid membrane to supply sensory fibers to the mucous membrane of the larynx above the level of the vocal folds and parasympathetic fibers to glands of the epiglottis, base of the tongue, and the upper larynx. The **external laryngeal nerve,** a long slender branch accompanying the superior thyroid artery, passes deep to the sternothyroideus muscle and the thyroid gland to supply the cricothyroideus mus-

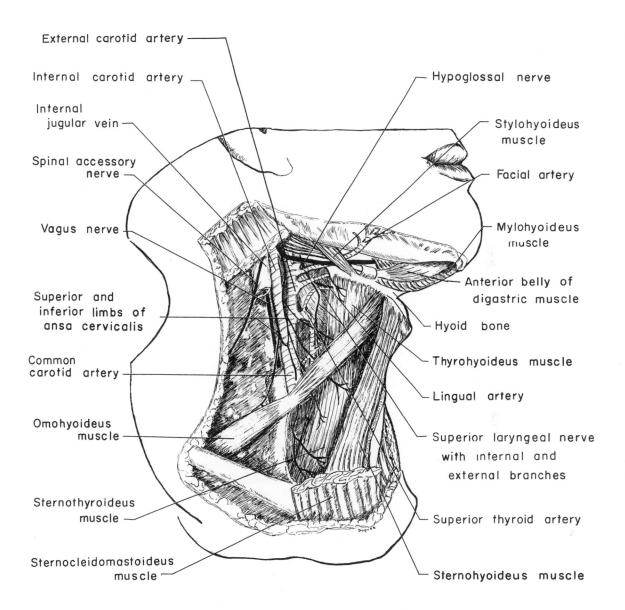

External carotid artery

Internal carotid artery

Internal jugular vein

Spinal accessory nerve

Vagus nerve

Superior and inferior limbs of ansa cervicalis

Common carotid artery

Omohyoideus muscle

Sternothyroideus muscle

Sternocleidomastoideus muscle

Hypoglossal nerve

Stylohyoideus muscle

Facial artery

Mylohyoideus muscle

Anterior belly of digastric muscle

Hyoid bone

Thyrohyoideus muscle

Lingual artery

Superior laryngeal nerve with internal and external branches

Superior thyroid artery

Sternohyoideus muscle

Fig. 57. Contents of the anterior triangle of the neck.

cle. The **superior cardiac branches** (two or three in number) arise at the level of the nodose ganglion and may join a sympathetic cardiac branch from the superior cervical ganglion as a common nerve to the heart. The **inferior cardiac branch** arises either from the vagus or from the recurrent laryngeal nerve at the root of the neck. All vagal cardiac branches from the right side and the superior cardiac branches from the left side pass behind the major vessels of the heart to terminate in the deep cardiac plexus. The inferior cardiac branch from the left side descends anterior to the arch of the aorta to end in the superficial cardiac plexus. Cardiac branches of the vagus nerve function to inhibit the rate and force of the heart beat.

Arising low in the neck, the **recurrent (inferior) laryngeal nerve** is sensory to the larynx below the level of the vocal folds and motor to all the intrinsic muscles of the larynx, except the cricothyroideus. The right recurrent nerve hooks around the subclavian artery, the left around the arch of the aorta, and both nerves pass posteriorly to ascend in the tracheoesophageal groove. At the larynx they penetrate the cricothyroid membrane to reach the interior of the larynx.

The **glossopharyngeal nerve** leaves the cranium through the jugular foramen together with the vagus and spinal accessory nerves, courses initially between the internal jugular vein and internal carotid artery, then forward between the internal carotid and the styloid process. It presents two **sensory ganglia,** the small **superior** and the larger **inferior (petrosal)** ganglion. From the inferior ganglion the **tympanic nerve** passes through the temporal bone to join the tympanic plexus on the promontory of the middle ear cavity. It carries parasympathetic fibers destined for the parotid gland and sensory fibers to the middle ear cavity. Filaments from the **promontory plexus** join to form the **minor petrosal nerve,** which passes through a small canal in the temporal bone to emerge into the middle cranial fossa and then continues through the fissure between the temporal and the sphenoid bones to reach the otic ganglion. A second branch of the glossopharyngeal, the **nerve to the carotid sinus,** descends from the main trunk at the jugular foramen and joins with fibers from the vagus to pass to the anterior surface of the internal carotid and supply pressor receptor fibers to the carotid sinus. Three or four **pharyngeal branches** join with branches from the vagus and the superior cervical sympathetic ganglion to supply sensory and motor innervation to the pharynx. The **nerve to the stylopharyngeus** is the only named muscular branch of the glossopharyngeal nerve. **Tonsillar branches** supply sensation to the palatine tonsil, soft palate, and fauces, and communicate with the lesser palatine nerve. Two **lingual branches** supply the posterior third of the tongue with both general and special (taste) sensation.

Cervical Sympathetic Trunk

The **cervical portion of the sympathetic trunk** is embedded within the connective tissue posterior to the carotid sheath and anterior to the prevertebral muscle. Unlike the sympathetic chain in the thorax, where typically one ganglion occurs for each spinal nerve, only three ganglia are present. The first four cervical spinal nerves receive branches from the superior cervical ganglion, the fifth and sixth cervical nerves from the middle cervical ganglion, and the seventh and eighth cervical nerves from the inferior cervical ganglion. The latter frequently unites with the first thoracic ganglion to form the stellate ganglion. **No white rami communicantes are present in the cervical region.** Each of the cervical spinal nerves receives at least one gray ramus communicans from their respective fused ganglia.

The **superior cervical ganglion,** the largest of the sympathetic chain, is located between the internal carotid artery and the longus capitis muscle at a level of the second and third cervical vertebrae. It is spindle-shaped, about an inch long, and sends twigs superiorly along the internal carotid artery as the internal carotid plexus. It also sends **communicating twigs** to the glossopharyngeal, vagus, spinal accessory, and hypoglossal cranial nerves; **gray rami** to the first four cervical spinal nerves; **pharyngeal branches** to the pharyngeal plexus; and a **cardiac branch** which on the left side passes to the superficial cardiac plexus and on the right to the deep cardiac plexus.

The small **middle cervical ganglion** is located opposite the summit of the loop of the inferior thyroid artery. It gives off **gray rami** to the fifth and sixth cervical nerves, a **thyroid branch** which forms a plexus around the inferior thyroid artery, **cardiac branches** to the deep cardiac plexus, and the **ansa subclavia** as filaments which descend arteriorly to hook around the subclavian artery and join the inferior cervical ganglion.

The **inferior cervical ganglion** is small, irregular in shape, located behind the common carotid artery, and usually joins with the ganglion of the first thoracic nerve to form the **stellate ganglion.** Its branches include **gray rami** to the seventh and eight cervical spinal nerves, branches to the **ansa subclavia,** contributions to the **subclavian** and **vertebral plexuses,** and a **cardiac branch** to the deep cardiac plexus.

Cervical Plexus (Fig. 58)

The **cervical plexus** is formed by the **anterior primary rami** of the first four cervical nerves. Except for the first cervical nerve, each of these primary rami divides into an **ascending** and a **descending division.** The ascending limb of the second cervical nerve joins with the first cervical nerve; the descending limb of the fourth cervical nerve contributes to the brachial plexus; and the remaining ascending and descending divisions unite to form **three loops** opposite the first four cervical vertebrae. The cervical plexus receives postganglionic sympathetic fibers from the superior cervical sympathetic ganglion. Branches of the plexus include the cutaneous nerves, to be described later with the posterior triangle (i.e., the **lesser occipital, greater auricular,** and **transverse cervical** from the loop between the second and third cervical nerves) and the **three supraclavicular nerves** from the loop between the third and fourth cervical nerves, the ansa cervicalis, segmental muscular branches to the prevertebral muscles, and the phrenic nerve.

The **ansa cervicalis,** which innervates the infrahyoid muscles, is derived from the first and second loops of the cervical plexus. Twigs from the first loop (C_1 and C_2) pass to the hypoglossal nerve, travel with it for one or two centimeters, where most of the fibers leave the hypoglossal as the **superior ramus** (descendens

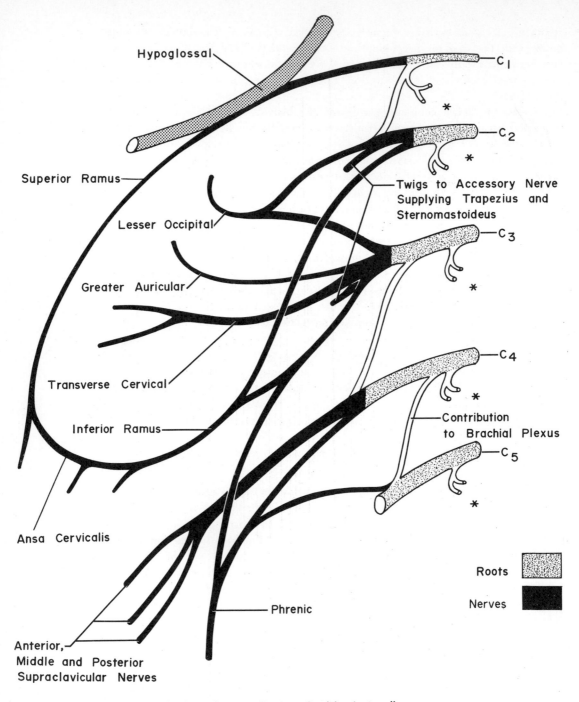

Hypoglossal

C₁

*

C₂

*

Twigs to Accessory Nerve
Supplying Trapezius and
Sternomastoideus

Superior Ramus

Lesser Occipital

C₃

*

Greater Auricular

Transverse Cervical

C₄

*

Contribution
to Brachial Plexus

Inferior Ramus

C₅

*

Ansa Cervicalis

Roots

Nerves

Phrenic

Anterior,
Middle and Posterior
Supraclavicular Nerves

* Segmental Branches to Rectus Capitis Lateralis,
Rectus Capitis Anterior, Longus Capitis, Longus Colli,
Scaleni Muscles and Levator Scapulae.

Fig. 58. Cervical plexus.

hypoglossi) of the ansa cervicalis and descend to form the ansa with a branch from the second loop (C_2 and C_3), the **inferior ramus** (descendens cervicalis). Fibers from the first and second cervical nerves, remaining with the hypoglossal nerve, branch off as independent twigs to supply the thyrohyoideus and geniohyoideus muscles. The superior ramus of the ansa cervicalis sends twigs to the superior belly of the omohyoideus; the inferior ramus supplies the inferior belly of the omohyoideus; and from the loop, branches pass to the sternohyoideus and sternothyroideus muscles.

Segmental muscular branches supply the prevertebral muscles. Twigs from the first loop of the cervical plexus pass to the rectus capitis lateralis, longus capitis, and rectus capitis anterior; from the second loop to the longus capitis and longus colli; and from the third loop to the middle scalenus and levator scapulae. Contributions from the cervical plexus to the spinal accessory nerve give additional innervation to the sternocleidomastoideus (C_2) and the trapezius (C_3 and C_4). The phrenic nerve is derived from the fourth cervical nerve with contributions from the third and fifth cervical nerves. It courses inferiorly to cross the scalenus anterior obliquely, passes deep to the transverse cervical and transverse scapular arteries to pass through the thorax, where it innervates the diaphragm.

PREVERTEBRAL REGION (TABLE XIX)

The **prevertebral muscles** form a longitudinal muscular mass anterior to the vertebral column which includes the **anterior, middle,** and **posterior scaleni;** the **longus capitis** and **colli;** and the **rectus capitis anterior** and **lateralis muscles.** The scaleni, longus capitis, superior portion of the longus colli, and rectus capitis lateralis muscles all arise from transverse processes of the cervical vertebrae. The inferior portion of the longus colli arises from the bodies of cervical vertebrae, and the rectus capitis anterior from the lateral mass of the atlas. The scaleni insert into the first two ribs, the rectus capitis anterior and lateralis into the occipital bone, and the colli muscles into the bodies or transverse processes of the cervical vertebrae. All the muscles are ensheathed by **prevertebral fascia,** are segmentally innervated, and act as a group in flexion and rotation of the head and neck.

Structures associated with the prevertebral region include the **vertebral artery,** the **carotid sheath** and its contents, the **cervical portion of the sympathetic trunk,** the **spinal nerves** emerging through the intervertebral foramina, and the **cervical plexus.**

POSTERIOR TRIANGLE OF THE NECK (FIG. 59)

The **posterior triangle** of the neck is bounded anteriorly by the posterior border of the sternocleidomastoideus and posteriorly by the anterior border of the trapezius. The **apex** is at the junction of the above muscles on the superior nuchal line, and the **base** is formed by the middle third of the clavicle. The posterior belly of the omohyoideus muscle divides the posterior triangle into a small **subclavian** and a large **occipital triangle.** From superior to inferior, six muscles form the

TABLE XIX. PREVERTEBRAL MUSCLES

Muscle	Origin	Insertion	Action	Nerve
Scalenus anterior	Transverse processes of third to sixth cervical vertebrae	Scalene tubercle on first rib	Bilaterally stabilize neck; unilaterally inclines neck to side	Twigs from cervical plexus and C_5 through C_7
Scalenus medius	Transverse processes of lower five cervical vertebrae	Upper surface of first and second ribs	As above	Cervical plexus and C_4 through C_8
Scalenus posterior	Transverse processes of fifth and sixth cervical vertebrae	Outer surface of second rib	As above	Twigs from C_7 or C_8
Longus capitis	Transverse processes of third through sixth cervical vertebrae	Basilar portion of occipital bone	Flexes and rotates head	Twigs from C_1 through C_4
Longus colli	Transverse processes and bodies of third cervical to third thoracic vertebrae	Anterior tubercle of atlas, bodies of second to fourth cervical vertebrae, and transverse processes of fifth and sixth cervical vertebrae	Flexes and rotates head	Twigs from C_2 through C_6
Rectus capitis anterior	Lateral mass of atlas	Basilar portion of occipital bone	Flexes and rotates head	Twigs from C_1 and C_2
Rectus capitis lateralis	Transverse process of atlas	Jugular process of occipital bone	Bends head laterally	C_1 and C_2

floor of the triangle: the semispinalis capitis; the splenius capitis; the levator scapulae; and the anterior, middle, and posterior scaleni.

Important structures within the posterior triangle include the spinal accessory, phrenic, lesser occipital, greater auricular, transverse cervical, and supraclavicular nerves; the roots of the brachial plexus; the subclavian, transverse scapular, and transverse cervical arteries; and the subclavian and **external jugular veins.** The latter, formed by the union of the posterior facial and posterior auricular veins, descends vertically from the angle of the mandible to pass obliquely across the sternocleidomastoideus, where it pierces the deep fascia an inch above the clavicle and empties into the subclavian vein. The **spinal accessory nerve** emerges from the posterior border of the sternocleidomastoideus to cross the triangle obliquely, dividing it into equal parts, and then disappears deep to the trapezius muscle, which it supplies. The **phrenic nerve,** arising from the third,

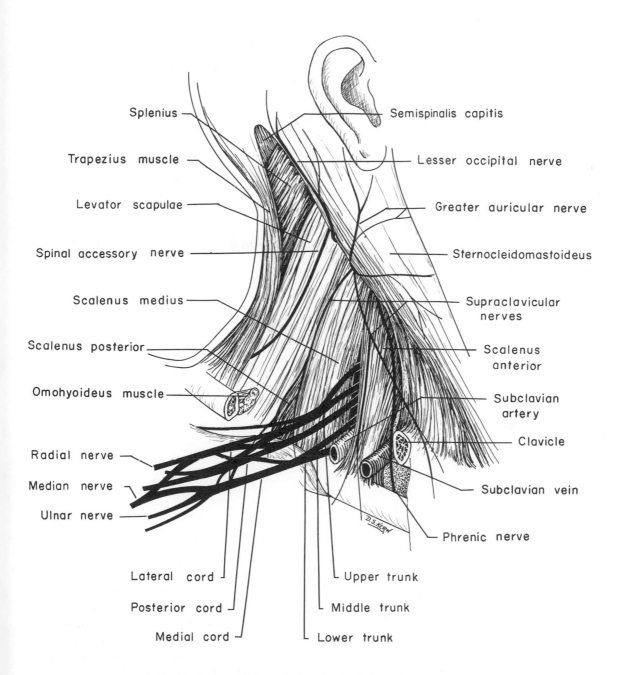

Splenius

Trapezius muscle

Levator scapulae

Spinal accessory nerve

Scalenus medius

Scalenus posterior

Omohyoideus muscle

Radial nerve

Median nerve

Ulnar nerve

Semispinalis capitis

Lesser occipital nerve

Greater auricular nerve

Sternocleidomastoideus

Supraclavicular nerves

Scalenus anterior

Subclavian artery

Clavicle

Subclavian vein

Phrenic nerve

D.S.KERN

Lateral cord

Posterior cord

Medial cord

Upper trunk

Middle trunk

Lower trunk

Fig. 59. Contents of the posterior triangle of the neck.

fourth, and fifth cervical nerves, crosses the scalenus anterior obliquely to descend into the thorax.

Inferior to the spinal accessory nerve, four cutaneous branches of the cervical plexus emerge from the posterior border of the sternocleidomastoideus. The **lesser occipital nerve** (C_2 and C_3) follows the posterior border of the sternocleidomastoideus cephalad to pierce the deep fascia near the mastoid process, where it supplies the scalp above and behind the ear and the medial surface of the auricula. The **greater auricular nerve** (C_2 and C_3) passes obliquely across the sternocleidomastoideus to ascend to the ear, where it gives a **mastoid branch** to the mastoid process, an **auricular branch** to both surfaces of the pinna, and **facial branches** to the skin in front of the ear and over the parotid gland. The **transverse cervical nerve** (C_2 and C_3) crosses the sternocleidomastoideus horizontally to divide into a **superior** and an **inferior branch,** which supply the skin over the anterior triangle of the neck. The **medial, intermediate,** and **lateral supraclavicular nerves** (C_3 and C_4) pierce the platysma near the clavicle to supply the skin of the chest as low as the third rib and the skin over the upper portion of the shoulder.

Within the posterior triangle, the **roots of the brachial plexus** emerge through the **scalene gap** between the anterior and middle scaleni muscles to continue through the cervicoaxillary canal into the axilla. The **subclavian artery** crosses the first rib to pass through the scalene gap in company with the brachial plexus, while the **subclavian vein** passes anterior to the scalenus anterior as it crosses the first rib. Two branches of the subclavian artery, the **transverse scapular** and the **transverse cervical,** cross the scalenus anterior from medial to lateral to pin down the phrenic nerve as they course toward the scapular region.

ROOT OF THE NECK (FIG. 60)

The **root of the neck,** the junctional area between the neck proper and the thorax, is limited laterally by the first rib, anteriorly by the manubrium, and posteriorly by the first thoracic vertebra. It transmits all the structures passing between the neck and the thorax.

Thyroid Gland

The **thyroid,** an encapsulated, endocrine, butterfly-shaped gland, is located in front and to the sides of the trachea at the level of the fifth through seventh cervical vertebrae. It is composed of a **right** and a **left lobe** connected by the narrow **isthmus** of glandular tissue located at the level of the third or fourth tracheal ring. Each lobe is somewhat conical in form and consists of a base situated at the level of the fifth or sixth tracheal ring and an apex resting against the side of the thyroid cartilage extending to its superior border. Its full, rounded lateral (superficial) surface is covered by infrahyoid muscles, and the medial (deep) surface is molded by the structures on which it lies, namely, the cricoid and thyroid cartilages and the cricothyroideus and inferior constrictor muscles superiorly, and the trachea and esophagus inferiorly. There may be a slender extension of the thyroid gland, the **pyramidal lobe,** passing from the isthmus or the left lobe superiorly to the hyoid bone. A narrow slip of muscle, the **levator glandulae thyroideae,** is sometimes attached to this lobe.

The thyroid gland is a highly vascularized organ supplied by two pairs of relatively large arteries: The **superior thyroid arteries,** branches from the external carotids, supply the apices, and the **inferior thyroid arteries,** from the thyrocervical trunks, supply the base and the deep surface. A single inconstant small branch, the **thyroidea ima artery,** may arise from the brachiocephalic, the left common carotid, or the arch of the aorta. These vessels anastomose freely within each lobe, but little communication occurs across the midline. **Venous drainage** is accomplished by three pairs of veins which form a superficial plexus; however, most of the blood is drained from the deep surface. The superior thyroid veins drain the upper portion of the gland and either across the common carotid to the internal jugular or follow the superior thyroid arteries to end in the common facial veins. The middle thyroid veins arise near the lower portion of the gland and cross the common carotids to empty into the internal jugulars; the inferior thyroids, largest of the thyroid veins, begin as a plexus over the isthmus and pass inferiorly to empty into the brachiocephalic veins.

Parathyroid Glands

Two or more pairs of small endocrine glands, the **superior** and **inferior parathyroids,** are usually embedded in the posterior aspect of the thyroid. The superior glands are more constant in position and usually lie at the level of the middle of the thyroid, while the inferior glands are situated near the base of the thyroid. Their vascular supply is usually derived from twigs of the inferior thyroid artery.

Arteries in the Root of the Neck

The arteries in the root of the neck originate from the arch of the aorta and include the brachiocephalic (innominate) on the right side and the common carotid and subclavian arteries on the left. The **brachiocephalic** arises from the arch of the aorta to pass superiorly and divide behind the sternoclavicular joint into right common carotid and subclavian arteries. Anteriorly the brachiocephalic artery is covered by the sternoclavicular joint and the sternohyoideus and sternothyroideus muscles; medially it rests on the trachea; laterally it is related to the right brachiocephalic vein; and posteriorly it is separated from the apical pleura by fat and connective tissue.

On the right side the **subclavian artery** originates behind the sternoclavicular joint as the terminal branch of the brachiocephalic; on the left it is a direct branch of the arch of the aorta and enters the root of the neck by passing behind the sternoclavicular joint. Both arteries arch laterally, groove the pleura, pass between the anterior and middle scaleni muscles to become axillary arteries at the lateral border of the first rib. The subclavian artery is arbitrarily divided into three parts by the anterior scalenus muscle. Branches from the first part (proximal to the muscle) include the vertebral, the thyrocervical trunk, and the internal thoracic arteries; the second part (deep to the muscle) gives off the costocervical trunk, while the dorsal scapular artery may arise as a single branch of the third part (distal to the muscle).

The **vertebral artery,** arising from the posterosuperior aspect of the subclavian, ascends vertically along the lateral border of the longus colli muscle

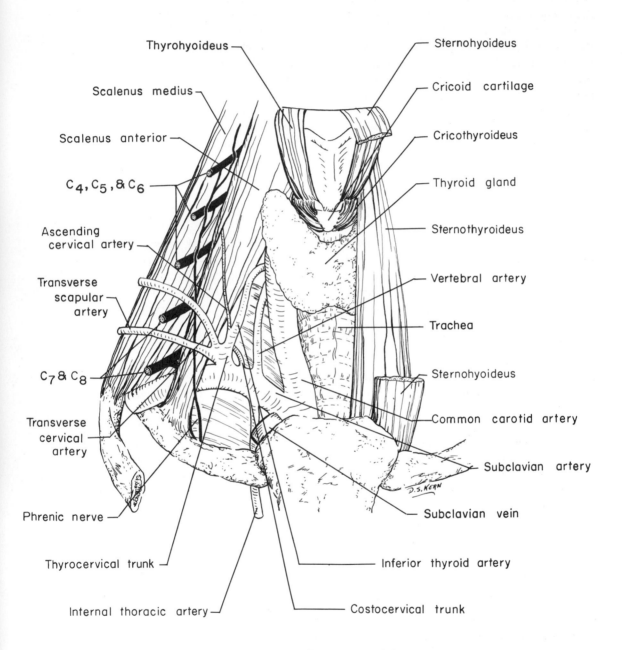

Thyrohyoideus

Scalenus medius

Scalenus anterior

$C_4, C_5, \& C_6$

Ascending
cervical artery

Transverse
scapular
artery

$C_7 \& C_8$

Transverse
cervical
artery

Phrenic nerve

Thyrocervical trunk

Internal thoracic artery

Sternohyoideus

Cricoid cartilage

Cricothyroideus

Thyroid gland

Sternothyroideus

Vertebral artery

Trachea

Sternohyoideus

Common carotid artery

Subclavian artery

Subclavian vein

Inferior thyroid artery

Costocervical trunk

Fig. 60. Root of the neck.

to the level of the cricoid cartilage, where it passes between the scalenus anterior and the longus colli to enter the foramen intertransversarium of the sixth cervical vertebra. It traverses similar foramina in each of the cervical vertebrae to finally enter the skull through the foramen magnum, where it contributes to the circle of Willis to supply the brain.

Arising from the anterior aspect of the subclavian at the medial margin of the anterior scalenus muscle, the short, wide **thyrocervical trunk** gives origin to a number of branches. The largest branch, the **inferior thyroid artery,** follows an S-shaped course, ascending along the medial border of the scalenus anterior to pass medially between the carotid sheath and vertebral vessels at the level of the cricoid cartilage. It then descends along the posterior border of the thyroid gland, which it supplies from its deep aspect. The **ascending cervical artery** is a small, constant branch of the trunk which ascends obliquely across the scalenus anterior to give twigs to prevertebral muscles and the vertebral canal. Coursing laterally across the scalenus anterior, anterior to the phrenic nerve, the **transverse cervical branch** traverses the posterior triangle of the neck. It courses deep to the omohyoid muscle to reach the anterior border of the trapezius, where it divides into an **ascending branch** (superficial cervical) ramifying on the deep surface of the trapezius and supplying it, and a **deep (descending) branch** which passes deep to the levator scapulae and rhomboidei to follow the vertebral border of the scapula and supply these muscles. The **suprascapular artery** follows the transverse cervical artery to pass to the scapular notch, where it meets the transverse scapular nerve. At the notch the artery passes superficial, the nerve deep, to the transverse scapular ligament, where both structures divide into **supraspinatus** and **infraspinatus branches** to supply muscles in their respective fossae on the dorsum of the scapula.

The **internal thoracic** (internal mammary) **artery,** arising from the inferior aspect of the subclavian, passes inferomedially to enter the thorax behind the first costal cartilage. It lies between the pleura and ribs and intercostal muscles and is usually crossed anteriorly by the phrenic nerve. This vessel continues inferiorly along the lateral border of the sternum to give **anterior intercostal branches** to the first six intercostal spaces, and then terminates by dividing into the **superior epigastric** and **musculophrenic arteries.**

The short **costocervical trunk** arises from the posterior aspect of the subclavian to pass superoposteriorly over the pleura to the neck of the first rib. Opposite the first intercostal space it gives a **deep cervical branch,** which ascends between the neck of the first rib and the transverse process of the seventh cervical vertebra to supply deep muscles of the neck. The **superior intercostal branch** of the trunk courses inferiorly, anterior to the neck of the first rib, to give posterior intercostal branches to the first and second intercostal spaces. As a **variation** of the branches of the subclavian artery, the **dorsal scapular artery** arises, in about half the cases, from the third part of the subclavian to course parallel to the vertebral border of the scapula. It supplies the levator scapulae and the rhomboidei and replaces the deep (descending) branch of the transverse cervical artery from the thyrocervical trunk. When the dorsal scapular artery is present, the transverse cervical supplies only the trapezius muscle, the normal distribution of its ascending cervical branch, and is called the superficial cervical artery.

DEEP BACK

DEEP MUSCLES (TABLE XX, FIG. 61)

The deep muscles of the back are arranged in two groups: a **longitudinal group** consisting of the **sacrospinalis** or **erector spinae** (**iliocostalis, longissimus,** and **spinalis**), the **semispinalis,** and the **splenius;** and a **transverse group** including the **multifidi,** the **rotatores,** the **interspinales,** and the **intertransversarii.** (The new PNA terminology lists the term erector spinae for all the deep muscles of the back.)

TABLE XX. DEEP MUSCLES OF THE BACK

Muscle	Origin	Insertion
Sacrospinalis	Series of muscles forming mass extending from sacrum to skull. Acting unilaterally, they bend vertebral column to that side; bilaterally they extend vertebral column. They are segmentally innervated by posterior primary rami of spinal nerves, as are all muscles of back listed below.	
Iliocostalis lumborum	Iliac crest and sacrospinal aponeurosis	Lumbodorsal fascia and tips of transverse processes of lumbar vertebrae and angles of lower six or seven ribs
Iliocostalis dorsi	Superior borders of lower seven ribs medial to angles	Angles of upper seven ribs and transverse process of seventh cervical vertebra
Iliocostalis cervicis	Superior borders at angles of third to seventh ribs	Transverse processes of fourth, fifth, and sixth cervical vertebrae
Longissimus dorsi	Sacrospinal aponeurosis, sacroiliac ligaments, transverse processes of lower six thoracic and first two lumbar vertebrae	Transverse processes of lumbar and thoracic vertebrae and inferior borders of ribs lateral to their angles
Longissimus cervicis	Transverse processes of upper five or six thoracic vertebrae	Transverse processes of second through sixth cervical vertebrae
Longissimus capitis	Transverse processes of first four cervical vertebrae and articular processes of last four cervical vertebrae	Mastoid process of temporal bone

Muscle	Origin	Insertion	Action
Spinalis dorsi	Spines of upper two lumbar and lower two thoracic vertebrae	Spines of second through ninth thoracic vertebrae	Extends vertebral column
Spinalis cervicis	Spines of upper two thoracic and lower two cervical vertebrae	Spines of second through fourth cervical vertebrae	Extends vertebral column

continued

The longitudinal group spans the interval from the spines of the vertebrae to the angles of the ribs and acts to extend the vertebral column. In width this group forms a mass of muscle about as broad as the palm of the hand. These muscles extend vertically from the fourth piece of the sacrum to the mastoid process of the temporal bone, and are placed side by side like three fingers.

The muscles of the transverse group extend from the spines of the vertebrae to the tips of the transverse processes and are present between the fourth sacral vertebra and the occipital bone. The muscles of the transverse group are placed one on top of the other like the layers of a sandwich and act primarily to twist the vertebral column. The deep muscles are innervated segmentally by posterior

TABLE XX. DEEP MUSCLES OF THE BACK *continued*

Muscle	Origin	Insertion	Action
Semispinalis capitis	Transverse processes of upper six thoracic and seventh cervical vertebrae	Between superior and inferior nuchal lines	Extends and inclines head laterally
Semispinalis dorsi	Transverse processes of lower six thoracic vertebrae	Spines of upper six thoracic and lower two cervical vertebrae	Extends and inclines head laterally
Semispinalis cervicis	Transverse processes of upper six thoracic vertebrae	Spines of second through sixth cervical vertebrae	Extends and inclines head laterally
Splenius cervicis	Spinous processes of third through sixth thoracic vertebrae	Transverse processes of first three cervical vertebrae	Inclines and rotates head and neck
Splenius capitis	Ligamentum nuchae and spinous processes of upper five thoracic vertebrae	Mastoid process and superior nuchal line	Inclines and rotates head and neck
Multifidus	Sacrum and transverse processes of lumbar, thoracic, and lower cervical vertebrae	Spinous processes of lumbar, thoracic, and lower cervical vertebrae	Abducts, rotates, and extends vertebral column
Rotatores	Transverse processes of second cervical vertebra to sacrum	Lamina above vertebra of origin	Rotate and extend vertebral column
Interspinales	Superior surface of spine of each vertebra	Inferior surface of spine of vertebra above vertebra of origin	Extend and rotate vertebral column
Intertransversarii	Extend between transverse processes of cervical, lumbar, and lower thoracic vertebrae. Unilaterally, they bend vertebral column laterally; bilaterally they stabilize column.		

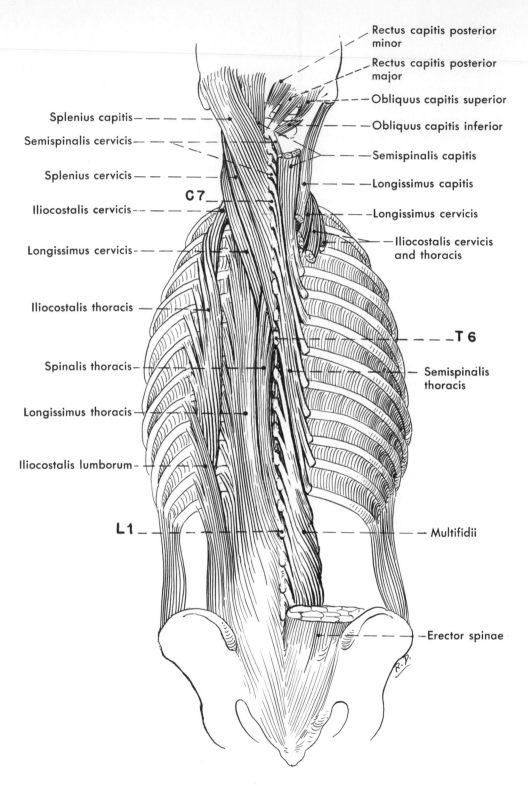

Rectus capitis posterior
minor

Rectus capitis posterior
major

Splenius capitis

Obliquus capitis superior

Semispinalis cervicis

Obliquus capitis inferior

Splenius cervicis

Semispinalis capitis

Iliocostalis cervicis

Longissimus capitis

C 7

Longissimus cervicis

Iliocostalis cervicis
and thoracis

Longissimus cervicis

Iliocostalis thoracis

T 6

Spinalis thoracis

Semispinalis
thoracis

Longissimus thoracis

Iliocostalis lumborum

L 1

Multifidii

Erector spinae

*Fig. 61. Deep muscles of the back. (From W. H. Hollinshead. Textbook of Anatomy, ed. 2.
New York, Hoeber, in press.)*

primary rami of the spinal nerves, except for some of the intertransversarii, which are supplied by anterior primary rami.

Fascia of the deep muscles forms thin muscular envelopes, except in the lumbar region, where it thickens and is disposed in three anteroposterior layers, or lamina, as the **lumbodorsal fascia.** The thick, strong **posterior layer** covers the sacrospinalis and continues superiorly onto the thorax; inferiorly it attaches to the iliac crest and sacrum. Medially it fuses with the periosteum of the vertebral spines and superiorly with the ligamentum nuchae; laterally it joins the middle and anterior layers at the lateral border of the sacrospinalis. The **middle** and **anterior layers** ensheathe the quadratus lumborum muscle, and at the lateral border of this muscle they fuse with the posterior layer to give insertion to the three muscles of the anterolateral abdominal wall.

SUBOCCIPITAL TRIANGLE (TABLE XXI, FIG. 62)

The muscles that bound the small **suboccipital triangle** are medially, the **rectus capitis posterior major,** which overlies the **minor;** laterally, the **obliquus capitis superior;** and inferiorly, the **obliquus capitis inferior.** The **semispinalis capitis** and the **longissimus capitis,** lying deep to the flattened, relatively extensive **splenius muscle,** form the roof of the triangle. The floor is formed by the posterior atlanto-occipital membrane and the posterior arch of the atlas. The triangle contains the **vertebral artery** as it passes into the skull through the foramen magnum and the **suboccipital nerve** (C_1), which supplies the muscles of the triangle. The **greater occipital nerve** (C_2) arches around the

TABLE XXI. MUSCLES OF THE SUBOCCIPITAL TRIANGLE

Muscle	Origin	Insertion	Action	Nerve
Rectus capitis posterior major	Spine of axis	Lateral half of inferior nuchal line	Extends and rotates head	Posterior primary ramus of C_1 (suboccipital nerve)
Rectus capitis posterior minor	Posterior tubercle of atlas	Occipital bone below medial portion of inferior nuchal line	Extends head	As above
Obliquus capitis superior	Transverse process of atlas	Occipital bone between superior and inferior nuchal lines	Extends head	As above
Obliquus capitis inferior	Spine of axis	Transverse process of atlas	Rotates and extends head	As above

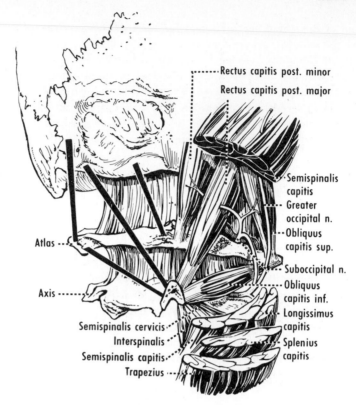

Fig. 62. Suboccipital triangle and contents. (From E. Gardner, D. J. Gray, and R. O'Rahilly. Anatomy. Philadelphia, Saunders, 1963.)

inferior border of the obliquus capitis inferior to supply sensation to the back of the scalp. The muscles of this triangle may act as extensors and rotators of the head, but function chiefly as postural muscles.

VERTEBRAL COLUMN (FIG. 63)

The **vertebral column** forms the central portion of the axial skeleton of the body and presents two **primary curvatures,** the thoracic and the sacral, which are convex posteriorly, and two **secondary curvatures,** the cervical and the lumbar, which are concave posteriorly. It is composed of seven cervical, twelve thoracic, five lumbar, five fused sacral, and three to five fused coccygeal vertebrae.

The component parts of a **typical vertebra** are the body and a number of processes which surround the centrally located vertebral foramen. The massive **body** gives strength to the vertebral column and is separated from adjacent vertebral bodies by the intervertebral discs. The **transverse processes** project laterally from the junction of the pedicles and the body. In the cervical region they contain a foramen for the passage of the vertebral artery, and in the thoracic region they afford articulation for the ribs. The short, slightly rounded **pedicles** project posteriorly from the body and are joined by the flattened **laminae** to form the arch. The pedicles, laminae, and posterior surface of the body form the vertebral foramen, with adjacent foramina forming the vertebral canal. At the junction of

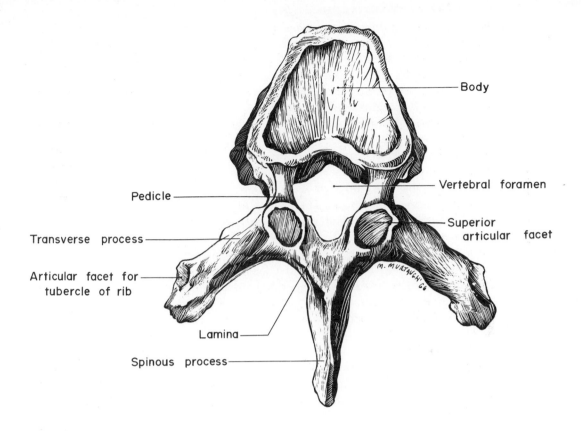

Body

Vertebral foramen

Superior articular facet

Pedicle

Transverse process

Articular facet for tubercle of rib

Lamina

Spinous process

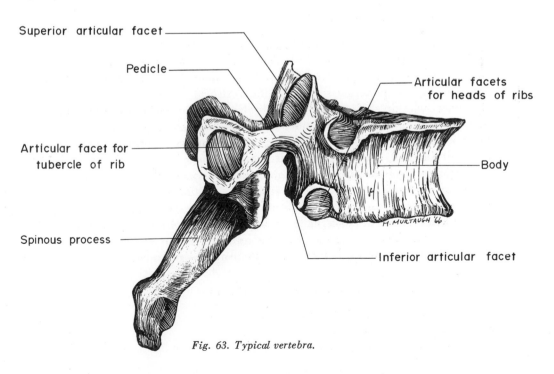

Superior articular facet

Pedicle

Articular facets for heads of ribs

Articular facet for tubercle of rib

Body

Spinous process

Inferior articular facet

Fig. 63. Typical vertebra.

the laminae the **spinous processes** project posteriorly. At the junction of the pedicle with the lamina the smaller **superior** and **inferior processes** bear articular facets which form synovial joints with adjacent vertebrae. The deep **vertebral notch** on the inferior edge, and the shallow notch on the superior edge, of each pedicle form between adjacent vertebrae **intervertebral foramina,** which transmit spinal nerves and vessels.

Regional characteristics differentiate vertebrae of the cervical, thoracic, and lumbar regions. Each cervical vertebra has a foramen within each transverse process, the **foramen transversarium,** which transmits the vertebral artery. The transverse processes present anterior and posterior tubercles, while the spinous processes of the third through sixth vertebrae are bifid. The first and second cervical vertebrae are atypical. The first, or **atlas,** lacks both a body and a spinous process. Instead of the usual articular processes, the lateral mass of the atlas articulates superiorly with the occipital condyles of the skull and inferiorly with the second cervical vertebra. These lateral masses are joined by the anterior and posterior arches which present, in the midline, anterior and posterior tubercles. The **odontoid process** projects superiorly from the upper part of the body of the second cervical vertebra, or **axis,** and represents the transposed body of the first vertebra. **Thoracic vertebrae** present **articular facets for the ribs,** one on the body for articulation with the head of the rib, and one at the transverse process for the rib tubercle. The long slender spinous processes of thoracic vertebrae are directed inferiorly. The **lumbar vertebrae** are differentiated by their lack of foramina transversarii and rib facets. They present massive bodies, broad somewhat quadrilateral horizontal spinous processes, and long slender transverse processes.

Ligaments of the Vertebral Column

The broad, thick **anterior longitudinal ligament** passes over the anterior surface of the vertebral bodies from the skull to the coccyx and is firmly attached to the bodies and the intervertebral discs. The **posterior longitudinal ligament** extends over the posterior surface of the vertebral bodies and, therefore, along the inner anterior surface of the vertebral canal. The **supraspinous ligament** attaches along the tips of the spinous processes, where it merges with the ligamentum nuchae in the cervical region. **Interspinous ligaments** pass between adjacent superior and inferior borders of spinous processes and fuse with the supraspinous ligament, while the **ligamentum flavum** extends from the anterior aspect of one lamina to the posterior aspect of the lamina below. **Intertransverse ligaments** form small bands between adjacent transverse processes.

Intervertebral discs unite adjacent, unfused vertebral bodies. They consist of an outer layer of fibrocartilage, the **annulus fibrosus,** while centrally they present a relatively soft gelatinous mass, the **nucleus pulposus.**

SPINAL CORD AND MENINGES (FIG. 64)

As an extension of the brain stem, the **spinal cord** extends from the foramen magnum to the level of the first or second lumbar vertebra. Below this level nerve rootlets and the filum terminale, a prolongation of pia mater, form the

cauda equina, which occupies the vertebral canal. The cylindrical cord is slightly flattened anteroposteriorly and has **cervical** and **lumbar enlargements** at the levels of origin of the nerves to the upper and lower extremities. The cord is grooved anteriorly by the **anterior median fissure,** and posteriorly by the **posterior median sulcus.** The designation of a spinal segment or **spinal level** refers to that portion of the cord associated with anterior and posterior roots of a specific spinal nerve.

The **blood supply** of the spinal cord is from the **vertebral arteries,** supplemented by segmental **intervertebral branches** of deep cervical, intercostal, lumbar, and sacral arteries. As the vertebral artery enters the cranial cavity, just prior to its union to the artery of the opposite side to form the basilar artery, it gives off **anterior** and **posterior spinal branches.** The branches from each side unite to form a single trunk anteriorly and paired trunks posteriorly. These arterial trunks extend distally along the entire length of the cord and receive segmental contributions from the above-named intervertebral branches.

The spinal cord, bathed in cerebrospinal fluid, is invested by three membranes (meninges): the dura, the arachnoid, and the pia mater. The outer, tough, dense **dura mater** is a fibrous tube which extends from the foramen magnum, where it is continuous with dura of the brain, to the coccyx. Below the level of the second sacral vertebra it narrows considerably and blends with the connective tissue covering the posterior aspect of the coccyx. As each spinal root emerges from

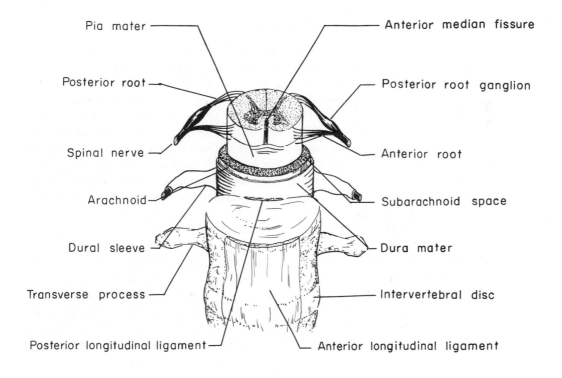

Fig. 64. Cross section of the spinal cord and meninges.

the vertebral canal, it carries with it for a short distance a prolongation of the dura as the **dural sleeve.** The **epidural space,** between the dura and walls of the vertebral canal, contains fat and a plexus of thin-walled veins. The **subdural space** is a capillary interval between the dura and the arachnoid, containing a small quantity of fluid.

The avascular, delicate, transparent **arachnoid mater,** coextensive with the dura mater, is also continuous through the foramen magnum with the arachnoid covering the brain. Filamentous extensions pass through the subarachnoid space to fuse with the pia mater. Laterally this membrane is prolonged a short distance with the sheath for the spinal nerve. The **subarachnoid space,** a wide, trabeculated interval between the arachnoid and the pia, contains the **cerebrospinal fluid,** which serves as a protective cushion for the cord.

The **pia mater,** a delicate, vascular membrane, is intimately adherent to the spinal cord. From the termination of the cord at the first or second lumbar vertebra the pia mater continues inferiorly as the **filum terminale. Denticulate ligaments,** serrated lateral extensions of the pia, anchor and eliminate torsion or twisting of the cord within the dural sac. The medial edge of this small ligament has a continuous attachment to the cord midway between the anterior and posterior nerve roots, while the serrated lateral border attaches to the dura at intervals between emerging spinal nerves.

FACE

Cutaneous Innervation (Fig. 65)

The cutaneous innervation to the face is supplied by all three divisions of the **trigeminal,** or fifth cranial, nerve. The **ophthalmic division** (V_1) divides into three branches, the lacrimal, the frontal, and the nasociliary nerves, which supply cutaneous innervation above the level of the eyes. The **lacrimal nerve** supplies the conjunctivum and skin of the upper eyelid. The **frontal nerve** divides into a **supratrochlear branch** that supplies skin of the forehead and upper eyelid, and a **supraorbital branch** passing through the supraorbital foramen and supplying the upper eyelid and the scalp as far posteriorly as the lambdoidal suture. The **nasociliary nerve** divides into an **external nasal twig,** which innervates the skin of the ala and apex of the nose, and an **infratrochlear branch** to the medial angle of the eye, lower eyelid, and side of the nose.

The **maxillary division** (V_2) divides into the infraorbital and zygomatic nerves, which supply an oblique area between the mouth and the eyes. The **infraorbital nerve** appears on the face at the infraorbital foramen and divides into an **inferior palpebral branch** to the skin and conjunctivum of the lower lid, an **external nasal branch** to the side of the nose, and a **superior labial branch** to the upper lip. The **zygomatic nerve** gives off the **zygomaticofacial branch,** which passes through the zygomaticofacial foramen to the skin over the prominence of the cheek, and a **zygomaticotemporal branch,** which passes through the zygomaticotemporal foramen to the skin over the temporal region.

The **mandibular division** (V_3) supplies the remainder of the face. Its cutaneous branches are derived from both the anterior and posterior divisions of this nerve. The **buccal branch,** from the anterior division, breaks up into a

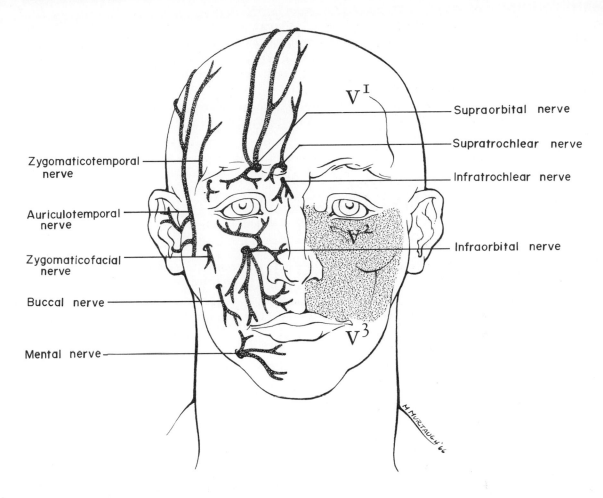

Zygomaticotemporal nerve

Auriculotemporal nerve

Zygomaticofacial nerve

Buccal nerve

Mental nerve

V^I

Supraorbital nerve

Supratrochlear nerve

Infratrochlear nerve

V^2

Infraorbital nerve

V^3

Fig. 65. Cutaneous innervation of the face.

series of twigs to supply the skin over the buccinator muscle of the cheek. The **auriculotemporal nerve,** from the posterior division, divides into an auricular branch to the external auditory meatus, tympanic membrane, skin of the tragus, and the upper and outer part of the auricula, and a **superficial temporal branch,** which supplies most of the temporal region. The terminal branch of the mandibular division is the **inferior alveolar nerve,** which passes through the mandibular foramen to course in the mandibular canal and then emerge from the mental foramen as the **mental branch,** supplying the skin of the chin, and the **inferior labial branch** to the lower lip.

Muscles (Table XXII, Fig. 66)

The muscles of facial expression lie within the superficial fascia of the face. They gain their origin from fascia or underlying bone and insert into the skin. They are usually described by their action on, or relation to, structures of the face; are frequently fused with adjacent muscles; and are innervated by the facial, or seventh cranial, nerve. Muscles associated with or adjacent to the eye include the **frontalis,** which wrinkles the forehead and raises the eyebrows, as in registering surprise or draws the skin of the scalp forward; the **corrugator,** which furrows and wrinkles the brow; and the **orbicularis oculi,** which acts in winking and blinking.

Muscles around the nose are the **procerus** (pyramidalis nasi) over the bridge of the nose, which wrinkles the skin between the eyebrows and draws the

TABLE XXII. MUSCLES OF THE FACE

Muscle	Origin	Insertion	Action	Nerve
Frontalis	Epicranial aponeurosis	Skin of frontal region (forehead)	Raises eyebrow; wrinkles forehead	Facial
Corrugator supercilii	Medial portion of supraorbital margin	Skin of medial half of eyebrow	Draws eyebrows downward and medialward	Facial
Orbicularis oculi	Medial orbital margin, medial palpebral ligament, and lacrimal bone	Skin and rim of orbit and tarsal plate	Acts as sphincter of eyelids	Facial
Procerus	Lower part of nasal bone, upper part of lateral nasal cartilage	Skin between eyebrows	Wrinkles skin over bridge of nose	Facial
Nasalis	Canine eminence lateral to incisive fossa	Nasal cartilages	Draws alae of nostril toward septum	Facial
Depressor septi	Incisive fossa of maxilla	Posterior aspect of ala and nasal septum	Draws nasal septum inferiorly	Facial
Dilator nares	Margin of piriform aperture of maxilla	Side of nostril	Widens nostril	Facial
Orbicularis oris	Surrounds oral orifice, forming intrinsic muscle of lips. Origin and insertion complicated; interlaces with other muscles associated with lips.		Acts in compression, contraction, and protrusion of lips	Facial
Quadratus labii superioris	Frontal process of maxilla, infraorbital region, and inner aspect of zygomatic bone	Greater alar cartilage, nasolabial groove, and skin of upper lip	Elevates lip, dilates nostril, and raises angle of mouth	Facial

continued

latter medially in registering a fierce expression; the **nasalis** (compressor nares), which compresses the nostril, drawing its margins toward the septum; the **dilator nares,** which enlarges the nostril; and the **depressor septi,** which draws the cartilaginous portion of the septum inferiorly and constricts the nostril.

The **orbicularis oris** ("kissing" muscle) encircles the mouth, forms the muscular bulk of the lips, interlaces with other muscles of the lips, and acts in compression, contraction, and protrusion of the lips. Three muscles are associated

TABLE XXII. MUSCLES OF THE FACE *continued*

Muscle	Origin	Insertion	Action	Nerve
Caninus	Canine fossa of maxilla	Angle of mouth	Raises angle of mouth	Facial
Zygomaticus	Zygomatic arch	Angle of mouth	Elevates and draws angle of mouth backward	Facial
Quadratus labii inferioris	Mandible between symphysis and mental foramen	Into orbicularis oris and skin of lower lip	Depresses and everts lower lip	Facial
Triangularis	Oblique line of mandible	Angle of mouth	Turns corner of mouth downward	Facial
Risorius	Fascia overlying masseter muscle	Angle of mouth	Retracts angle of mouth	Facial
Platysma	Superficial fascia of pectoral and deltoid region	Mandible, skin of neck and cheek, angle of mouth, and orbicularis oris	Depresses lower jaw; tenses and ridges skin of neck	Facial
Buccinator	Pterygomandibular raphe, alveolar processes of jaw opposite molar teeth	Angle of mouth	Compresses cheek as accessory muscle of mastication	Facial
Mentalis	Incisive fossa of mandible	Skin of chin	Elevates and protrudes lower lip	Facial
Auricularis anterior, superior, and posterior (rudimentary)	Temporal fascia, epicranial aponeurosis, and mastoid process	Front of helix, triangular fossa, and convexity of concha	May retract and elevate ear	Facial

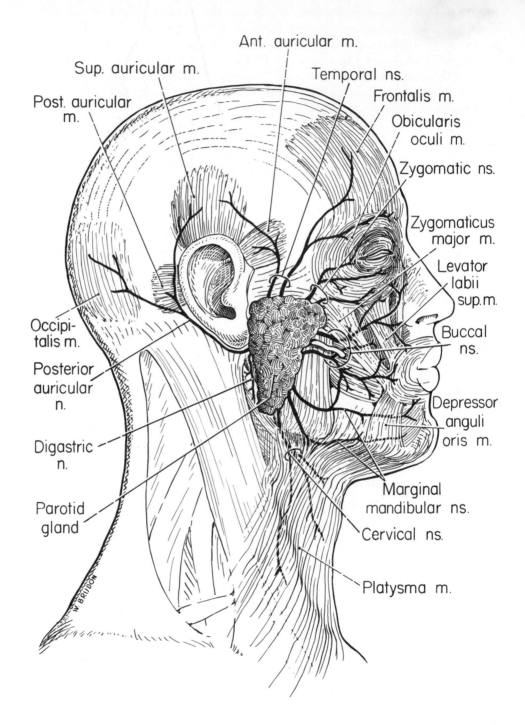

Sup. auricular m.

Post. auricular
m.

Ant. auricular m.

Temporal ns.

Frontalis m.

Obicularis
oculi m.

Zygomatic ns.

Zygomaticus
major m.

Levator
labii
sup.m.

Buccal
ns.

Occipi-
talis m.

Posterior
auricular
n.

Digastric
n.

Parotid
gland

Depressor
anguli
oris m.

Marginal
mandibular ns.

Cervical ns.

Platysma m.

W BRUDON

Fig. 66. Muscles of the face and the facial nerve. (From R. T. Woodburne. Essentials of Human
Anatomy, *ed. 3. New York, Oxford, 1965.)*

with the upper lip; the **quadratus labii superioris,** which functions in elevation of the lips, dilation of the nostril, and raising the angle of the mouth; the **caninus,** acting to elevate the corner of the mouth; and the **zygomaticus,** ("laughing" muscle), which draws the angle of the mouth backward and upward.

Muscles of the lower lip are four in number: the **depressor labii inferioris** expresses terror or grief in depressing and everting the lip; the **depressor anguli oris** draws the angle of the mouth downward; the **risorius** retracts the angle of the mouth in grinning; and the **platysma,** interdigitating with muscles of the lower lip, depresses the lower lip and jaw and tenses or ridges the skin of the neck.

The **buccinator** muscle makes the cheek rigid in sucking or blowing, and is an accessory muscle of mastication by eliminating the space of the vestibule between the cheek and the jaws. The **mentalis** muscle of the chin elevates and protrudes the lower lip and, when well developed, may form with its member of the opposite side the dimple in the chin.

Three poorly developed muscles of the ear, the **auricularis anterior, superior,** and **posterior,** insert into the auricula and act in feeble movements of the ear.

Arteries and Nerves (Fig. 66)

The **facial nerve** follows a complicated course from its origin on the brain stem to its emergence from the cranium at the stylomastoid foramen. Here its branches include the **posterior auricular nerve,** with an **auricular branch** to the posterior auricular muscle of the ear, and an **occipital branch** to the occipitalis muscle. The **digastric branch** supplies the posterior belly of the digastricus muscle, and the **stylohyoid branch,** the stylohyoideus muscle. The facial nerve then turns anteriorly to pass lateral to the styloid process and enters the substance of the parotid gland, where it divides into an **upper (temporozygo- matic)** and a **lower (cervicofacial) division.**

The upper division supplies all the superficial muscles above the zygomatic arch, with a **temporal branch** innervating the anterior and superior auricular, frontalis, orbicularis oculi, and corrugator muscles, and a **zygomatic branch** to the orbicularis oculi and zygomaticus muscles. The lower division gives a **buccal branch** to the muscles of expression below the orbit and around the mouth, a **mandibular branch** to the quadratus labii inferioris and mentalis muscles, and a **cervical branch** to the platysma.

The **facial artery** appears on the face at about the middle of the inferior border of the mandible and passes from the anterior border of the masseter muscle toward the medial angle of the eye. In its course it gives off the **superior** and **inferior labial branches** to the upper and lower lips, respectively, and the **lateral nasal branch** to the ala and dorsum of the nose; it terminates as the **angular artery** at the medial corner of the eye. The latter anastomoses with the dorsal nasal and palpebral branches of the ophthalmic artery to establish a com- munication between branches of the internal and external carotid arteries. Addi- tional anastomoses are present between the facial artery and the infraorbital branches of the internal maxillary.

The **superficial temporal branch** of the external carotid artery arises in the substance of the parotid gland and courses superficially toward the temporal region. It gives off the **transverse facial artery,** which parallels the course of the parotid duct to supply the parotid gland and duct, the masseter and buccinator muscles, and the skin over the cheek, and anastomoses with branches of the facial artery. The superficial temporal artery terminates by bifurcating into the **frontal (anterior) branch,** which anastomoses with branches of the ophthalmic artery, and the **parietal (posterior) branch,** which anastomoses with the posterior auricular and occipital arteries.

PAROTID GLAND

The **parotid gland,** largest of the three major salivary glands, occupies the depression between the sternocleidomastoideus muscle and the ramus of the mandible. It is roughly quadrilateral in shape and somewhat flattened, with a **deep process** passing to the inner aspect of the mandible. The **superficial facial process** (accessory parotid) extends anteriorly beyond the ramus of the mandible, surrounds the proximal part of the large parotid (Stensen's) duct, and overlies the masseter muscle. The gland is enclosed within the investing layer of deep cervical fascia. The thick-walled excretory **duct of the parotid** emerges from the facial process to continue across the masseter muscle, turns deep to pass through the suctorial fat pad and buccinator muscle, and terminates inside the oral cavity opposite the upper second molar tooth.

The parotid gland is related laterally to the skin and superficial fascia of the face, branches of the greater auricular nerve, and parotid lymph nodes, and superiorly to the external auditory meatus. The posteromedial surface of the parotid overlies the mastoid process, the sternocleidomastoideus, posterior belly of the digastricus, and stylohyoideus muscles, and the styloid process. The antero-medial surface is molded to the posterior border of the ramus of the mandible and the structures attaching to it, i.e., the masseter and medial pterygoideus muscles, and the temporomandibular ligament. The most superficial structures passing through the substance of the gland are the terminal branches of the facial nerve, with the division of this nerve into upper and lower trunks occuring within the gland. The posterior facial vein, the external carotid artery and some of its branches, and the auriculotemporal and greater auricular nerves are related to the deep aspect of the parotid. The above structures radiate from the periphery of the gland to pass to their destinations. The superficial temporal artery and vein, the auriculo-temporal nerve, and the temporal branch of the facial nerve pass superiorly; the zygomatic, buccal, and mandibular branches of the facial nerve and the transverse facial artery pass anteriorly; the cervical branch of the facial nerve passes inferiorly; and the posterior auricular artery and nerve pass posteriorly to cross the middle of the sternocleidomastoideus muscle.

TEMPORAL AND INFRATEMPORAL FOSSAE

The **temporal fossa,** an oval area on the lateral aspect of the skull, is bounded by the temporal lines on the frontal and parietal bones superiorly, the temporal border of the zygomatic bone anteriorly, the superior border of the zygoma and its processes inferiorly, and the supramastoid crest posteriorly. It is continuous inferiorly with the infratemporal fossa and contains the fan-shaped **temporalis muscle** of mastication.

The **infratemporal fossa** is the area bounded laterally by the ramus of the mandible, anteriorly by the body of the maxilla, superiorly by the infraorbital fissure, and inferiorly by the upper second and third molar teeth and their alveolar processes. The **medial wall** consists of the lateral or muscular plate of the pterygoid process, and the **roof** is formed by the inferior surface of the greater wing of the sphenoid and part of the temporal bone, with the infratemporal crest separating the roof from the medial wall. The medial and lateral pterygoidei muscles, the pterygoid plexus of veins, the mandibular nerve, and the internal maxillary artery are within the infratemporal fossa. The foramen ovale penetrates the roof of the fossa at the posterior border of the lateral pterygoid plate; the infraorbital fissure opens into it at right angles to the pterygopalatine fissure; and the foramen spinosum is situated just posterolateral to the fossa.

Muscles (Table XXIII, Fig. 67)

The four muscles of mastication, located in the temporal and infratemporal fossae, act in movements of the mandible and are innervated by the mandibular division of the fifth cranial nerve. The fan-shaped **temporalis muscle** originates from the temporal fossa, inserts into the coronoid process, and elevates and retracts the mandible. The thick quadrilateral **masseter muscle** covers the lateral surface

TABLE XXIII. TEMPORAL AND INFRATEMPORAL MUSCLES

Muscle	Origin	Insertion	Action	Nerve
Temporalis	Temporal fossa and temporal fascia	Coronoid process and anterior border of ramus of mandible	Raises and retracts mandible	Mandibular division of trigeminal
Masseter	Lower border and deep surface of zygomatic arch	Lateral surface of ramus and coronoid process of mandible	Raises and helps protract mandible	Mandibular division of trigeminal
Lateral pterygoid	Infratemporal surface of sphenoid and lateral surface of lateral pterygoid plate	Neck of mandible and capsule of temporomandibular joint	Protrudes and depresses mandible; draws it toward opposite side	Mandibular division of trigeminal
Medial pterygoid	Maxillary tuberosity and medial surface of lateral pterygoid plate	Mandible between mandibular foramen and angle	Raises and protrudes mandible; draws it toward opposite side	Mandibular division of trigeminal

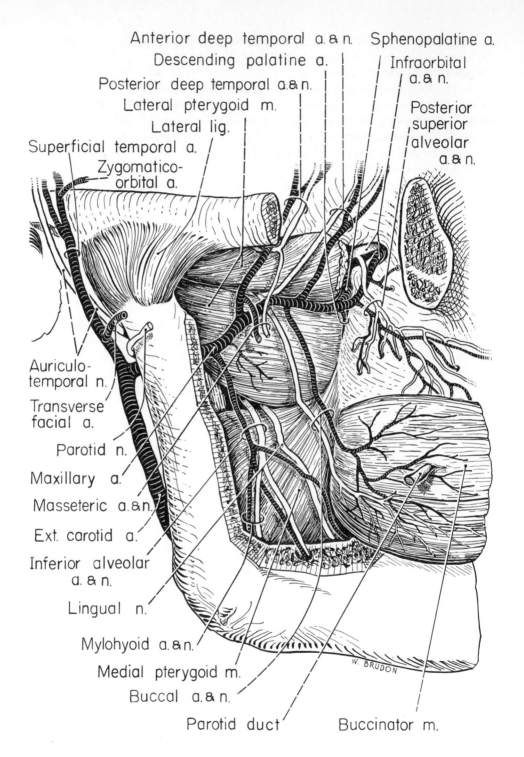

Anterior deep temporal a. & n.
Descending palatine a.
Posterior deep temporal a. & n.
Lateral pterygoid m.
Lateral lig.
Superficial temporal a.
Zygomatico-orbital a.
Sphenopalatine a.
Infraorbital a. & n.
Posterior superior alveolar a. & n.
Auriculo-temporal n.
Transverse facial a.
Parotid n.
Maxillary a.
Masseteric a. & n.
Ext. carotid a.
Inferior alveolar a. & n.
Lingual n.
Mylohyoid a. & n.
Medial pterygoid m.
Buccal a. & n.
Parotid duct
Buccinator m.

W. BRUDON

Fig. 67. Infratemporal fossa. (From R. T. Woodburne. Essentials of Human Anatomy, ed. 3. New York, Oxford, 1965.)

of the ramus, the angle, and the coronoid process of the mandible and raises the lower jaw. In forcible clenching of the jaw this muscle can be felt as it bulges over the angle of the mandible. The **medial** and **lateral pterygoids** are both situated deep to the mandible in the infratemporal fossa. Both have two heads partially originating from the lateral pterygoid plate and act to protrude and move the mandible from side to side. In addition the medial pterygoid elevates, and the lateral pterygoid depresses, the mandible.

Arteries and Nerves (Fig. 67)

The **internal maxillary artery,** the larger of the two terminal branches of the external carotid, begins at the neck of the mandible and passes anteriorly across the lower border of the lateral pterygoideus muscle to disappear into the pterygopalatine fossa. It is divided into three parts by the lateral pterygoideus. The **first part,** proximal to this muscle, gives four branches: the **deep auricular artery,** which follows the auriculotemporal nerve to supply the skin of the external auditory meatus and outer aspect of the tympanic membrane; the **anterior tympanic branch,** which ascends behind the capsule of the temporomandibular joint to pass into the tympanic cavity via the petrotympanic fissure; the **middle meningeal artery,** which ascends medial to the lateral pterygoideus muscle to pass through the foramen spinosum to supply to meninges; and the **inferior alveolar,** which accompanies the inferior alveolar nerve as it passes through the mandibular foramen to traverse the mandibular canal and supply the lower teeth. The latter vessel terminates as the **mental branch,** which passes on to the face through the mental foramen. The **second part** of the internal maxillary artery gives **muscular branches** to the lateral and medial pterygoidei, the masseter, and the temporalis muscles; the terminal, or **third part** of the artery passes into the pterygopalatine fossa and will be described with that area.

The sensory portion of the **mandibular division** of the trigeminal nerve originates from the trigeminal ganglion and enters the infratemporal fossa by passing through the foramen ovale, where it is joined by the small **motor root** of the trigeminal. Two branches originate from the main trunk, one the **recurrent meningeal** (nervus spinosus), which re-enters the skull through the foramen spinosum with the middle meningeal artery to supply the meninges, and the other the **nerve to the medial pterygoideus,** which supplies that muscle and sends sensory twigs to the otic ganglion. The main trunk then divides into an anterior and a posterior division. The smaller **anterior division,** essentially motor, gives four branches to the muscles of mastication: the **masseteric branch** to the masseter, the **deep temporal branch** to the temporalis, and the **nerves to the lateral** and **medial pterygoidei.**

The **posterior division,** mostly sensory, has three main branches: the auriculotemporal, the lingual, and the inferior alveolar. The **auriculotemporal nerve,** which embraces the middle meningeal artery near its origin, sends **communicating branches** to the facial nerve and the otic ganglion. In the latter the fibers continue through the ganglion without synapsing to innervate the tensor veli palatini and the tensor tympani muscles. An **anterior auricular branch** of the auriculotemporal nerve supplies sensation to the front of the ear. The tympanic membrane and skin of the external auditory meatus are innervated by the **external acoustic branch,** and the small **superficial temporal branch** of the auriculotemporal nerve supplies the parotid gland and skin over the temporal region.

The **lingual nerve** descends anteroinferiorly, medial to the lateral pterygoideus and anterior to the inferior alveolar nerve. Passing between the medial pterygoideus and the mandible, it reaches the submandibular region where it supplies general sensation to the mucous membrane of the floor of the mouth and the anterior two-thirds of the tongue. **Communicating branches** are given to the inferior alveolar and hypoglossal nerves and the submaxillary ganglion. The **chorda tympani branch** from the facial nerve, supplying special sensory (taste) fibers to the anterior two-thirds of the tongue and preganglionic parasympathetic fibers to the submandibular ganglion, joins the lingual nerve in the infratemporal fossa.

The **inferior alveolar nerve** descends with the inferior alveolar artery to enter the mandibular foramen and traverses the mandibular canal to emerge at the mental foramen as the mental nerve. The **mylohyoid branch** arises as the inferior alveolar nerve enters the mandibular foramen and supplies the anterior belly of the digastricus and the mylohyoideus muscles. Within the mandibular canal the inferior alveolar nerve sends twigs to all the lower teeth; its terminal branches, the **mental** and **inferior labial nerves,** supply the skin of the chin and the skin and mucous membrane of the lower lip.

SKULL

REGIONS

The **skull** is the most complex osseous structure of the body. It is adapted to house the brain and a group of special sensory organs, and encloses the openings into the digestive and respiratory tracts. It is composed of twenty-two flattened, irregular bones which, except for the mandible, are joined by immovable, sutural-type articulations. For descriptive purposes the skull is subdivided into the **cranium,** which houses the brain and special sense organs and is formed by eight bones, and the **facial skeleton,** composed of fourteen bones. There is no special demarcation of this subdivision, but the junctional area contributes to the support of nasal, ocular, and auditory organs. The major **cranial sutures** are the **sagittal,** passing in the midline between the two parietal bones, and two transverse sutures, the **coronal** between the frontal and the parietal bones and the **lamboidal** between the occipital and parietal bones.

Basic points of reference of the skull include the **nasion,** the midpoint of the nasofrontal sutures; the **bregma,** at the junction of the sagittal and coronal sutures; the **obelion,** that portion of the sagittal suture adjacent to the parietal foramina; the **lambda,** at the junction of the sagittal and lambdoidal sutures; the **inion,** or external occipital protuberance; the **asterion,** at the junction of the occipital, parietal, and temporal bones; and the **pterion,** at the junction of the frontal, sphenoid, parietal, and temporal bones.

CRANIAL CAVITY (TABLE XXIV, FIG. 68)

Superiorly in the median plane of the internal aspect of the **calvarium,** or skull cap, a shallow groove lodges the superior sagittal venous sinus, with numerous small adjacent pits indicating the position of the arachnoid granulations. Many grooves on the inner aspect of the calvarium are formed by the meningeal vessels. The largest and most prominent of these grooves, extending laterally over the inner surface from the foramen spinosum, lodges the middle meningeal artery and its branches.

The **floor** of the cranial cavity is subdivided into anterior, middle, and posterior cranial fossae. The **anterior cranial fossa** is formed by portions of the ethmoid, sphenoid, and frontal bones and is adapted for the reception of the frontal lobes of the brain. Posteriorly this fossa is limited by the posterior border of the lesser wings of the sphenoid and the anterior margin of the chiasmatic groove. The **crista galli,** a midline process of the ethmoid bone, affords attachment for a longitudinal fold of dura mater, the **falx cerebri.** The **cribriform plate of the ethmoid,** at either side of the crista galli, admits passage of filaments of the olfactory nerve from the nasal mucosa to synapse in the olfactory bulb. Posteromedially the **anterior** and **posterior clinoid processes** give attachment to another dural fold, the tentorium cerebelli.

The floor of the **middle cranial fossa** is composed of the body and great wings of the sphenoid and the squamosal and petrous portions of the temporal bones and contains the temporal lobes of the brain laterally. It is limited posteriorly by the superior angle of the petrous portion of the temporal bone and the dorsum sellae centrally. The **sella turcica,** the site of the hypophyseal fossa, is bounded by the tuberculum sellae anteriorly, the dorsum sellae posteriorly, and the anterior and posterior clinoid processes laterally. A crescentic arrangement of the **foramina spinosum, ovale,** and **rotundum** and the **superior orbital fissure** is present in the floor of the middle cranial fossa. The **trigeminal impression** on the anterior surface of the petrous portion of the temporal bone lodges the trigeminal ganglion (semilunar or gasserian) of the fifth cranial nerve. The **tegmen tympani,** the lateral part of the anterior and superior surfaces of the petrous bone, forms the roof of the tympanic cavity, the mastoid antrum, and the auditory canal.

The **posterior cranial fossa** comprises the remainder of the cranial cavity, its floor being formed by parts of the sphenoid, temporal, and occipital bones. The posterior cranial fossa contains the cerebellum, pons, and medulla oblongata, with the **tentorium cerebelli** extending in a transverse plane to separate the cerebellum from the cerebrum. The basilar part of the occipital bone articulates with the sphenoid at the dorsum sellae and is related to the pons and medulla of the brain stem. The **internal occipital protuberance** is located at the region of the confluence of the dural sinuses. The inferiormost portion of the posterior cranial fossa presents the large **foramen magnum,** through which the spinal cord passes. At either side of the foramen magnum, the **hypoglossal canal** transmits the hypoglossal nerve. Laterally the deep groove for the **lateral (transverse** and **sigmoid) dural sinus** extends from the internal occipital protuberance to the **jugular foramen.** At the foramen the glossopharyngeal, vagus, and spinal

TABLE XXIV. FORAMINA OF THE SKULL

Name	Bone	Position on bone	Structures passing through
Foramina Associated with Floor of Skull			
Cecum	Frontal	Between frontal and ethmoid (crista galli) at anterior end of crista galli in midline	Vein from nasal cavity to superior sagittal sinus
Olfactory	Ethmoid	In cribriform plate of ethmoid	Olfactory nerve branches and nasociliary nerve
Pterygoid (vidian canal)	Sphenoid	Through root of pterygoid process	Nerve, artery, and vein of pterygoid canal
Sphenopalatine	Sphenoid and palatine	Between vertical part of palatine and under surface of body of sphenoid	Superior nasal nerve, nasopalatine nerves, and sphenopalatine vessels
Rotundum	Sphenoid	At junction of anterior and medial parts of sphenoid	Maxillary nerve
Vesali	Sphenoid	Opposite root of pterygoid process and medial to foramen ovale	Small vein from cavernous sinus
Ovale	Sphenoid	Base of lateral pterygoid plate, in greater wing of sphenoid	Mandibular nerve, accessory meningeal artery, sometimes lesser superficial petrosal nerve
Spinosum	Sphenoid	Posterior angle of sphenoid, medial to spine of sphenoid	Middle meningeal vessels and recurrent branch from mandibular nerve
Lacerum	Sphenoid and petrous part of temporal	Bounded in front by sphenoid, behind by apex of petrous, medially by sphenoid and occipital bones	Internal carotid artery through upper and inner part of foramen, surrounded by nerve plexus; vidian nerve; meningeal branch of ascending pharyngeal artery
Jugular	Temporal and occipital	Behind carotid canal, between petrous part of temporal and occipital	Inferior petrosal sinus and bulb of internal jugular vein; ninth, tenth, and eleventh cranial nerves
Hypoglossal	Occipital	Above base of condyles	Hypoglossal nerve; meningeal branch of ascending pharyngeal artery

continued

TABLE XXIV. FORAMINA OF THE SKULL *continued*

Name	Bone	Position of bone	Structures passing through
Magnum	Occipital	Center of posterior cerebral fossa	Medulla oblongata and membranes, spinal accessory nerve, vertebral arteries, spinal arteries, and tectorial membrane

Foramina Associated with Orbit

Name	Bone	Position of bone	Structures passing through
Anterior ethmoidal	Frontal and ethmoid	In frontoethmoidal suture on medial wall of orbit	Anterior ethmoidal vessels and anterior ethmoidal nerve
Posterior ethmoidal	Frontal and ethmoid	One inch posterior to anterior ethmoidal	Posterior ethmoidal vessels
Optic	Sphenoid	Between upper and lower roots of small wing of sphenoid	Optic nerve and ophthalmic artery
Superior orbital fissure	Sphenoid	Between greater and lesser wings of sphenoid	*Above* superior head of lateral rectus: trochlear, frontal, and lacrimal nerves; sympathetic branches from carotid plexus. *Between* heads of lateral rectus: abducens, oculomotor, and nasociliary nerves; ophthalmic veins
Inferior orbital fissure	Sphenoid and maxilla	Between greater wing of sphenoid and maxilla	Maxillary and zygomatic nerves, infraorbital vessels, and veins to pterygoid plexus

Foramina Associated with Mouth

Name	Bone	Position of bone	Structures passing through
Mandibular	Mandible	Center of medial surface of ramus of mandible	Inferior alveolar nerve and vessels
Greater palatine	Maxilla and palatine	At either posterior angle of hard palate	Greater palatine nerve and descending palatine vessels
Lesser palatine	Palatine	In pyramidal process of palatine bone (two or more)	Lesser palatine nerves
Incisive	Maxilla	Anterior end of median palatine suture just behind incisor teeth	Terminal branches of descending palatine vessels and nasopalatine nerve
Scarpa's	Maxilla	Incisive foramen in midline	Nasopalatine nerve

continued

TABLE XXIV.   FORAMINA OF THE SKULL *continued*

Name	Bone	Position of bone	Structures passing through
Stensen's	Maxilla	In each maxilla in incisive foramen	Terminal branch of descending palatine artery

Foramina Associated with Face

Name	Bone	Position of bone	Structures passing through
Supraorbital	Frontal	Supraorbital margin of orbit	Supraorbital nerve and artery
Infraorbital	Maxilla	Above canine fossa and below orbit	Infraorbital nerve and artery
Zygomatico-orbital (2)	Zygoma	Anteromedial surface of orbital process	Zygomaticotemporal and zygomaticofacial nerves
Zygomaticofacial	Zygoma	Near center of deep surface of zygoma	Zygomaticofacial nerve and vessels
Zygomaticotemporal	Zygoma	Near center of temporal surface of zygoma	Zygomaticotemporal nerve
Mental	Mandible	Below second premolar tooth	Mental nerve and vessels

Foramina Associated with External Aspects of Skull

Name	Bone	Position of bone	Structures passing through
Stylomastoid	Temporal	Between styloid and mastoid processes	Facial nerve and stylomastoid artery
Mastoid	Temporal	Near posterior border of external surface of mastoid part of temporal bone	Vein to transverse sinus, small branch of occipital artery to dura
Parietal	Parietal	Posterior aspect of parietal close to midline	Emissary vein to superior sagittal sinus

accessory nerves leave the cranial cavity, and the sigmoid sinus becomes the internal jugular vein. On the posterior surface of the petrous portion of the temporal bone, the prominent **internal acoustic meatus** transmits the seventh and eighth cranial nerves as well as branches of the basilar artery to the internal ear.

CRANIAL MENINGES

Three distinct connective tissue membranes (**meninges**), the dura, the arachnoid, and the pia mater cover the brain. The **dura mater** forms a tough outer covering and is composed of two closely adherent layers. The **outer layer** lines the cranium as the periosteum (endosteum) and is continuous through the foramina of the skull with the ectocranial periosteum. Within this outer layer **arachnoid**

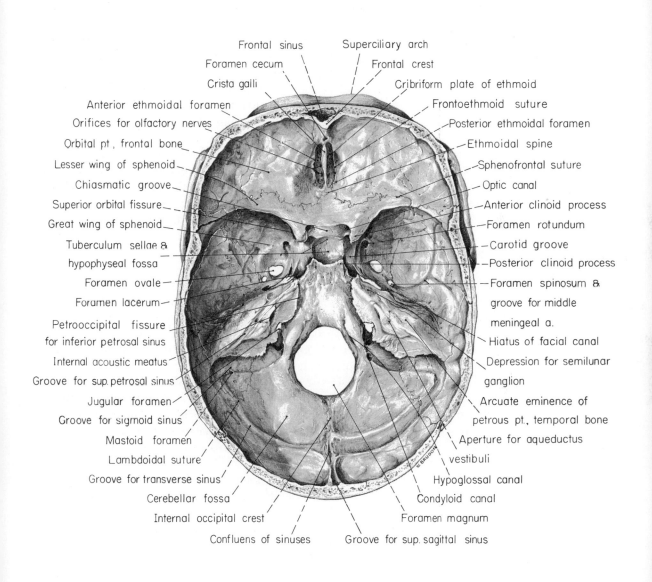

Frontal sinus
Superciliary arch
Foramen cecum
Frontal crest
Crista galli
Cribriform plate of ethmoid
Anterior ethmoidal foramen
Frontoethmoid suture
Orifices for olfactory nerves
Posterior ethmoidal foramen
Orbital pt, frontal bone
Ethmoidal spine
Lesser wing of sphenoid
Sphenofrontal suture
Chiasmatic groove
Optic canal
Superior orbital fissure
Anterior clinoid process
Great wing of sphenoid
Foramen rotundum
Tuberculum sellae &
Carotid groove
hypophyseal fossa
Posterior clinoid process
Foramen ovale
Foramen spinosum &
Foramen lacerum
groove for middle
Petrooccipital fissure
meningeal a.
for inferior petrosal sinus
Hiatus of facial canal
Internal acoustic meatus
Depression for semilunar
Groove for sup. petrosal sinus
ganglion
Jugular foramen
Arcuate eminence of
Groove for sigmoid sinus
petrous pt., temporal bone
Mastoid foramen
Aperture for aqueductus
Lambdoidal suture
vestibuli
Groove for transverse sinus
Hypoglossal canal
Cerebellar fossa
Condyloid canal
Internal occipital crest
Foramen magnum
Confluens of sinuses
Groove for sup. sagittal sinus

Fig. 68. Cranial cavity. (From R. T. Woodburne. Essentials of Human Anatomy, ed. 3. New York, Oxford, 1965.)

granulations, bulging cauliflower-like masses, pit the inner surface of the parietal bones. The meningeal vessels, grooving the calvarium, also run in this layer. The **inner layer** forms four inward-projecting reduplicated folds, namely, the falx cerebri, the falx cerebelli, the tentorium cerebelli, and the diaphragma sellae, which partially divide the cranial cavities into compartments. At the points of separation of the outer and inner layer, venous spaces, the dural sinuses, are present.

The midline sickle-shaped **falx cerebri** projects inwardly between the cerebral hemispheres. Anteriorly it is attached to the crista galli of the ethmoid bone; superiorly the convex upper border extends from the crista galli, along the midline of the inner surface of the calvarium, to the internal occipital protuberance, and is the site of the superior sagittal sinus; the lower concave border is free anteriorly and contains the inferior sagittal sinus. Posteriorly the lower border unites with the tentorium cerebelli and contains the straight sinus at this union. The **tentorium cerebelli** is situated between the cerebellum and the occipital and posterior portions of the temporal lobes of the cerebrum. The falx cerebelli is a slight fold, attached posteriorly to the internal occipital crest and the tentorium. Anteriorly it is free and projects between the cerebellar hemispheres, while the occipital sinus is at its posterior attachment. The **diaphragma sellae** bridges over the sella turcica and covers the hypophysis cerebri, where a large central aperture admits the stalk of the hypophysis.

The **arachnoid** is separated from the dura by a capillary (subdural) space which contains just sufficient fluid to keep the adjacent surfaces moist. From the inner surface of the arachnoid, cobweb-like trabeculae extend across the subarachnoid space to become continuous with the pia mater. Between the arachnoid and the pia the cerebrospinal fluid is contained within the relatively large **subarachnoid space.** The **arachnoid villi** and **granulations** project into the superior sagittal sinus to permit absorption of the cerebrospinal fluid. At certain areas around the base of the brain the arachnoid and the pia are widely separated as the **cerebello-medullary, pontine, interpeduncular, chiasmatic,** and **ambiens cisternae** containing large amounts of cerebrospinal fluid. The subarachnoid space communicates with the ventricular system of the brain via small apertures in the roof of the fourth ventricle and is continuous with the perineural space around nerves emerging from the brain and spinal cord.

The **pia mater** is a thin, highly vascular layer intimately adherent to the cortex of the brain and following closely the contours of the brain. It is invaginated into certain parts of the ventricles, where it forms the **tela chorioidea.** It also ensheathes for a short distance the roots of the cranial nerves.

DURAL SINUSES (FIG. 69)

The **dural sinuses** are venous channels for the brain. They contain no valves and are located between the inner and outer layers of the dura, except for the inferior sagittal and straight sinuses, which are between the reduplications of the inner layer. The **superior sagittal sinus** is triangular in cross section, occupies the entire length of the attached superior portion of the falx cerebri, and increases in size as it passes posteriorly. At the internal occipital protuberance it usually

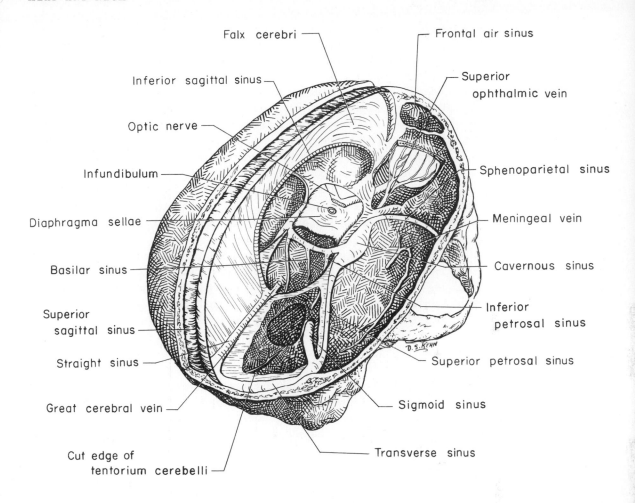

Fig. 69. Venous sinuses.

continues as the right lateral sinus. Arachnoid granulations bulge into its lateral expansions, the **lacunae laterales.** The superior sagittal sinus receives several cerebral veins, two to four diploic veins, and some drainage from the meningeal veins. The smaller **inferior sagittal sinus** occupies the free inferior edge of the falx cerebri. It receives adjacent cerebral veins and, at the junction of the falx cerebri with the tentorium cerebelli, receives the great cerebral vein (of Galen) to become the **straight sinus.** The latter occupies the union of the falx cerebri and the tentorium cerebelli. At the internal occipital protuberance the straight sinus usually continues as the left lateral sinus. The **lateral sinuses** are continuations of either the superior sagittal or straight sinuses as noted above, but at their origin may form a common space, the confluence of sinuses. The lateral sinus is subdivided into transverse and sigmoid portions. The **transverse sinus** occupies the attached portion of the tentorium cerebelli and receives as tributaries the superior petrosal sinus, diploic veins, and adjacent cerebral and cerebellar veins.

The **sigmoid sinus,** a continuation of the transverse, follows an S-shaped course internal to the junction of the petrous and mastoid portions of the temporal bone. It receives the occipital sinus and, at the jugular foramen, becomes the internal jugular vein.

The **confluence of sinuses,** as noted above, consists of a dilatation commonly at the beginning of the right transverse sinus and forms a wide, shallow depression where the right and left transverse sinuses communicate. It may receive the superior sagittal and straight sinuses and may give origin to the **occipital sinus.** The latter occupies the attached border of the falx cerebelli and is variable in size. Inferiorly the occipital sinus bifurcates, partially encircles the foramen magnum, and ends in the sigmoid sinus. It receives cerebellar veins and communicates with the vertebral plexus of veins. The **cavernous sinus,** an expanded, trabeculated dilatation at either side of the hypophyseal fossa, extends laterally to the trigeminal ganglion and the maxillary nerve. The oculomotor, trochlear, ophthalmic, and maxillary nerves are embedded in its lateral wall, while the internal carotid artery with its sympathetic plexus and the abducens nerve pass through the sinus close to its medial wall. It receives opthalmic and cerebral veins and the sphenoparietal sinus, and is drained by the superior and inferior petrosal sinuses. The **intercavernous (circular) sinus** connects the two cavernous sinuses. The **sphenoparietal sinus,** beneath the lesser wing of the sphenoid, receives the anterior branch of the middle meningeal vein and diploic veins, and drains into the cavernous sinus. Within the attached margin of the tentorium cerebelli at the superior border of the petrous bone, the **superior petrosal sinus** bridges the trigeminal ganglion and drains the cavernous sinuses to the transverse sinus. The **inferior petrosal sinus,** larger than the superior, occupies a groove between the petrous and basioccipital bones, where the abducens nerve passes. This sinus drains the cavernous sinus and the internal auditory and adjacent veins, and passes independently through the jugular foramen to empty into the internal jugular vein. The **basilar sinus** is a wide, trabeculated space on the posterior aspect of the dorsum sellae and the superior surface of the basioccipital bone. It unites the cavernous and inferior petrosal sinuses and communicates inferiorly with the vertebral plexus of veins. All the dural sinuses ultimately drain to the lateral sinuses and finally into the **internal jugular vein,** except for the inferior petrosal sinus, which empties directly into the internal jugular.

Diploic veins drain the diploë (the marrow-filled space between the inner and outer tables of the cranial bones) into dural sinuses adjacent to the bones. They have no accompanying arteries, the diploë being supplied by meningeal and ectocranial arteries.

Emissary veins pass through foramina of the skull and connect the dural sinuses with the veins on the external surface of the skull. These vessels include a connection between the veins of the nose and the superior sagittal sinus through the foramen cecum; a connection between the veins of the scalp and the superior sagittal sinus through the parietal foramina; a connection (the largest of the emissary veins) between the posterior auricular vein and the sigmoid sinus through the mastoid foramen; and a connection between the suboccipital veins and the sigmoid sinus via the condylar foramen. Additional emissary veins include communications between the pterygoid plexus and the cavernous sinus through the foramen ovale; between supraorbital, ophthalmic, and facial veins and the cavernous sinus through the supraorbital fissure and the optic foramen; and between the pharyngeal venous plexus and the cavernous sinus by way of the carotid canal.

The **hypophysis cerebri** is an endocrine gland situated in the sella turcica. Superiorly the sella turcica is roofed by the diaphragma sellae, which has a central aperture through which the **infundibulum,** or stalk, of the hypophysis connects the posterior lobe of the gland to the **tuber cinereum** of the hypophysis. The cavernous sinuses are at either side of the sella turcica, while anteriorly the diaphragma sellae separates the anterior lobe of the hypophysis from the optic chiasma.

Most of the brain consists of two **cerebral hemispheres** separated by the deep **longitudinal cerebral fissure** and joined at the base of the fissure by a thick band of transverse fibers, the **corpus callosum.** Each hemisphere has a convex lateral surface, a flattened vertical medial surface, and a slightly concave base. Each is subdivided into **frontal, parietal, occipital,** and **temporal lobes,** which are adjacent to the bones of the same name. The surface of the brain is marked by irregular grooves, the **sulci,** with raised areas between them, the **gyri.** Some gyri and sulci may vary in different individuals, but the important ones are sufficiently constant to be named and are demonstrable in nearly all specimens. The prominent **central sulcus,** flanked by the **pre-** and **postcentral gyri,** separates the frontal from the parietal lobe. At the posterior aspect of the cerebrum the **parieto-occipital sulcus** divides the occipital from the parietal lobe. On the inferolateral surface of each hemisphere a deep fissure, the **lateral sulcus,** demarcates the temporal from the parietal and frontal lobes.

Within the posterior cranial fossa the smaller **cerebellum** is similarly composed of two hemispheres connected by a midline structure, the **vermis.** The cerebellum is separated from the cerebrum by a dural reduplication, the **tentorium cerebelli.** The sulci of the cerebellum parallel one another and are relatively shallow; the gyri are much smaller than those of the cerebrum.

The **brain stem,** consisting of the midbrain, pons, and medulla oblongata, lies beneath the cerebrum and cerebellum. It is formed primarily by brain tracts passing between the brain and spinal cord, contains nuclei of the cranial nerves and association tracts between the various parts of the brain, and serves as the site of emergence of most of the cranial nerves.

Four cavities (ventricles) of varying sizes are associated with the brain. The large paired **lateral ventricles** within the cerebral hemispheres communicate via the **interventricular foramina** with the third ventricle of the midbrain. The narrow, slit-like **third ventricle** is continuous via the **cerebral aqueduct** with the large, rhomboid-shaped **fourth ventricle** between the pons and medulla oblongata and the cerebellum. The fourth ventricle is continuous with the minute **central canal** of the spinal cord.

Blood Vessels

The brain is supplied by two pairs of arteries, the internal carotid and the vertebral arteries, which form an anastomosis at the base of the brain called the **circulus arteriosus cerebri,** or the circle of Willis. The **internal carotid** is subdivided for descriptive purposes into four parts. The **cervical portion** begins at the bifurcation of the common carotid artery opposite the upper border of the thyroid cartilage and passes vertically upward anterior to the transverse processes of the upper three cervical vertebrae. In its course it is crossed by the twelfth cranial nerve, the digastricus and stylohyoideus muscles, and the occipital and posterior auricular arteries. At the base of the skull the ninth, tenth, and eleventh cranial nerves pass between the artery and the internal jugular vein. **The internal carotid artery has no branches in the neck.** Its **petrous portion** follows an S-shaped course through the petrous portion of the temporal bone within the carotid canal. It is separated by a thin layer of bone from the tympanic cavity and the trigeminal ganglion and gives the **caroticotympanic branch** to the tympanic cavity. The **cavernous portion** of the carotid artery, within the cavernous sinus, follows a second sigmoid course passing upward to the posterior clinoid process, then forward and superiorly again at the anterior clinoid process. Branches within the sinus include twigs to the cavernous sinus, the hypophysis, the trigeminal ganglion, and the meninges. The **ophthalmic artery** arises just as the internal carotid passes through the roof of the cavernous sinus.

Passing between the second and third cranial nerves, the **cerebral portion** of the internal carotid artery extends to the medial end of the lateral cerebral fissure, where it divides into terminal branches. Its **posterior communicating branch** courses posteriorly beneath the optic tract to join the posterior cerebral branch of the basilar artery. The internal carotid artery supplies the optic tract and cerebral peduncles and gives deep branches to the internal capsule and thalamus of the brain. Its small **choroidal branch** follows the optic tract and cerebral peduncles to the choroid plexus. The **anterior cerebral artery** passes antero-medially above the optic chiasma, then along the fissure over the corpus callosum to the parieto-occipital sulcus, giving cortical branches to the medial surface of the hemisphere and deep central branches. The **anterior communicating branch** connects the anterior cerebral arteries of either side as they course over the corpus callosum. The direct continuation of the internal carotid, the **middle cerebral artery,** passes upward and laterally in the lateral cerebral fissure to spread out over the surface of the brain, giving orbital, frontal, temporal, and parietal cortical branches to the lateral surface of the hemisphere, and **central striate branches** (the arteries of cerebral hemorrhage) which pass deeply into the corpus striatum of the brain.

The **vertebral artery,** a branch of the subclavian, courses superiorly through the foramina intertransversarii to enter the cranial cavity via the foramen magnum. As it enters the cranium it gives off **anterior** and **posterior spinal arteries,** which descend on either surface of the spinal cord to anastomose with each other and with segmental spinal branches to form longitudinal vessels along the length of the cord. The **meningeal branch** supplies the meninges of the posterior cranial fossa. The largest branch of the vertebral artery, the **posterior**

inferior cerebellar, passes between the tenth and eleventh cranial nerves to supply the undersurface of the cerebellum.

The **basilar artery** is formed by the union of the two vertebral arteries. It passes in the midline of the inferior surface of the pons and gives the following branches: the **anterior inferior cerebellar** to the under surface of the cerebellum, the **pontine branches** to the pons, and the **labyrinthine artery,** which passes through the internal auditory meatus to the internal ear. Its **superior cerebellar branch** courses laterally just posterior to the third cranial nerve, supplies the superior surface of the cerebellum, and anastomoses with the anterior and posterior inferior cerebellar arteries. The **posterior cerebral branch** passes laterally to join the **posterior communicating vessel** from the internal carotid and contributes to the circle of Willis. The latter branch winds around the cerebral peduncle, giving cortical branches to the occipital lobe, to the area adjacent to the parieto-occipital fissure, and to the temporal lobe.

The **meningeal arteries** are periosteal arteries which groove the inner surface of the calvarium, lie in the outer layer of the dura mater, and supply the dura, the inner table of the skull, and the diploë. The **middle meningeal** is a branch of the internal maxillary artery and enters the cranial cavity through the foramen spinosum to divide into anterior and posterior branches which supply most of the meninges. Other arteries to the meninges include branches from the anterior and posterior ethmoidal arteries to the anterior cranial fossa; the accessory meningeal and branches of the internal carotid to the middle cranial fossa; branches of the vertebral, the ascending pharyngeal, and the occipital artery to the posterior cranial fossa.

CRANIAL NERVES (TABLE XXV)

Ten of the **twelve cranial nerves** originate directly from the brain stem. Each has a superficial attachment as well as a deeply located nucleus of origin or termination. The olfactory (I) and optic (II) nerves are unusual in that they do not arise from the brain stem and are actually brain tracts rather than nerves. Five of the twelve cranial nerves attach to the ventral aspect of the brain: the olfactory (I) at the olfactory bulb on the cribriform plate; the optic (II) at the anterolateral angle of the optic chiasma; the oculomotor (III) in a groove, the oculomotor sulcus, between the cerebral peduncle and the interpeduncular fossa; the abducens (VI) in a groove between the pons and the lateral aspect of the pyramid; and the hypoglossal (XII) as a row of rootlets in a groove between the pyramid and the olive. Six cranial nerves attach to the lateral aspect of the brain stem: the trigeminal (V) by two roots, a large sensory and a small motor at the side of the pons; the facial and vestibulocochlear (VII and VIII) in line with the trigeminal at the border of the pons and the inferior cerebellar peduncle; and the glossopharyngeal, vagus, and spinal accessory (IX, X, and XI) as a row of rootlets in a narrow groove along the entire lateral side of the medulla. This origin of the spinal accessory is the cranial or accessory portion of that nerve; the spinal portion is derived from the upper five cervical segments of the cord. Only one cranial nerve, the trochlear (IV), attaches to the dorsum of the brain stem, emerging immediately posterior to the inferior colliculus of the midbrain at the superior medullary velum.

TABLE XXV. CRANIAL NERVES AND THEIR COMPONENTS

Number	Name	Component	Cell bodies	Distribution
I	Olfactory	Sensory (smell)	Olfactory mucosa	Nasal mucosa, upper part of septum, and superior concha
II	Optic	Sensory (vision)	Ganglion layer of retina	Retina
III	Oculomotor	Somatic motor	Brain stem	Superior, inferior, and medial rectus; inferior oblique and levator palpebrae superiorus muscles
		Parasympathetic	Preganglionics, brain stem; postganglionics, ciliary ganglion	Sphincter muscle of iris; ciliary muscle
IV	Trochlear	Somatic motor	Brain stem	Superior oblique muscle
V	Trigeminal	Sensory (general)	Semilunar ganglion	Skin and mucosa of head; meninges
		Branchiomeric motor	Brain stem	Muscles derived from first branchial arch: muscles of mastication (masseter, temporal, external and internal pterygoids); mylohyoid; anterior belly of digastric; tensor tympani; and tensor veli palatini
VI	Abducens	Somatic motor	Brain stem	Lateral rectus muscle
VII	Facial	Branchiomeric motor	Brain stem	Muscle derived from second branchial arch: Facial muscles, posterior belly of digastric, stylohyoid, and stapedius
		Parasympathetic	Preganglionics, brain stem; postganglionics, pterygopalatine ganglion	Nasal, palatine, and lacrimal glands
			Preganglionics, brain stem; postganglionics, submaxillary ganglion	Submaxillary and sublingual glands
		Sensory (general)	Geniculate ganglion	Skin of mastoid region and external acoustic meatus

continued

TABLE XXV. CRANIAL NERVES AND THEIR COMPONENTS *continued*

Number	Name	Component	Cell bodies	Distribution
		Sensory (taste)	Geniculate ganglion	Anterior two-thirds of tongue via chorda tympani; soft palate via greater superficial petrosal
VIII	Acoustic	Sensory (hearing)	Spiral ganglion	Organ of Corti
		Sensory (equilibrium)	Vestibular ganglion	Semicircular canals, utricle, and saccule
IX	Glossopharyngeal	Branchiomeric motor	Brain stem	Stylopharyngeus muscle and pharyngeal muscles
		Parasympathetic	Preganglionics, brain stem; postganglionics, otic ganglion	Parotid gland
		Sensory (general)	Petrosal ganglion	Mucosa of pharynx, tympanic cavity, posterior one-third of tongue, and carotid sinus
		Sensory (taste)	Petrosal ganglion	Posterior one-third of tongue
X	Vagus	Branchiomeric motor	Brain stem	Muscles of pharynx, larynx, levator veli palatini, glossopalatinus
		Parasympathetic	Preganglionics, brain stem; postganglionics, on, in, or near viscera	Thoracic and abdominal viscera
		Sensory (general)	Jugular ganglion	Skin of external acoustic meatus
		Sensory (general)	Nodose ganglion	Pharynx, larynx, and thoracic and abdominal viscera
		Sensory (taste)	Nodose ganglion	Epiglottis and base of tongue
XI	Accessory			
	Cranial root	With motor branches of vagus		
	Spinal root	Somatic motor	Spinal cord	Sternocleidomastoid and trapezius
XII	Hypoglossal	Somatic motor	Brain stem	Intrinsic and extrinsic muscles of tongue

The **olfactory nerve (I)** is entirely sensory, arises in the nasal mucosa as bipolar neurons, and is limited in origin to the mucous membrane covering the superior nasal concha and adjacent nasal septum. Numerous filaments from this distribution area pierce the cribriform plate to synapse with secondary neurons in the **olfactory bulb.** The **olfactory tract** passes posteriorly from the olfactory bulb to the olfactory trigone of the brain.

The **optic nerve (II)** is also entirely sensory and originates in the **ganglionic cells** of the retina. The orbital portion of the nerve is two inches long, invested by meninges, and passes posteriorly through the optic foramen to the **optic chiasma,** which rests on the tuberculum sellae. Fibers of this first portion partially decussate at the optic chiasma to continue posteriorly as the **optic tract,** which winds around the cerebral peduncle and terminates in the lateral geniculate body of the mesencephalon.

The **oculomotor nerve (III),** from its origin at the oculomotor sulcus, passes between the posterior cerebral and superior cerebellar arteries. Lateral to the clinoid processes it pierces the dura to traverse the cavernous sinus and enter the orbital cavity through the superior orbital fissure. The oculomotor nerve is accompanied by the abducens and nasociliary nerves, all of which pass between the heads of the lateral rectus muscle. Its terminal distribution will be described with the section on the orbit.

The **trochlear nerve (IV)** is motor in function. It is the most slender of the cranial nerves, yet has the longest intracranial course. Originating from the dorsum of the brain stem, it winds around the midbrain, enters the edge of the tentorium cerebelli, and passes with the third nerve between the posterior cerebral and the superior cerebellar arteries. It continues forward around the cerebral peduncle to penetrate the dura and enter the cavernous sinus between the third and sixth nerves, and contiuues along the lateral wall of the sinus to enter the orbit through the supraorbital fissure above the origin of the ocular muscles. Its orbital course will be given regionally with the description of the orbital cavity.

The large **trigeminal nerve (V)** is both motor and sensory. It is formed by a large **sensory root from the trigeminal ganglion** and a smaller **motor root.** The trigeminal ganglion occupies a cavity (cavum trigeminale) in the dura at the sutural area between the petrous portion of the temporal and the greater wing of the sphenoid bones. From the ganglion the **ophthalmic division (V_1)** courses anteriorly to enter the orbit via the superior orbital fissure, the **maxillary division (V_2)** passes through the foramen rotundum to the pterygopalatine fossa, and the **mandibular division (V_3)** traverses the foramen ovale to reach the infratemporal fossa. Attached to branches of this nerve by sensory roots are four small parasympathetic ganglia, but the nerve has no parasympathetic components in its brain stem nuclei. The **ophthalmic division** will be discussed with the orbital cavity; the **maxillary division** will be described with the pterygopalatine fossa; and the **mandibuar division** has been covered with the infratemporal fossa.

The **abducens nerve (VI)** is motor in function and pierces the dura at the dorsum sellae to pass below the posterior clinoid process and enter the cavernous sinus at the lateral side of the internal carotid artery. Traversing the sinus, it passes through the superior orbital fissure to enter the orbital cavity above the ophthalmic artery. Its distribution will be discussed in connection with the orbital cavity.

The **facial nerve (VII)** contains both motor and sensory fibers. The large **motor** and smaller **sensory (nervus intermedius) roots** traverse the internal auditory meatus (in company with the eighth nerve) to unite at the **geniculate ganglion,** which is located on the sharp posterior bend of the seventh nerve within the facial canal. From the geniculate ganglion the **major petrosal nerve,** transmitting preganglionic parasympathetic fibers, traverses the petrous portion of the temporal bone to enter the middle cranial fossa through the hiatus of the facial canal. This branch then courses forward between the dura and the trigeminal ganglion, passing deep to the latter, to unite with the **deep petrosal nerve** carrying postganglionic sympathetic fibers from the internal carotid plexus with their cell bodies located in the superior cervical sympathetic ganglion. The junction of these two nerves forms the **nerve of the pterygoid canal** (vidian nerve), which passes through the pterygoid (vidian) canal in the sphenoid bone to terminate in the pterygopalatine ganglion. Distal to the geniculate ganglion the facial nerve passes through the facial canal to emerge at the stylomastoid foramen. Within the facial canal the nerve gives rise to the **branch to the stapedius muscle, communicating twigs** to the auricular branch of the vagus, and the **chorda tympani nerve.** The latter turns upward through a separate small canal to enter the tympanic cavity through the posterior wall, and courses forward on the internal surface of the tympanic membrane. Arching across the handle of the malleus, it leaves the tympanic cavity by passing through the anterior wall. It then traverses the petrotympanic fissure and joins the lingual branch of the trigeminal nerve in the infratemporal fossa. The **chorda tympani** carries preganglionic parasympathetic fibers to the submandibular ganglion and special taste fibers to the anterior two-thirds of the tongue. The **terminal branches** of the facial nerve have been described with the face.

The **vestibulocochlear nerve (VIII),** entirely sensory in function, consists of two parts, the cochlear and vestibular portions, which differ in peripheral endings, central connections, and function. The eighth nerve courses with the facial nerve through the internal auditory meatus, where it divides at the termination of the canal into its respective parts. The **cochlear portion,** the nerve of hearing, consists of bipolar neurons associated with the **spiral ganglion** of the cochlea. The peripheral processes pass to the spiral organ (of Corti), while the central processes pass from the modiolus to the lateral end of the internal auditory canal. The **vestibular portion,** the nerve of equilibrium, consists of the bipolar cells of the **vestibular ganglion** located in the superior part of the lateral end of the internal auditory canal. Peripheral processes of these bipolar neurons pass to the utricle, the saccule, and the ampullae of the semicircular ducts. The central processes join with those of the cochlear division to form the eighth nerve.

The **glossopharyngeal nerve (IX),** both motor and sensory, exits through the jugular foramen in company with the tenth and eleventh nerves. Two **sensory ganglia,** the **superior** and the **inferior (petrosal),** are associated with the glossopharyngeal nerve as the nerve passes through the foramen. The **tympanic branch** (nerve of Jacobson), transmitting preganglionic parasympathetic fibers to the otic ganglion, passes through a small canal (of Jacobson) within the temporal bone to the tympanic cavity, where it joins with branches of the facial nerve to form the **tympanic (promontory) plexus,** which supplies the mucous membrane of the tympanic cavity. From this plexus, the minor **petrosal nerve** is reconstituted and courses through the petrous portion of the temporal bone to run forward in the middle cranial fossa, traverses the foramen ovale, and synapses in the **otic ganglion.** At its exit from the jugular foramen, the glossopharyngeal nerve passes deep to the styloid process, gives a **branch to the stylopharyngeus muscle,** then joins with branches of the vagus and sympathetic fibers to form the **pharyngeal plexus. Terminal branches** of the glossopharyngeal nerve supply the posterior third of the tongue with general and special (taste) sensation.

The **vagus nerve (X),** containing both motor and sensory fibers, has the most extensive course and distribution of any of the cranial nerves. It leaves the cranial cavity via the jugular foramen in company with the ninth and eleventh nerves. Sensory ganglia of the vagus, the **jugular** superiorly and the **nodose** inferiorly, are located within the jugular foramen or just below it. Passing to the cervical region in company with the internal jugular vein, the vagus nerve gives a **recurrent branch** to the meninges, **auricular branches** to the ear, **pharyngeal branches** to the pharyngeal plexus and soft palate, the **nerve to the carotid sinus, cervical cardiac branches,** and a **superior** and a **recurrent (inferior) laryngeal branch** to the larynx. At the root of the neck, the left vagus passes between the common carotid and subclavian arteries to pass anterior to the arch of the aorta and posterior to the root of the lung, where it joins with the right vagus to form the **esophageal plexus.** The right vagus passes anterior to the subclavian artery, then descends along the trachea to the posterior aspect of the root of the lung and joins the left as above. The **recurrent (inferior) laryngeal nerves** loop under the arch of the aorta on the left side and the subclavian artery on the right to reach the tracheoesophageal groove and ascend to supply all the intrinsic musculature of the larynx, except the cricothyroideus. In the thorax, the vagus gives off **cardiac** and **pulmonary branches** and then forms the **esophageal plexus.** After passing through the esophageal hiatus, the right vagus re-forms as the **posterior gastric nerve,** the left as the **anterior gastric nerve,** to aid in the formation of the **celiac plexus.** The vagi contribute to the innervation of all abdominal viscera except those portions of the gastrointestinal tract distal to the splenic flexure of the colon.

The **spinal accessory nerve (XI)** is a motor nerve formed from both cranial and spinal components. The smaller **cranial portion** units with the spinal part to pass through the jugular foramen, then separates to join with the vagus for distribution to the pharynx and larynx. It probably supplies the musculus uvulae, the levator veli palatini, and the pharyngeal constrictor muscles. The **spinal portion,** originating in the motor cells of the ventral horns of the first through the fifth cervical nerves, passes superiorly along the side of the spinal cord and through the foramen magnum, where it joins with the cranial portion. It continues a short distance with the latter as it exits via the jugular foramen, then separates to pass inferiorly behind the internal jugular vein, the stylohyoideus, the digastricus, and the upper part of the sternocleidomastoideus. It crosses the posterior triangle of the neck picking up communicating twigs of the cervical plexus (C_2 and C_3) and passes to the deep surface of the trapezius to supply this muscle and the sternocleidomastoideus.

The **hypoglossal nerve (XII),** the motor nerve to the tongue musculature, passes through the hypoglossal canal to descend almost vertically to a point opposite the angle of the mandible. It courses deep to the internal carotid artery and internal jugular vein, then lies between the artery and the vein, deep to the stylohyoideus and digastricus muscles. At the intermediate tendon of the digastricus it loops around the occipital artery and passes anteriorly between the hypoglossus and mylohyoideus muscles to **supply the intrinsic and extrinsic muscles of the tongue.** Communicating twigs from the first loop of the cervical plexus join the hypoglossal nerve and run with it for a short distance before most of the fibers leave the hypoglossal nerve as the anterior limb (descendens hypoglossi) of the ansa cervicalis to supply infrahyoid muscles of the neck. Some of the fibers from this communication with the cervical plexus continue with the hypoglossal nerve to branch from the latter as individual twigs to supply the thyrohyoideus and geniohyoideus muscles.

CRANIAL PARASYMPATHETIC GANGLIA

The small **ciliary ganglion,** located within the orbital cavity, receives preganglionic parasympathetic fibers from the **short ciliary branch of the oculomotor nerve.** The postganglionic parasympathetic fibers from cell bodies within the ganglion leave via the **short ciliary nerves** to the ciliary and sphincter pupillae muscles. Sensory fibers from the **long ciliary branch of the nasociliary nerve** traverse the ganglion without synapsing and become components of the short ciliary nerves, which supply general sensation to the eyeball. Sympathetic fibers from the ophthalmic plexus also pass through the ganglion and are distributed with the short ciliary nerves to innervate the dilator pupillae muscle and the smooth muscle of orbital blood vessels.

Within the pterygopalatine fossa, the **pterygopalatine ganglion** is attached to the maxillary division of the trigeminal nerve by two **short sensory roots.** Preganglionic parasympathetic fibers pass with the **nervus intermedius of the seventh nerve** to the ganglion via the **major petrosal nerve.** Postganglionic parasympathetic fibers are distributed with branches of the maxillary division of the trigeminal nerve to the lacrimal gland, while branches from the ganglion supply the nasopharynx, nasal cavity, palate, upper lip, and gingiva. Post ganglionic sympathetic fibers, transmitted along the internal carotid plexus, pass as the **deep petrosal nerve** to join the **major petrosal nerve** in the middle cranial cavity and form the **nerve of the pterygoid canal.** The sympathetic fibers pass through the ganglion uninterrupted to be distributed with its branches. **Sensory fibers,** via the two roots to the ganglion from the maxillary division of the fifth cranial nerve, also pass through uninterrupted and are distributed as sensory components of the ganglionic branches.

The **otic ganglion,** located in the infratemporal fossa, is attached to the mandibular division of the trigeminal immediately distal to the foramen ovale. Its preganglionic parasympathetic fibers are derived from a branch of the glossopharyngeal nerve, **the nerve of Jacobson,** which passes to the promontory plexus. From the latter, the **minor petrosal nerve** is reconstituted and transmits the preganglionic parasympathetic fibers to the otic ganglion. Postganglionic fibers are distributed to the parotid gland by the auriculotemporal branch of the trigeminal. Sympathetic fibers passing uninterrupted through the ganglion are derived from the plexus surrounding the middle meningeal artery and are distributed to the blood vessels of the parotid, along with sensory fibers derived from the mandibular nerve.

The **submandibular ganglion** is adjacent to the submandibular gland. Its preganglionic parasympathetic fibers are derived from the seventh cranial nerve via the **chorda tympani.** The latter nerve branches from the facial nerve within the facial canal to course through the middle ear cavity, and traverses the petrotympanic fissure to reach the infratemporal fossa, where it joins the lingual nerve. The preganglionic fibers pass to the submandibular ganglion via two short roots that suspend this ganglion from the lingual nerve. Postganglionic parasympathetic fibers are distributed to the submandibular and sublingual glands. Fibers from the sympathetic plexus around the external maxillary artery may pass through the ganglion and continue with its branches. Sensory fibers from the lingual nerve are distributed with the branches of the ganglion to the submandibular and sublingual glands and to mucous membranes of the oral cavity.

ORBITAL CAVITY (FIGS. 70 AND 71)

The pyramid-shaped **orbital cavity** presents a base, an apex, and four walls. The optic foramen is located at the **apex,** while the quadrangular **base** opens onto the face and is formed about equally by the frontal, maxillary, and zygomatic bones. Each bone transmits a cutaneous nerve: the supraorbital in the frontal, the infraorbital in the maxillary, and the zygomaticofacial in the zygoma. The **medial walls** of the cavities are parallel, about an inch apart, separated by the nasal cavities, and are formed by the fragile lacrimal bone and the orbital plates of the ethmoid. The strong **lateral walls,** at right angles to each other, are formed by processes of the zygomatic and the greater wings of the sphenoid bones. The fossa for the lacrimal gland is in the superolateral portion of the lateral wall. The **superior wall,** or roof of the cavity, is formed by the orbital plate of the frontal bone; the orbital plate of the maxillary and a small part of the zygomatic bone form the **inferior wall** or floor. In the floor of the orbital cavity the **infraorbital groove** continues anteriorly as the **infraorbital canal** to open onto the face at the **infraorbital foramen.**

The **orbital periosteum,** a funnel-shaped sheath attached to the bony walls of the orbital cavity, is continuous posteriorly with the outer layer of the dura and anteriorly with the periosteum covering the external surface of the skull. It encloses the contents of the orbit, except for the zygomatic nerves and the infraorbital nerves and vessels, which lie between the periosteum and the bone. The thin, membranous **fascia bulbi (Tenon's capsule)** encloses the eyeball, forming a socket in which it moves, and separates the eyeball from the orbital fat pad. Its smooth inner surface forms, with the sclera, the **periscleral space.** Expansions from the fascial sheath pass to the lateral and medial recti muscles as the **check ligaments.** The sheath reflects onto and encloses the eye muscles as they attach to the sclera. Posteriorly the bulbar fascia is perforated by ciliary vessels and nerves at the **lamina cribrosa sclerae.**

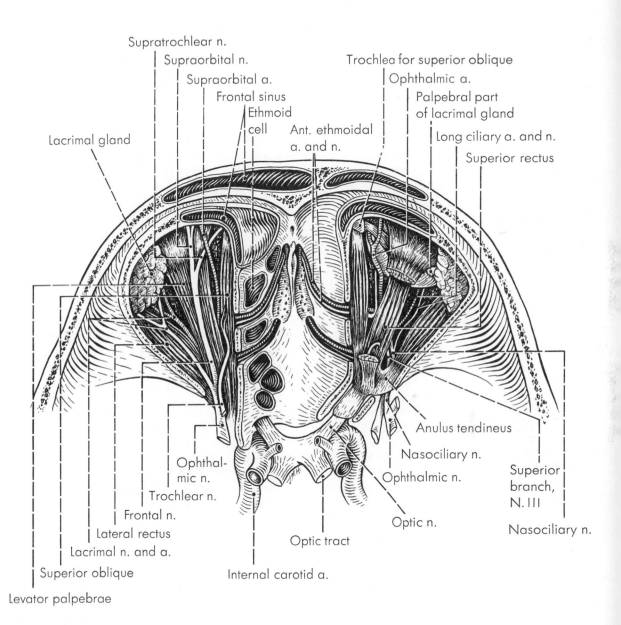

Supratrochlear n.

Supraorbital n.

Supraorbital a.

Frontal sinus

Ethmoid cell

Ant. ethmoidal a. and n.

Trochlea for superior oblique

Ophthalmic a.

Palpebral part of lacrimal gland

Long ciliary a. and n.

Superior rectus

Lacrimal gland

Anulus tendineus

Nasociliary n.

Ophthalmic n.

Superior branch, N. III

Nasociliary n.

Optic n.

Optic tract

Internal carotid a.

Ophthalmic n.

Trochlear n.

Frontal n.

Lateral rectus

Lacrimal n. and a.

Superior oblique

Levator palpebrae

Fig. 70. Superior view of the interior of the orbit. (From W. H. Hollinshead. Textbook of Anatomy, ed. 2. New York, Hoeber, in press.)

Muscles (Table XXVI)

The **extrinsic muscles** of the eye consist of four straight muscles, the superior, inferior, medial, and lateral recti; two oblique muscles, the superior and inferior; and the levator palpebrae superioris. The **recti muscles** originate from the margin of a **fibrous cuff,** which is fixed posteriorly to periosteum and the dural sheath of the optic nerve at the optic foramen, and laterally to the margins of the supraorbital fissure. The lateral rectus is split into upper and lower heads at its origin, with vessels and nerves entering the orbital cavity between the two heads. The recti muscles spread out like the staves of a barrel to insert into a band-like aponeurosis encircling the sclera just behind the corneoscleral junction. Each muscle has a fascial sheath, with adjacent sheaths joining to form a **fibro-muscular cone.**

The **levator palpebrae superioris** is separated superiorly from the superior rectus and inserts into the tarsal plate and the superior fornix of the conjunctiva. The tendon of the **superior oblique** passes through a fascial pulley, the **trochlea,** attached to the medial wall of the orbit, and reverses direction before inserting into the sclera. The **inferior oblique,** located in the anterior part of the orbital cavity, has an origin apart from the other extrinsic ocular muscles. The lateral rectus is supplied by the **abducens nerve,** the superior oblique by the **trochlear nerve,** and the remaining muscles by the **oculomotor nerve.** The medial, superior, and inferior recti acting together move the eye medially, while the inferior and superior oblique and the lateral rectus muscles acting in concert shift it laterally. The inferior oblique and superior rectus direct the eye upward; the superior oblique and inferior rectus move it downward. The superior rectus and superior oblique medially rotate the eye, and the inferior oblique and inferior rectus are lateral rotators. Additional actions include the recti muscles acting as retractors and the oblique muscles as protractors to keep the eye in balance.

Blood Vessels and Nerves (Fig. 71)

As the internal carotid artery leaves the cavernous sinus, it gives off the **ophthalmic artery,** which passes through the optic foramen inferior to the optic nerve, pierces the dural sheath, and lies free within the fibromuscular cone of the orbital cavity. It courses above the optic nerve to give several branches to the structures within the cavity. A very important branch, the small, **central artery to the retina,** pierces the optic nerve sheath about half an inch posterior to the eyeball and gains the center of the optic nerve to reach and supply the retina. Several **short posterior ciliary arteries** arise from the ophthalmic to pierce the sclera, form a plexus in the choroid, and send forward two **long posterior ciliary branches** to anastomose with the anterior ciliary artery at the margin of the iris. The **anterior ciliary arteries** arise from muscular branches to the recti muscles, pierce the sclera just behind the corneoscleral junction, supply the ciliary body and iris, and give twigs to the deep conjuctival plexus. The relatively large **lacrimal branch** of the ophthalmic artery begins near the optic foramen and courses with the lacrimal nerve along the lateral wall above the lateral rectus muscle. It supplies the latter, the superior oblique muscle, the lacrimal gland, and the upper eyelid,

TABLE XXVI. EXTRINSIC MUSCLES OF THE EYE

Muscle	Origin	Insertion	Action	Nerve
Rectus superior, inferior, medial, and lateral	All originate from fibrous cuff fixed posterior to optic foramen and anteriorly to dural sheath of optic nerve, and insert superiorly, inferiorly, medially, and laterally by band-line aponeurosis into sclera just behind corneoscleral junction	See below		Lateral rectus, abducens; others, oculomotor
Levator palpebrae superioris	Orbital roof anterior to optic foramen	Upper tarsal plate and superior fornix of conjunctivum	Elevates upper lid	Oculomotor
Superior oblique	Roof of orbital cavity between superior and medial recti and anterior to optic foramen	Slender tendon passes through fibrous ring (trochlea), reverses direction to insert deep to superior rectus	See below	Trochlear
Inferior oblique	Floor of orbital cavity lateral to lacrimal fossa for lacrimal sac	To sclera between superior and lateral recti	See below	Oculomotor

Action of Eye Muscles

Action	Muscle
Adduction	**Medial,** superior, and inferior recti
Abduction	Inferior and superior oblique; **lateral rectus**
Elevation	Inferior oblique; **superior rectus**
Depression	Superior oblique; **inferior rectus**
Medial rotation	Superior rectus; superior oblique
Lateral rotation	Inferior oblique; inferior rectus

and gives twigs to the conjunctiva. Terminal branches of the ophthalmic artery include the **supraorbital, supratrochlear, dorsal nasal, anterior ethmoidal,** and **posterior ethmoidal,** which pass from the orbital cavity to anastomose freely with branches of the external carotid in the upper face.

Venous drainage of the orbital cavity is accomplished by the **superior** and **inferior ophthamic veins.** The former, formed by the junction of the supra-orbital and supratrochlear veins, drains into the cavernous sinus. The inferior ophthalmic vein, originating in the floor of the cavity, communicates through the infraorbital fissure with the pterygoid plexus or through the supraorbital fissure with the cavernous sinus.

The **optic nerve** enters the orbital cavity through the **optic foramen,** while all the other nerves to the orbit traverse the superior orbital fissure. The optic nerve passes anterolaterally and slightly inferiorly from the optic foramen to penetrate the posterior aspect of the eyeball slightly medial to the posterior pole of the eye, where its meningeal coverings fuse with the sclera of the eyeball. It is slightly longer than its course and therefore does not interfere with movements of the eyeball. Within the retina it spreads out as the third-order neuron in the visual pathway.

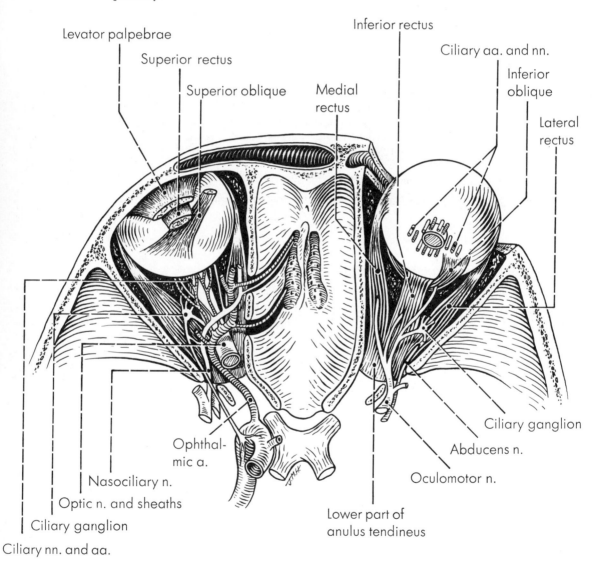

Fig. 71. Deep aspect of the orbital cavity. (From W. H. Hollinshead. Textbook of Anatomy, ed. 2. New York, Hoeber, in press.)

The **oculomotor nerve** is motor to the superior, medial, and inferior recti, the inferior oblique, and the levator palpebrae superioris muscles, and carries pre-ganglionic parasympathetic fibers to the ciliary ganglion. Passing between the heads of the lateral rectus muscle, it divides into an **upper division,** supplying the superior rectus and the levator palpebrae superioris, and a **lower division** to the medial and inferior recti and the inferior oblique muscles. The **trochlear nerve** innervates the superior oblique muscle as it passes along the superior surface of that muscle. The **abducens nerve** lies between the heads of the lateral rectus to course on the ocular surface of this muscle, which it innervates.

The smallest division of the trigeminal nerve, the **ophthalmic nerve,** is sensory and terminates as frontal, lacrimal, and nasociliary branches, which are distributed to structures within the orbital cavity. The **frontal nerve** passes through the supraorbital fissure above the lateral rectus muscle to course between the levator palpebrae superioris and the orbital plate, and terminates as **supra-orbital** and **supratrochlear branches,** which supply the eyelids, forehead, and scalp. The **lacrimal nerve,** passing just below the frontal branch, follows the upper border of the lateral rectus muscle to supply the lacrimal gland and terminates as twigs to the conjunctivum and skin of the eyelids and the skin over the zygomatic process. Communications between the lacrimal nerve and the zygomatic branch of the maxillary division of the trigeminal form the pathway for postganglionic para-sympathetic fibers to pass from the pterygopalatine ganglion to the lacrimal gland. The **nasociliary nerve** courses between the heads of the lateral rectus muscle to cross to the medial wall of the orbital cavity above the optic nerve. Its branches include the **long ciliary nerves,** carrying sensory and postganglionic sympathetic fibers to the iris; **posterior ethmoidal nerves,** supplying the ethmoidal and sphenoidal air sinuses; the **infratrochlear nerve** supplying the lacrimal sac, con-junctivum, eyelids, and upper nose; and the **anterior ethmoidal nerve.** The latter passes through the anterior ethmoidal foramen to enter the anterior cranial fossa, courses on the cribriform plate, and enters the nasal cavity by traversing the naso-ciliary slit, where it then terminates as the **internal** and **external nasal branches.**

The **ciliary ganglion** located in the posterior third of the orbital cavity is a synaptic station for parasympathetic neurons and has been previously described.

Lacrimal Apparatus (Fig. 72)

The **lacrimal gland** is located in the superolateral aspect of the orbital cavity, partly within the **lacrimal fossa** and partially embedded in the upper eyelid. It drains into six to ten **lacrimal ducts,** which pierce the superior fornix of the conjunctivum to empty onto the apposing palpebral and ocular surfaces of the conjunctivum. The action of blinking spreads a uniform layer of lacrimal fluid over the conjunctivum. At the medial canthus of the eye the **punctum lacrimale** opens at the summit of the **lacrimal papilla** on the free margin of the lid as the beginning of the **lacrimal canaliculi.** The latter drain the lacrimal fluid into an expansion of the proximal end of the nasolacrimal duct, the **lacrimal sac.** The **nasolacrimal duct** passes through the nasolacrimal canal of the maxilla and lacrimal bones to open deep to the inferior nasal concha, where it drains into the inferior meatus.

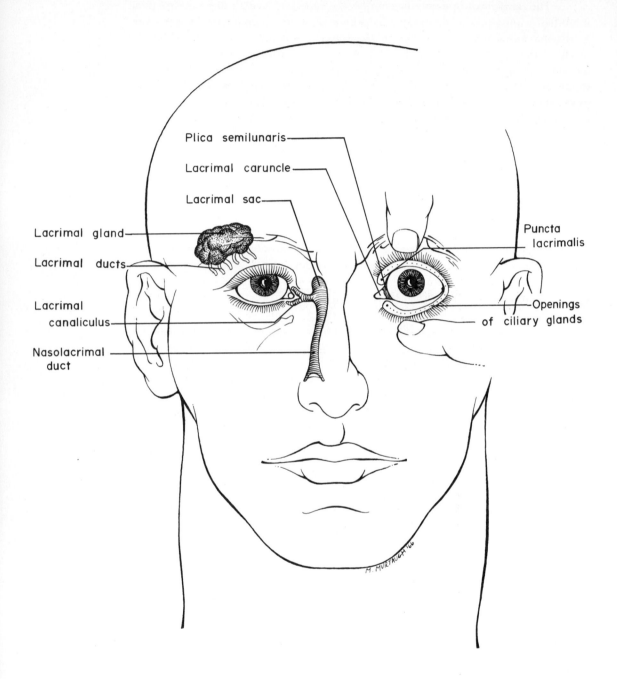

Plica semilunaris

Lacrimal caruncle

Lacrimal sac

Lacrimal gland

Lacrimal ducts

Lacrimal canaliculus

Nasolacrimal duct

Puncta lacrimalis

Openings of ciliary glands

M. MURTAUGH '66

Fig. 72. Lacrimal apparatus.

The lacrimal gland is innervated by parasympathetic fibers originating from the facial nerve passing with the lacrimal branch of the ophthalmic division of the trigeminal nerve. It receives its blood supply via the lacrimal branch of the ophthalmic artery.

Eyeball (Fig. 73)

The **eyeball,** approximately an inch in diameter, is essentially spherical with a slight anterior bulge. Its wall consists of three concentric coats: an outer fibrous, a middle vascular, and an inner nervous tunic. The sclera and cornea compose the outer **fibrous tunic,** with the **sclera** forming a firm fibrous cup covering the posterior five-sixths of the eyeball. Its outer surface is smooth, separated from the bulbar fascia by loose connective tissue, and perforated posteriorly by the optic nerve and the central artery and vein at the lamina cribrosa. At the corneoscleral junction it is continuous with the transparent **cornea,** which bulges slightly over the anterior one-sixth of the eyeball. The cornea is nonvascular and receives its nutrient supply by diffusion from a capillary network at its margin. The cornea is richly supplied with free sensory nerve endings derived from the ciliary nerves.

The **vascular tunic** lies internal to the sclera and consists of the choroid, the ciliary body, and the iris. The **choroid,** a thin, highly vascular membrane, brown in color from pigmented cells covers the posterior two-thirds of the eyeball extending to the ora serrata of the retina. The choroid consists of a dense capillary network of small arteries and veins held together with connective tissue. It is loosely connected to the sclera except at the entrance of the optic nerve, where it is firmly fixed. It is intimately attached to the inner pigmented layer of the retina. The **ciliary body,** consisting of a thickening of the vascular tunic as the ciliary ring, ciliary processes, and ciliary muscle, connects the choroid at the **ora serrata** to the peripheral circumference of the iris. The **ciliary ring** extends from the ora serrata to the **ciliary processes,** while the latter, sixty to eighty small projections, are continuous peripherally with the ciliary ring and give attachment centrally to the **suspensory ligament of the lens.** The nonstriated **ciliary muscle** originates at the posterior margin of the scleral spur and inserts into the ciliary ring and processes. It contracts in accommodation to draw the ciliary processes forward, which relaxes the suspensory ligament permitting the natural elasticity of the lens to result in a bulging of the lens, and so effects focus. The **iris** is a thin, pigmented, contractile diaphragm with a central aperture, the **pupil.** The opening varies in size, either by contracting by the action of the circularly arranged **sphincteric muscle,** which is innervated by parasympathetic fibers from the ciliary ganglion and third cranial nerve, or by dilating through the action of the radially arranged **dilator muscle,** which is innervated by sympathetic fibers from the superior cervical ganglion. The iris, the conspicuous colored portion of the eye, separates the **anterior chamber** (posterior to the cornea and anterior to the iris) from the **posterior chamber** (posterior to the iris and anterior to the suspensory ligament and ciliary processes). Both chambers are continuous with each other through the pupil and are filled with a clear refractile fluid, the **aqueous humor.**

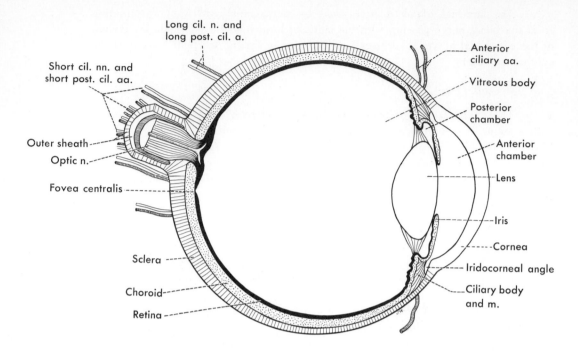

Long cil. n. and
long post. cil. a.

Short cil. nn. and
short post. cil. aa.

Outer sheath

Optic n.

Fovea centralis

Sclera

Choroid

Retina

Anterior
ciliary aa.

Vitreous body

Posterior
chamber

Anterior
chamber

Lens

Iris

Cornea

Iridocorneal angle

Ciliary body
and m.

Fig. 73. Cross section of the eyeball. (From W. H. Hollinshead. Textbook of Anatomy, ed. 2. New York, Hoeber, in press.)

The **nervous tunic** or **retina** is developmentally an evagination of the brain which results in an outer pigmented layer and an inner light-receptor portion. Three regions of the retina are differentiated: the optic, ciliary, and iridial portions. The optic part is light-sensitive and contains a three-neuron pathway. The first neuron constitutes the light-receptor **rods and cones;** the second, **bipolar** cells; and the third, the **ganglion cells,** whose axons form the fibers of the optic nerve. The optic portion occupies the posterior part of the bulb and ends at the ora serrata. It is firmly attached at the ora serrata anteriorly and at the entrance of the optic nerve posteriorly. The **ciliary portion** of the retina begins at the ora serrata and continues anteriorly to line the internal surface of the ciliary body. The **iridial (iris) portion** of the retina covers the posterior aspect of the iris to the pupillary muscle, with both cellular layers being pigmented.

The **macula lutea** is a yellowish oval area at the posterior pole of the eye which presents a slight central depression, the **fovea centralis,** the area of greatest visual acuity. Light rays are focused at the fovea if the eyes are correctly accommodated. The **optic disc,** the site of emergence of the optic nerve, is about three millimeters from the macula lutea toward the nasal side of the eye. Axons of the third-order neuron of the retina converge at this point in an area devoid of light-receptor cells, known as the **blind spot** of the eye. At the center of the optic disc, the central artery of the retina emerges and distributes to the retina.

The refractile **lens,** a transparent biconvex body more flattened anteriorly than posteriorly, is composed of laminated transparent lens fibers. It is enclosed by a transparent **capsule** and held in place by the **suspensory ligament.** Its shape is modified in focusing by the action of the ciliary muscle. Posterior to the lens, the refractile **vitreous humor,** or **body,** occupies the central portion of the eyeball.

MOUTH AND PHARYNX

ORAL CAVITY (FIG. 74)

The **oral cavity** is subdivided for descriptive purposes into the **vestibule** and the **mouth cavity proper.** The former is the cleft separating the lips and cheeks from the teeth and gingivae, or gums. With the mouth closed the vestibule communicates with the mouth cavity through the interval between the last molar teeth and the ramus of the mandible. At the lips the skin of the face is continuous with the mucous membrane of the oral cavity. The bulk of the **lips** is formed by the orbicularis oris muscle and contains a vascular arch arising from labial branches of the facial artery. The **cheeks,** consisting for the most part of the buccinator muscle and the buccal fat pads, are pierced by the parotid duct which opens into the vestibule opposite the upper second molar tooth. The **gingivae** are composed of dense fibrous tissue covered by a smooth vascular mucosa, which is attached to the alveolar margins of the jaws, where it embraces the necks of the teeth as the **periodontal membrane.** Thirty-two **teeth** are normally present in the adult: two incisors, one canine, two premolars, and three molars are found in each half of each jaw.

Posteriorly the mouth cavity communicates with the pharynx through the **fauces.** The **hard** and **soft palates** make up the roof of the mouth, and the floor is formed by the tongue and mucous membrane. Anteriorly the tongue lies more or less free in the mouth, with a median fold of mucous membrane, the **frenulum linguae,** passing from the floor of the mouth to the under surface of the tongue. The transverse **sublingual fold** overlies the sublingual glands and the minute orifices of these glands open along the summit of the fold. The sublingual papillae at the medial ends of the sublingual fold surround the openings of the submandibular ducts.

The tongue, a mobile mass of muscle and mucous membrane, functions in taste, chewing, swallowing, and speech. It is shaped like an upside-down, high-topped shoe, with the sole of the shoe being the dorsum of the tongue and the upper portion of the shoe the root of the tongue. At the back of the tongue a V-shaped groove, the **sulcus terminalis,** is flanked anteriorly by a ridge of large **circumvallate papillae,** which divides the dorsum of the tongue into two parts, an **anterior horizontal (palatine) portion** and a **posterior vertical (pharyngeal) portion** (root). A small pit, the **foramen cecum,** is present at the vertex of this sulcus. **Fungiform** and **filiform papillae** are distributed over the palatine portion of the tongue. With the mouth open only the palatine portion of the tongue is visible; the less apparent vertical pharyngeal portion forms the anterior wall of the oropharynx and is related inferiorly to the epiglottis. On the ventral surface of

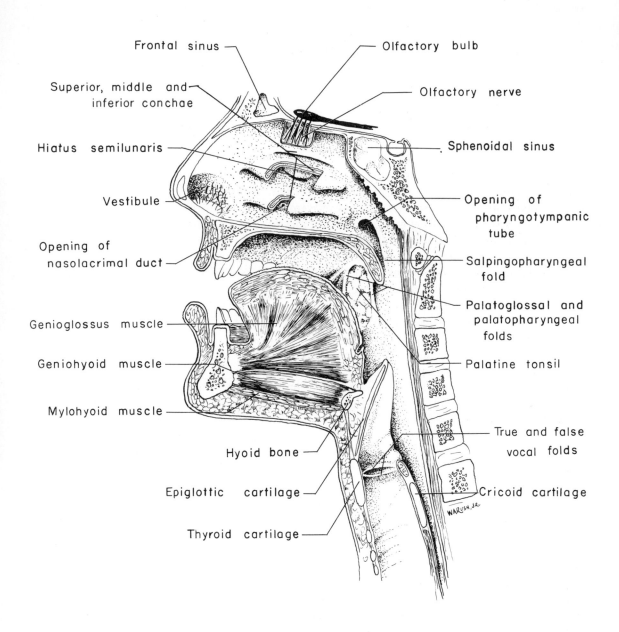

Frontal sinus

Superior, middle and inferior conchae

Hiatus semilunaris

Vestibule

Opening of nasolacrimal duct

Genioglossus muscle

Geniohyoid muscle

Mylohyoid muscle

Hyoid bone

Epiglottic cartilage

Thyroid cartilage

Olfactory bulb

Olfactory nerve

Sphenoidal sinus

Opening of pharyngotympanic tube

Salpingopharyngeal fold

Palatoglossal and palatopharyngeal folds

Palatine tonsil

True and false vocal folds

Cricoid cartilage

WARUSH, JR

Fig. 74. Hemisection of the oral cavity and pharynx.

the tongue, the midline **frenulum linguae,** flanked by the **deep lingual veins,** attaches the tongue to the floor of the mouth. A delicate fringed ridge of mucous membrane, the **fimbriated fold,** is present on the lateral aspect of the ventral surface of the tongue. Numerous lymph follicles constituting the **lingual tonsil** are present on the pharyngeal portion of the tongue. As the mucous membrane reflects onto the epiglottis, it forms **median** and **lateral glossoepiglottic folds.**

Muscles of the Tongue (Table XXVII)

The muscles of the tongue consist of four pairs of intrinsic and three pairs of extrinsic muscles, with the muscles of either side separated by a midline fibrous septum. The **superior longitudinal muscle** extends from the tip to the root of the tongue, and the **inferior longitudinal muscle** is present in the interval between the extrinsic genioglossus and the hyoglossus muscles. The **transversus linguae** extends from the septum to the sides of the tongue, while the **verticalis linguae** originates from the dorsum of the tongue and sweeps inferiorly and laterally to interdigitate with the other tongue musculature.

Extrinsic muscles include the fan-shaped **genioglossus,** radiating from the genial tubercle of the mandible into the tongue, with its lowermost fibers inserting into the hyoid bone. The quadrilateral **hyoglossus,** under cover of the mylohyoideus, passes from the body and greater horn of the hyoid to the sides of the tongue. The slip-like **styloglossus** sweeps forward from the tip of the styloid

TABLE XXVII. MUSCLES OF THE TONGUE

Muscle	Origin	Insertion	Action	Nerve
Genioglossus	Genial tubercle of mandible	Ventral surface of tongue and body of hyoid bone	Aids in protrusion, retraction, and depression of tongue	Hypoglossal
Hyoglossus	Body and greater cornu of hyoid bone	Sides of tongue	Depresses and draws tongue laterally	Hypoglossal
Styloglossus	Styloid process	Sides of tongue	Aids in retraction and elevation of tongue	Hypoglossal
Palatoglossus	Soft palate	Dorsum and sides of tongue	Elevates tongue and narrows fauces	Pharyngeal plexus
Longitudinalis linguae (superior and inferior); Transversus and verticalis linguae	Form intrinsic musculature of tongue; named according to their relationship		Alter shape of tongue	Hypoglossal

process and stylomandibular ligament to blend with and insert into the hyoglossus and palatoglossus with some of its fibers extending along the side of the tongue as far as the tip. The **palatoglossus** originates from the palate, passes to the side of the tongue, and forms the anterior pillar of the palatine fossa. All the muscles are innervated by the hypoglossal nerve; the intrinsic muscles act to alter the shape of the tongue, and the extrinsic group function to change the position and to a limited extent the shape of the tongue. The anterior two-thirds of the tongue is supplied with special (taste) sensation by the chordi tympani branch of the facial nerve and with general sensation by the lingual branch of the mandibular division of the trigeminal nerve. The glossopharyngeal nerve supplies both general and special sensation to the posterior one-third of the tongue.

The **roof of the mouth,** formed by the hard and soft palates, is a vaulted dome. The **hard palate** is composed of the palatine processes of the maxillary bones anteriorly and the anterior part of the palatine bones posteriorly; the **soft palate** consists of muscles, glands, and the palatine aponeurosis. The soft palate is attached anteriorly to the posterior margin of the hard palate and laterally to the wall of the pharynx. Posteriorly it forms, in the midpoint of its free margin, the conical **uvula** directed inferiorly into the fauces. During deglutition the soft palate helps to close the nasopharynx.

Muscles of the Palate (Table XXVIII)

Five pairs of muscles are associated with the soft palate. The **palatoglossus** and **palatopharyngeus** originate from the palatine aponeurosis and the posterior part of the hard palate and are contained within the palatoglossal and palatopharyngeal folds, respectively. The palatoglossus inserts into the dorsum and side of the tongue, while the palatopharyngeus splits to pass to either side of the levator veli palatini and musculus uvulae, reunites, and then blends with the salpingopharyngeus before inserting into the thyroid cartilage and pharynx. Both **musculi uvulae** arise from the posterior nasal spine and unite as they pass backward to insert into the mucous membrane of the uvula. The rounded **levator veli palatini** originates from the temporal bone adjacent to the opening of the carotid canal to pass obliquely downward and insert into the palatine aponeurosis, interdigitating with fibers of the muscle from the opposite side. The flat, triangular **tensor veli palatini muscle** arises from the scaphoid fossa, spine of the sphenoid, and cartilaginous portion of the auditory tube. It tapers to form a rounded tendon which hooks around the pterygoid hamulus, turns medially, and then spreads out to insert into the palatine aponeurosis and posterior border of the hard palate.

The region of communication between the oral cavity and the pharynx, the **fauces,** is bounded superiorly by the soft palate, inferiorly by the dorsum of the tongue, and laterally on each side by the palatoglossal and palatopharyngeal arches, which enclose the two palatine tonsils.

PHARYNX

The **pharynx** is a wide muscular tube, about five inches long, and lined with mucous membrane. It extends from the base of the cranium to the level of the sixth cervical vertebra, where it becomes the esophagus. The attachments of

TABLE XXVIII. MUSCLES OF THE PALATE

Muscle	Origin	Insertion	Action	Nerve
Tensor veli palatini	Scaphoid fossa, spine of sphenoid, and cartilaginous portion of pharyngotympanic tube	Tendon passes around hamulus of pterygoid to insert into palate	Tenses soft palate	Mandibular division of trigeminal
Levator veli palatini	Petrous portion of temporal bone and cartilaginous portion of pharyngotympanic tube	Midline of soft palate	Elevates palate	Pharyngeal plexus
Palatoglossus	Soft palate	Dorsum and sides of tongue	Narrows fauces and elevates tongue	Pharyngeal plexus
Palatopharyngeus	Soft palate	Posterior border of thyroid cartilage and musculature of pharynx	Elevates pharynx and helps to close nasopharynx	Pharyngeal plexus
Uvulus	Palatine aponeurosis	Mucous membrane of uvula	Elevates uvula	Pharyngeal plexus

the pharynx, from superior to inferior, are the pharyngeal tubercle at the base of the skull, the medial pterygoid lamina, the pterygomandibular raphe, the inner aspect of the ramus of the mandible, the hyoid bone, and the thyroid and cricoid cartilages. The wall of the pharynx consists of the three overlapping constrictor muscles (superior, middle, and inferior), the stylopharyngeus and palatopharyngeus muscles, various fascial layers, and mucous membrane.

It is subdivided into the nasal, oral, and laryngeal portions. Anteriorly the wall is interrupted by, and related to, structures associated with openings into these portions. The **nasal pharynx** is situated above the level of the soft palate, posterior to the nasal cavity, and is related superiorly to the sphenoid and basilar portions of the occipital bone. It is the widest part of the pharynx and normally remains patent for the passage of air. Anteriorly it is bounded by the **choanae** (internal nares), which open into the nasal cavity, and laterally it receives the opening of the **auditory** or **pharyngotympanic tube,** around which the mucous membrane is raised as the **torus tubarius.** A mucous membrane covering the salpingopharyngeal muscle, the **salpingopharyngeal fold,** descends vertically from the torus tubarius. The roof and the posterior wall of the nasopharynx form a continuous curve, with no sharp demarcation, and contain an aggregate of lymphoid tissue between the roof and pharyngeal recesses, the **pharyngeal tonsils,** when enlarged these are called the adenoids. The pharyngeal isthmus, located between the nasal and oral parts of the pharynx, is bounded laterally by the palatopharyngeal arch and the mucous membrane covering the palatopharyngeal muscle. It is closed during swallowing by the elevation of the soft palate and contraction of the superior constrictor muscle of the pharynx.

The **oropharynx,** whose posterior wall has no characteristic features, is located posterior to the oral cavity. The lower portion of the anterior wall is formed by the root of the tongue and by the epiglottic cartilage. Three mucous membrane folds, a median glossoepiglottic fold between the tongue and the epiglottic cartilage and the two pharyngoepiglottic folds between the epiglottis and the junction of the tongue and pharynx, bound depressions, the **epiglottic vallecu-lae.** The lateral wall houses a mass of lymphoid tissue, the **palatine** or **(true) tonsil,** located between the **palatine arches** formed anteriorly by the palatoglossus muscle and posteriorly by the palatopharyngeus muscle. The lingual tonsil is a diffuse collection of lymphoid tissue at the root of the tongue.

The **laryngopharynx** lies behind the larynx, extending from the inlet of the larynx to the cricoid cartilage, where it becomes the esophagus. The posterior and lateral walls of the laryngopharynx have no characteristic features. Superiorly, the anterior wall presents the **inlet** of the larynx with the epiglottis anteriorly, the aryepiglottic folds laterally, and the **piriform recesses** to either side of the folds. These recesses lie between the aryepiglottic membrane medially and the thyroid cartilage and thyrohyoid membrane laterally. Inferiorly, the muscles and mucous membrane on the posterior aspect of the arytenoid and cricoid cartilages form the anterior wall of the laryngopharynx.

Muscles of the Pharynx (Table XXIX, Fig. 75)

The wall of the pharynx is formed, in large part, by the three paired superior, middle, and inferior constrictor muscles, which overlap or telescope into one another. All the constrictors insert posteriorly into the median raphe, with the **inferior constrictor** originating from the oblique line of the thyroid and arch of the cricoid cartilages; the **middle constrictor** from the greater cornu of the thyroid cartilage and the stylohyoid ligament; and the **superior constrictor** from the medial pterygoid plate and hamulus, the pterygomandibular raphe, the mylohyoid line of the mandible, and the pharyngeal tubercle. Fibers from the inferior constrictor ascend obliquely toward the median raphe to overlap the middle constrictor; fibers from the middle fan out to descend internal to the inferior, and ascend to overlap the superior constrictor; and fibers of the superior constrictor form a gap inferiorly through which the stylopharyngeus muscle passes, and are deficient superiorly at the pharyngeal recess.

The thin conical **stylopharyngeus** passes from the tip of the styloid process anteroinferiorly to interdigitate and insert between the superior and middle constrictors. The **salpingopharyngeus** descends vertically from the auditory tube to insert with the **palatoglossus,** which passes from the palatine aponeurosis into the wall of the pharynx internal to the constrictors. All the muscles are innervated by the vagus and glossopharyngeal nerves through the pharyngeal plexus, except the stylopharyngeus, which is supplied solely by the glossopharyngeal nerve.

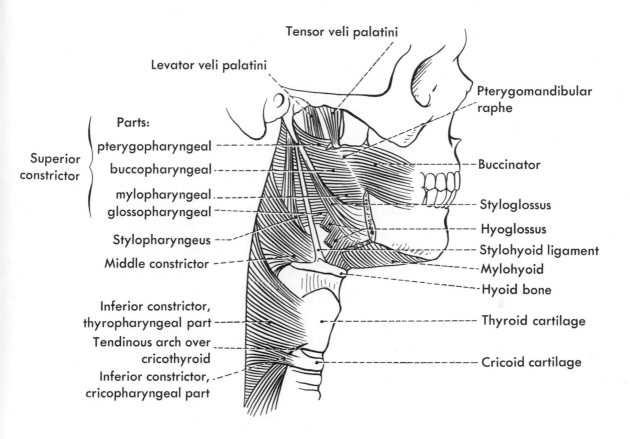

Fig. 75. Musculature of the pharynx. (From W. H. Hollinshead. Textbook of Anatomy, ed. 2. New York, Hoeber, in press.)

NASAL CAVITY (FIGS. 74 AND 76)

Situated above the hard palate and divided by the nasal septum, the **nasal cavity** opens anteriorly at the external nares (nostrils) and posteriorly into the nasopharynx by the internal nares (choanae). The **external nares** are kept patent by the presence of the U-shaped greater alar cartilages. The oblong **internal nares** are rigid, being bounded by bone.

The horizontal **floor** of the nasal cavity is formed by the superior surface of the hard palate, the palatine process of the maxilla, and the horizontal plate of the palatine bone. It is approximately three inches long and a half inch wide. The long, very narrow **roof** is formed anteriorly by the upper nasal cartilage and nasal bones, and posteriorly by the cribriform plate of the ethmoid, which is pierced by twelve to twenty filaments of the olfactory nerve. The osseous portion of the **medial wall** of the nasal cavity, or nasal septum, is formed by the thin vertical (perpendicular) plate of the ethmoid superiorly and the vomer inferiorly, with septal cartilages present anteriorly and between the bones noted above.

TABLE XXIX. MUSCLES OF THE PHARYNX

Muscle	Origin	Insertion	Action	Nerve
Inferior constrictor	Side of cricoid and oblique line of thyroid cartilages	Median raphe of pharynx	Constricts pharynx in swallowing	Pharyngeal plexus
Middle constrictor	Greater and lesser cornua of hyoid and stylohyoid ligament	Median raphe	Constricts pharynx in swallowing	Pharyngeal plexus
Superior constrictor	Continuous line from medial pterygoid plate, pterygoid hamulus, pterygomandibular ligament, and side of tongue	Median raphe; superiormost fibers reach pharyngeal tubercle of skull	Constricts pharynx in swallowing	Pharyngeal plexus
Stylopharyngeus	Styloid process	Superior and posterior borders of thyroid cartilage and musculature of pharynx	Raises pharynx	Pharyngeal plexus
Palato-pharyngeus	Soft palate	Posterior border of thyroid cartilage and musculature of pharynx	Elevates pharynx and helps to close nasopharynx	Pharyngeal plexus
Salpingo-pharyngeus	Cartilaginous portion of pharyngotympanic tube	Musculature of pharynx	In swallowing, opens pharyngotympanic tube	Pharyngeal plexus

The **lateral wall** of the nasal cavity presents bony projections, the **conchae,** which shelter a number of openings. The conchae (turbinate bones) are three curled bony plates projecting from the lateral wall into the nasal cavity and covered by thick mucous membrane. The **superior concha,** a process of the ethmoid, is very short; the **middle concha,** also a process of the ethmoid, is larger; the **inferior concha,** longer than the middle, is an individual bone located midway between the middle concha and the floor of the nasal cavity. The **meatuses** are passageways lying deep to, or under cover of, their respective conchae. The area above the superior concha, into which the sphenoidal air sinuses open, is designated the **sphenethmoidal recess.** The short, narrow **superior meatus** between the superior and middle conchae receives drainage from the posterior and middle ethmoidal air sinuses. Between the middle and inferior conchae, the rather extensive **middle meatus** receives the **infundibulum,** an anterosuperior funnel-shaped opening of the frontal air sinus. Located posterior to the infundibulum a deep, curved groove, the **hiatus semilunaris,** drains the anterior and middle ethmoidal and the maxillary air sinuses. The **bulla ethmoidalis** is a prominent bulging of the ethmoidal air sinuses forming the upper margin of the hiatus semilunaris. The **inferior meatus** is the horizontal passage deep to the inferior concha into which the **nasoacrimal duct** opens.

Mucoperiosteum, consisting of mucous membrane closely adherent to periosteum, lines the nasal cavity except for the area of the vestibule, which is lined with skin, and the roof, the superior concha, and adjacent septum, which are lined with olfactory epithelium. The mucoperiosteum is continuous through the nasolacrimal duct with the conjunctiva, through various apertures with the mucous membrane lining the several air sinuses, and through the choanae with the mucous membrane of the pharynx. It is thick and spongy due to the presence of rich sinusoidal venous plexuses and numerous mucous cells. It functions to moisten and warm the incoming air.

Arteries and Nerves

All the vessels to the nasal cavity form a rich irregular anastomosis deep to the mucous membrane, with the **sphenopalatine artery,** a branch of the internal maxillary, as the principal supply. Branches of the sphenopalatine artery

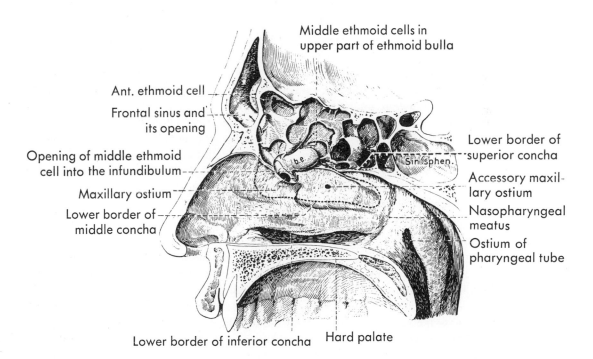

Fig. 76. Lateral wall of the nasal cavity. (From W. H. Hollinshead. Textbook of Anatomy, ed. 2. New York, Hoeber, in press.)

include the **posterior lateral nasal branch,** supplying the conchae and the ethmoidal, frontal, and maxillary air sinuses; a **posterior septal branch** to the upper part of the septum; and the **nasopalatine artery,** which continues anteriorly on the septum to pass through the incisive foramen and anastomose with the greater palatine artery supplying the hard palate. The ophthalmic artery gives **anterior** and **posterior ethmoidal branches,** which supply the anterior portion of the superior and middle conchae and adjacent septal areas and give twigs to supply the frontal and ethmoidal air sinuses.

Nerves to the nasal cavity include the olfactory nerve, nerves of general sensation from branches of both the ophthalmic and the maxillary divisions of the trigeminal nerve, and the autonomic nerves from the pterygopalatine ganglion.

The cells of origin of the **olfactory nerve** are limited to the small area of **olfactory epithelium** lining the roof and adjacent surfaces of the septum and superior nasal concha. Central processes of these bipolar neurons pass through the **cribriform plate** to synapse in the **olfactory bulb,** which gives rise to the **olfactory tract** leading to the brain. Anterior and posterior ethmoidal nerves are branches of the nasociliary nerve from the ophthalmic division of the trigeminal. The **posterior ethmoidal nerve** passes through the posterior ethmoidal foramen to the posterior ethmoidal and sphenoidal air sinuses, while the **anterior ethmoidal nerve** passes through the anterior ethmoidal foramen to re-enter the anterior cranial fossa. It then crosses the cribriform plate and enters the nasal cavity via the nasal slit (fissure) at the side of the crista galli. In the nasal cavity this nerve divides into an **external nasal branch,** which passes down the nasal bone to supply the skin of the lower part of the nose, and an **internal nasal branch,** which sends a medial branch to the superoanterior part of the nasal septum and a lateral branch to the anterior portion of the superior and middle conchae. From the maxillary division of the trigeminal nerve, **sensory twigs** pass to the **sphenopalatine ganglion** and distribute with its branches. These include the **lateral posterior superior nasal branch** to the posterior part of the superior and middle conchae; the **nasopalatine branch,** which crosses the roof of the nasal cavity to supply the septum and then follows the nasopalatine artery through the incisive foramen to supply the anterior portion of the hard palate; and the **greater palatine nerve,** which passes through the palatine canal to give branches to the inferior concha and terminate in the mucous membrane of the hard and soft palates.

Paranasal Air Sinuses (Fig. 77)

The bilateral **paranasal air sinuses** are located in bones adjacent to the nasal cavity. The **sphenoidal air cavities,** occupying the body of the sphenoid, are rarely symmetrical, and their ostia usually open into the middle or superior part of the sphenoethmoidal recesses. The large **maxillary sinuses** are four-sided, hollow pyramids between the lateral nasal walls and the infratemperal fossae. The slit-like ostium of each sinus opens into the posterior part of the hiatus semilunaris. The sockets of the upper molar or premolar teeth may project into these sinuses. The numerous **ethmoidal air cells** are usually limited to the lamina papyracea and the orbital portion of the ethmoid bone. The posterior air cells drain into the

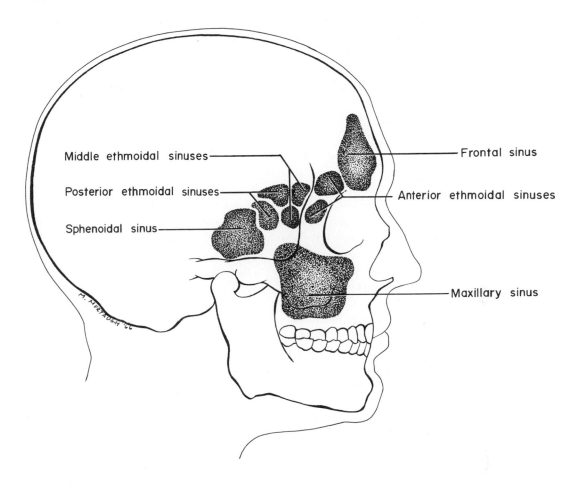

Middle ethmoidal sinuses

Posterior ethmoidal sinuses

Sphenoidal sinus

Frontal sinus

Anterior ethmoidal sinuses

Maxillary sinus

Fig. 77. Paranasal air sinuses.

superior meatus, and the middle and the anterior into the hiatus semilunaris. **Frontal sinuses,** forming the brow ridges, are developmentally anterior ethmoidal air cells that migrate or extend into the frontal bone. Each drains inferiorly into each middle meatus by way of the infundibulum.

PTERYGOPALATINE FOSSA (FIG. 78)

The **pterygopalatine fossa** is an elongated triangular area between the posterior aspect of the maxillary bone and the pterygoid processes of the sphenoid bone. The **medial wall** opens into the nasal cavity via the sphenopalatine foramen; the **roof** is formed by the great wing of the sphenoid; the **lateral wall** is relatively open as the pterygomaxillary fissure. Openings into the pterygopalatine fossa include the **sphenopalatine foramen** at the junction of the roof and the medial wall, for the passage of vessels and nerves to the nasal cavity; the **greater** and

lesser palatine canals inferiorly, for the passage of the greater and lesser palatine nerves and arteries; and posteriorly the **foramen rotundum,** for the maxillary division of the trigeminal nerve, and the **pterygoid** canal, for the passage of its nerve and artery. The fossa communicates with the orbital cavity via the **inferior orbital fissure** and with the infratemporal fossa by way of the **pterygomaxillary fissure.**

Arteries and Nerves

Contents of the pterygopalatine fossa include the third portion of the **internal maxillary artery** and its companion **veins,** the **maxillary division of the trigeminal nerve,** and the **pterygopalatine ganglion.** The pterygopalatine, or third portion of the internal maxillary, artery lies in the fossa lateral to the sphenopalatine ganglion and gives branches to the nasal and orbital cavities, the palate, the upper teeth, and the face. As the artery enters the fossa, its **posterior superior alveolar branch** descends on the maxillary tuberosity to enter the superior alveolar canal and supply the gingivae and upper molar and premolar teeth. The **greater palatine artery** passes through the pterygopalatine canal to emerge at the greater palatine foramen. It passes forward on the hard palate supplying glands and mucous membrane of the palate and gingivae, and anastomosing with the long sphenopalatine branch through the incisive foramen. Within the pterygopalatine canal the greater palatine artery gives rise to the **lesser palatine branch,** which emerges at the lesser palatine foramen to supply the soft palate and palatine tonsil. The **artery to the pterygoid canal** passes posteriorly to supply twigs to the pharynx, pharyngotympanic tube, and tympanic cavity. **Pharyngeal branches** of the internal maxillary are distributed to the upper pharynx and auditory tube by way of the pharyngeal canal. The major supply of the nasal cavity, the **sphenopalatine artery,** passes through the sphenopalatine foramen to give posterior lateral nasal branches to the conchae, meatuses, and sinuses. It then descends on the nasal septum, where it anastomoses with the greater palatine and the superior labial arteries as it passes through the incisive foramen. The terminal direct continuation of the internal maxillary, the **infra-orbital artery,** enters the orbital cavity through the infraorbital fissure to traverse the infraorbital groove and canal and emerges on the face at the infraorbital foramen. In the canal it gives branches to the inferior oblique and inferior rectus muscles, the lacrimal sac, mucous membranes of the maxillary air sinuses, and the **anterior superior alveolar branch** to the incisor and canine teeth. Its terminal branches on the face ramify and anastomose with branches of the external maxillary artery.

From the midportion of the trigeminal ganglion, the maxillary division of the trigeminal nerve passes through the foramen rotundum, traverses the pterygopalatine fossa, enters the orbit by way of the infraorbital fissure, and passes in the infraorbital groove and canal to emerge on the face at the infraorbital foramen. Its branches are entirely sensory and supply the skin and the mucous membrane of all structures in the region of the face between the lower eyelid and upper lip.

Within the cranial cavity the **maxillary division** of the fifth cranial nerve gives branches which follow the middle meningeal artery to supply the meninges.

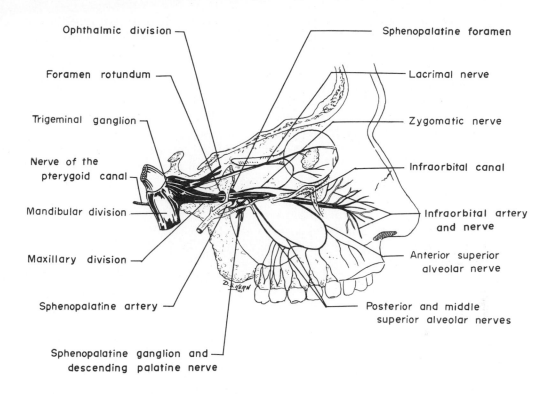

Ophthalmic division

Foramen rotundum

Trigeminal ganglion

Nerve of the
pterygoid canal

Mandibular division

Maxillary division

Sphenopalatine artery

Sphenopalatine ganglion and
descending palatine nerve

Sphenopalatine foramen

Lacrimal nerve

Zygomatic nerve

Infraorbital canal

Infraorbital artery
and nerve

Anterior superior
alveolar nerve

Posterior and middle
superior alveolar nerves

Fig. 78. Pterygopalatine fossa.

The zygomatic, sphenopalatine, and posterior superior alveolar branches arise
from the pterygopalatine portion of this nerve. The **zygomatic branch** enters
the orbital cavity through the infraorbital fissure and sends a **temporal branch**
through the lateral wall of the orbit to the temporal fossa, a **communicating
branch** to the lacrimal nerve which carries postganglionic parasympathetic fibers
from the sphenopalatine ganglion to the lacrimal gland, and a **facial branch**
passing through the inferolateral angle of the orbit to supply the skin over the
prominence of the cheek. The **sphenopalatine nerve** sends two short sensory
roots to the sphenopalatine ganglion to be distributed with branches from the
ganglion as an orbital branch to the periosteum of the orbit and the posterior
ethmoidal sinuses; a **greater palatine branch** which passes through the pterygopalatine canal and out the greater palatine foramen to supply the hard and soft
palates, the middle and inferior meatuses, and the inferior concha; a **lesser palatine branch** which follows the same course as the greater palatine but emerges
through the lesser palatine foramen to supply the soft palate, uvula, and palatine
tonsil. Additional branches of the sphenopalatine nerve include the **posterior
superior nasal branch,** which traverses the sphenopalatine foramen and distributes to the superior and middle conchae and posterior ethmoidal sinus; direct
branches to the superior and middle conchae, posterior ethmoidal sinus, and posterior part of the septum; a **pharyngeal branch** passing through the pharyngeal

canal to the nasopharynx; and the **long sphenopalatine (nasopalatine) branch,** which supplies the roof of the nasal cavity and the nasal septum. This latter nerve courses downward on the septum to pass through the incisive canal and communicate with the greater palatine branch. The **posterior superior alveolar nerve** enters the orbital fissure to pass in the posterior alveolar canals to supply upper molar teeth, gums, and mucous membrane of the cheek.

Within the infraorbital canal, the maxillary nerve gives off a **middle superior alveolar branch** which supplies the maxillary sinus and the premolar teeth, an **anterior superior alveolar branch** to the maxillary sinus and the canine and incisor teeth, and a **nasal branch** which innervates the anterior part of the inferior meatus and floor of the nasal cavity.

The terminal (facial) portion of the maxillary nerve emerges at the infra-orbital foramen as the **infraorbital nerve** and divides into the **inferior palpebral branch** to the lower lid, the **external nasal branch** to the skin at the side of the nose, and the **superior labial branch** to the skin, mucous membrane, and glands of the upper lip.

EAR (FIG. 79)

External Ear

For descriptive purposes the ear is divided into external, middle, and internal portions. The **external ear** comprises the auricula (pinna) and the external auditory meatus. The **auricula** collects sound waves and directs them into the external auditory canal, where they strike the tympanic membrane. Parts of the auricula include the **concha,** the well of the ear leading into the external auditory canal; the **helix,** the outer rim of the external ear beginning at the concha and ending at the **lobule;** the **antihelix,** rimming the concha opposite the helix; the **tragus,** the small lip overlapping the concha; the **fossa triangularis,** the tri-

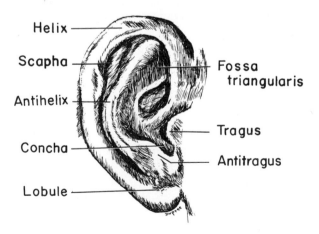

Fig. 79. External ear.

angular depression above the concha; and the **scapha,** which forms a depressed groove in front of the helix.

The lateral third of the **external acoustic canal** is cartilaginous, and the remainder is formed by the tympanic part of the temporal bone. The **tympanic membrane** slopes obliquely inferomedially with the lateral surface slightly concave; the maximal point of the concavity is designated as the **umbo.** The handle of the malleus can be seen through the membrane extending inferiorly to the umbo. A flaccid, less tense portion of the tympanic membrane, the **pars flaccida,** lies above the lateral process of the malleus. The whole of the peripheral margin, except for the flaccid part, is lodged in the **tympanic groove.**

Middle Ear (Fig. 80)

The **middle ear,** or **tympanic cavity,** is filled with air and communicates anteromedially with the pharynx via the **auditory (pharyngotympanic) tube** and posterosuperiorly with the tympanic antrum and mastoid air cells through the aditus. The tympanic cavity contains the auditory ossicles, the stapedius and tensor tympani muscles, the tympanic plexus of nerves, and the chorda tympani nerve. The tympanic cavity has a roof, a floor, and four walls. The **roof** of the cavity,

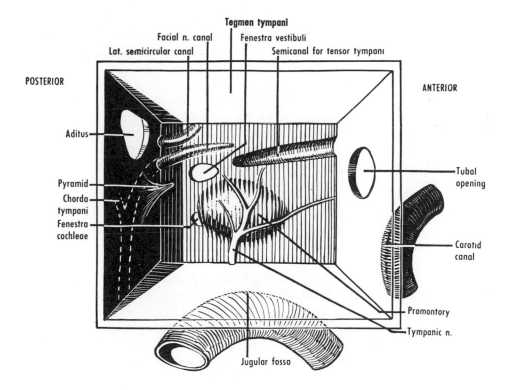

Fig. 80. Middle ear cavity. (From E. Gardner, D. J. Gray, and R. O'Rahilly. Anatomy. Philadelphia, Saunders, 1963.)

the **tegmen tympani,** is a thin plate of bone separating it from the middle cranial fossa. The **floor** of the cavity, or **jugulum,** is a thin plate of bone separating the cavity from the jugular fossa and the bulb of the jugular vein. The **posterior (mastoid) wall** contains an opening, the **aditus,** from the **epitympanic recess** into the **tympanic antrum.** In the lower part of the posterior wall a small conical projection, the **pyramid,** lodges the **stapedius muscle,** and lateral to the pyramid an opening admits the chorda tympani nerve. Owing to the convergence of the medial and lateral walls, the **anterior (carotid) wall** is narrow, and an opening in the upper portion leads to the canal which houses the tensor tympani muscle. An opening in the midportion leads into the pharyngotympanic tube. A septum, between the canal for the tensor tympani and the pharyngotympanic tube, is prolonged posteriorly on the medial wall as the **processus cochleariformis,** which affords a pulley around which the tensor tympani tendon turns laterally to its insertion. In the lower portion of the anterior wall a thin lamina of bone separates the cavity from the carotid canal. The **medial (labyrinthine) wall** forms the boundary between the middle and internal parts of the ear, where anteriorly the rounded **promontory** is formed by the underlying basal turn of the cochlea. Above the posterior part of the promontory is a depression in which the **fenestra vestibuli (oval window)** is closed by the foot plate of the stapes. Above the oval window, an anteroposterior ridge demarcates the postion of the canal containing the facial nerve. Immediately above the ridge of the facial canal, a horizontal projection indicates the site of the horizontal semicircular canal. Below and behind the promontory is a fossa which contains the **fenestra cochleae (round window),** which is closed by the **secondary tympanic membrane** and opens into the scala tympani.

The auditory ossicles, the malleus (hammer), incus (anvil), and stapes (stirrup), extend in a chain from the lateral to the medial wall of the middle ear cavity. The **malleus** is described as having a handle, a neck, and anterior and lateral processes. The **handle,** or **manubrium,** of the malleus is attached along its length to the tympanic membrane, extends to the umbo, and receives into its medial surface the insertion of the tendon of the tensor tympani muscle. Just above this insertion the chorda tympani nerve passes between the manubrium and the tympanic membrane. The **head** of the malleus articulates with the body of the incus. The **incus** consists of a body and short (horizontal) and long (vertical) crura. The **lenticular process** is a small knob on the end of the long crus which articulates with the stapes. The **short crus** is attached via the ligament of the incus to the posterior aspect of the epitympanic recess, and the **body** receives the articulating head of the malleus. The **stapes** presents a head, a neck, a foot plate, and anterior and posterior limbs. The incus articulates at the concave socket on the head of the stapes, and the **foot plate** is attached by the **annular ligament** to the margin of the fenestra vestibuli. The stapedius muscle inserts into the posterior surface of the **neck** of the stapes.

The **tympanic antrum,** located immediately behind the epitympanic recess, communicates through the **aditus** with the mastoid air cells. The **tegmen tympani** separates the recess noted above and the tympanic cavity from the middle cranial fossa. The lateral wall of the recess is formed by the squamosal portion of the temporal bone, immediately above and behind the external auditory meatus.

Internal Ear

The **internal ear** is located within the petrous portion of the temporal bone and consists of the osseous labyrinth which contains the membranous labyrinth. The **osseous labyrinth** is composed of bony cavities: the vestibule, three semicircular canals, and the cochlea, all filled with perilymph in which the membranous labyrinth is suspended. The **vestibule** is centrally located, and the superior, posterior, and lateral semicircular canals open into it posteriorly by way of five openings, with the adjoining ends of the superior and posterior canals forming a common terminal canal. Laterally the **fenestra vestibuli** is closed by the foot plate of the stapes, while the medial wall of the vestibule presents depressions with small openings for the emergence of filaments of the eighth cranial nerve.

The **semicircular canals** are each approximately 0.8 millimeter in diameter, and each presents a dilatation, the ampulla, at one end. The vertical **superior canal** is at right angles to the similarly vertical **posterior canal,** which parallels the posterior surface of the petrous portion of the temporal bone. The horizontal **lateral canal** is in the angle between the superior and posterior canals and bulges into the medial wall of the tympanic cavity.

Located anterior to the vestibule, the bony **cochlea** resembles a snail's shell. It is a tapering tube which spirals about two and one-half turns around a central core, the **modiolus.** The osseous tube opens into the tympanic cavity via the **fenestra cochlea** (round window) and is closed in the fresh state by the secondary tympanic membrane. The basal, or first, turn around the modiolus bulges as the promontory on the medial wall of the tympanic cavity. The modiolus is thick at the base and tapers rapidly to the apex, with a thin narrow shelf of bone, the **spiral lamina,** turning around the modiolus like the threads of a screw.

Two membranous sacs, the utricle and the saccule, the three semicircular ducts, and the cochlear duct compose the **membranous labyrinth,** which lies within the bony labyrinth, but does not completely fill it. The membranous labyrinth contains the endolymph, while the perilymph occupies the space between the membranous and osseous labyrinths. Lying in the posterosuperior part of the vestibule, the **utricle** receives the openings of the semicircular ducts. The smaller **saccule** lies in the anteroinferior part of the vestibule. A short canal, the **ductus reuniens,** extends from the lower part of the saccule to the cochlear duct. The blind **endolymphatic duct** leaves the posterior part of the saccule, is joined by the short **utriculosaccular duct** from the utricle, then traverses the aqueduct of the vestibule. It ends under the dura mater on the posterior surface of the petrous portion of the temporal bone as a dilatation, the **endolymphatic sac.** The **semicircular ducts** and their terminal **ampullae** are attached to the convex sides of the semicircular canals and open into the utricle.

Within the bony canal of the cochlea the **membranous labyrinth** consists of a closed spiral tube, the **cochlear duct,** which is separated from the internally located **scala vestibuli** by the **vestibular membrane,** and from the externally placed **scala tympani** by the **basilar membrane.** The basilar membrane supports the **spiral organ (of Corti),** which contains the peripheral nerve endings associated with sound reception. The scalae vestibuli and tympani are continuous with each other at the apex of the cochlea via a tiny opening, the **helicotrema.**

LARYNX

The **larynx** is specially modified for vocalization. Situated anteriorly in the neck below the hyoid bone and the tongue, part of it forms a marked anterior projection, the laryngeal prominence (Adam's apple). It is related anteriorly to skin and fascia and laterally to the thin strap muscles of the neck, the thyroid gland, the great vessels of the neck, and the vagus nerves. Posteriorly it is separated from the vertebral column and prevertebral muscles by the laryngopharynx.

The **skeleton of the larynx** is formed by three single cartilages, the thyroid, cricoid, and epiglottic; and three paired cartilages, the arytenoids, corniculates, and cuneiforms. The thin, leaf-shaped, **epiglottic cartilage** forms the anterior boundary of the inlet (aditus) as well as the vestibule of the larynx. The superior end of the cartilage is broad and free, with the lateral margins enclosed in the aryepiglottic folds; the lower end is pointed and connected to the thyroid cartilage by the thyroepiglottic ligament. The large **thyroid cartilage** has two broad quadrilateral **laminae,** which are fused anteriorly, open posteriorly, and separated anterosuperiorly by the V-shaped **thyroid notch.** The junction of the notch and the fused lamina forms the **laryngeal prominence.** The posterior border of the thyroid cartilage is thick and rounded and is prolonged upward and downward as the **superior** and **inferior cornua.** The superior border gives attachment to the **thyrohyoid membrane,** which is pierced by the internal laryngeal nerve and the superior laryngeal vessels. The thyrohyoid membrane, between the greater horn and the hyoid bone, is free posteriorly and encloses the small cartilago triticea. The relatively flat lateral surface of the thyroid cartilage gives attachment to the sternothyroideus, thyrohyoideus, and inferior pharyngeal constrictor muscles. The medial (internal) surface is smooth and gives attachment to the thyroepiglottic, vestibular, and vocal ligaments, and to the thyroarytenoideus and vocalis muscles. The short, thick inferior horn articulates with the cricoid cartilage.

The signet-ring-shaped **cricoid cartilage** presents posteriorly a broad, quadrilateral **lamina** with two convex facets on the upper border that articulate with the base of the arytenoid cartilages. The anterior arch gives attachment to the cricothyroidei muscles and the cricovocal ligament. The superior border of the cricovocal ligament attaches to the vocal process of the arytenoid cartilage and presents a free edge which attaches to the vocal ligament.

The **arytenoid cartilages** are three-sided pyramidal structures with their bases articulating on the upper border of the cricoid lamina and their apices curving posteromedially. The posterolateral angle of the base presents a thick, projecting **muscular process,** which gives insertion to the cricoarytenoideus muscle, and a spine-like **anterior (vocal) process,** for attachment of the vocal ligament. The **corniculate cartilages** are small conical bodies at the apex of the arytenoid cartilages located in the posterior edge of the aryepiglottic folds. The small, rod-shaped **cuneiform cartilages** are embedded in the aryepiglottic folds above the level of the corniculate cartilages.

Interior of the Larynx (Fig. 81)

The interior of the larynx is smaller than might be expected and is sub-divided into three portions by vocal and vestibular folds which extend anteroposteriorly and project inwardly from the sides of the cavity. The upper subdivision, the **vestibule,** extends from the aditus to the vestibular folds. It diminishes in width from superior to inferior, and its anterior wall is longer than the posterior. The anterior wall is formed in part by the epiglottic cartilage, the thyroid lamina, and the thyroepiglottic ligament; the lateral walls by the **aryepiglottic folds,** which cover the aryepiglottic muscle; and the posterior wall is the interarytenoid membrane.

The middle portion, the **ventricle,** is the smallest of the three regions and is bounded by the vestibular folds above and the vocal folds below. The soft, flaccid **vestibular folds** stretch anteroposteriorly across the side of the cavity, and the interval between them, the **rima vestibuli** is wider than the interval between the **vocal folds.** The latter are sharp, prominent bands which enclose the **vocal ligament.** They are prismatic in cross section and pearly white in the fresh state. The elongated interval between the vocal folds, the **rima glottidis,** forms the narrowest part of the laryngeal cavity, and the shape of the opening varies with respiration and vocalization. The vocal folds and the interval between them form the glottis.

The remainder of the laryngeal cavity, the **infraglottic portion,** extends from the rima glottidis to the trachea. Superiorly it is narrow and compressed from side to side, then gradually widens to become circular as it becomes the trachea.

Muscles (Table XXX)

The suprahyoid and infrahyoid musculature of the neck aids in phonation. The former muscles elevate the larynx in the production of high notes, while the latter depress the larynx in the production of low notes. The intrinsic muscles control the airway through the larynx: The cricothyroideus, lateral cricoarytenoideus, transverse aryetenoideus, and thyroarytenoideus **adduct,** or close, the vocal folds; the important posterior cricoarytenoideus, "the safety muscle of the larynx," **abducts** the vocal folds and opens the glottis. In phonation the cricothyroideus tenses the vocal folds, while the vocalis muscle acts to relax them.

The **cricothyroideus** bridges the lateral portion of the interval between the cricoid and thyroid cartilages. The **posterior cricoarytenoideus** passes from the lamina of the cricoid cartilage to the muscular process of the arytenoid cartilage. The only unpaired muscle in the larynx, the **transverse arytenoideus,** extends from the posterior aspect of one arytenoid cartilage to the other. The **oblique arytenoidei** lie on the posterior aspect of the arytenoid cartilage, where they cross like the limbs of an X, superficial to the transverse arytenoideus. Some of the fibers of the oblique arytenoideus insert into the apex of the arytenoid cartilage, but most of the fibers are prolonged anteriorly as the **aryepiglottic muscle,** which inserts into the margin of the epiglottis. The **lateral cricoarytenoideus,** applied to the upper border and side of the cricoid arch, passes posterosuperiorly

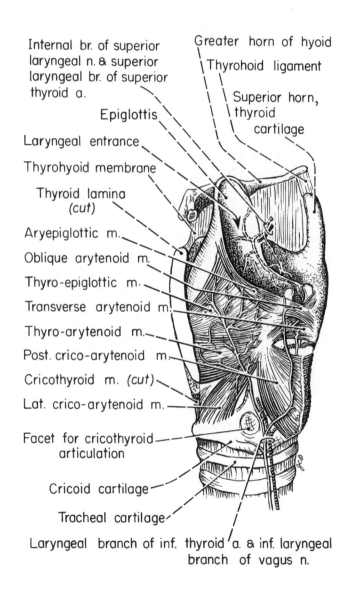

Internal br. of superior
laryngeal n. & superior
laryngeal br. of superior
thyroid a.

Epiglottis

Laryngeal entrance

Thyrohyoid membrane

Thyroid lamina
(cut)

Aryepiglottic m.

Oblique arytenoid m.

Thyro-epiglottic m.

Transverse arytenoid m.

Thyro-arytenoid m.

Post. crico-arytenoid m.

Cricothyroid m. (cut)

Lat. crico-arytenoid m.

Facet for cricothyroid
articulation

Cricoid cartilage

Tracheal cartilage

Greater horn of hyoid

Thyrohoid ligament

Superior horn,
thyroid
cartilage

Laryngeal branch of inf. thyroid a. & inf. laryngeal
branch of vagus n.

*Fig. 81. Lateral view of the larynx. (From R. T. Woodburne. Essentials of Human Anatomy,
ed. 3. New York, Oxford, 1965.)*

to insert into the muscular process of the arytenoid cartilage. The **thyroary-tenoideus muscle** extends as a sheet between the thyroid and arytenoid cartilages, where the uppermost fibers continue superiorly as the **thyroepiglottic muscle,** and the deepest fibers stretch from the thyroid cartilage to the lateral side of the vocal process as the **vocalis muscle.** All the intrinsic muscles of the larynx are supplied by the recurrent (inferior) laryngeal branch of the vagus nerve, except the cricothyroideus, which is innervated by the external laryngeal branch of the superior laryngeal nerve of the vagus.

TABLE XXX.   MUSCLES OF THE LARYNX

Muscle	Origin	Insertion	Action	Nerve
Cricothyroideus	Arch of cricoid	Inferior horn and lower border of thyroid cartilage	Chief tensor of vocal ligament	External laryngeal branch of superior laryngeal
Posterior crico-arytenoideus	Posterior surface of lamina of cricoid cartilage	Muscular process of arytenoid cartilage	Abductor of vocal fold	Inferior laryngeal
Transverse artytenoideus (only unpaired muscle of larynx)	Passes from posterior aspect of one arytenoid cartilage to other		Closes rima glottidis	Inferior laryngeal
Oblique arytenoideus	Muscular process of arytenoid cartilage	Some fibers into apex of arytenoid; most prolonged as aryepiglottic muscle	Closes rima glottidis	Inferior laryngeal
Lateral crico-arytenoideus	Upper border of cricoid arch	Muscular process of arytenoid cartilage	Adducts vocal folds	Inferior laryngeal
Thyro-arytenoideus	Inner surface of lamina of thyroid	Anterolateral surface of arytenoid cartilage	Slackens vocal folds and closes rima glottidis	Inferior laryngeal
Thyroepiglottis	Anteromedial surface of lamina of thyroid cartilage	Lateral margin of epiglottic cartilage	Aids in closure of laryngeal inlet	Inferior laryngeal
Vocalis	Anteromedial surface of lamina of thyroid cartilage	Vocal process	Adjusts tension of vocal ligament	Inferior laryngeal

Arteries and Nerves

The innervation of the larynx is from the **vagus nerve.** The **superior laryngeal branch,** originating high in the cervical region, passes inferiorly to divide opposite the hyoid bone into **internal** and **external laryngeal nerves.** The former pierces the thyrohyoid membrane to supply sensation to the mucous membrane above the vocal folds, while the **external laryngeal nerve** passes along the external surface of the larynx to supply the cricothyroideus muscle. The **right recurrent (inferior) laryngeal branch** of the vagus nerve loops around the right subclavian artery, and the **left recurrent (inferior) branch** loops around the arch of the aorta. Both nerves then ascend in the tracheoesophageal groove to supply all the intrinsic muscles of the larynx except the cricothyroideus, and to supply sensation to the interior of the larynx below the vocal folds.

The **superior laryngeal branch of the superior thyroid artery** accompanies the internal laryngeal nerve to pass through the thyrohyoid membrane and ramify and supply the internal surface of the larynx. The **inferior laryngeal branch of the inferior thyroid artery** accompanies the recurrent laryngeal nerve in the tracheoesophageal groove to supply the larynx from its inferior aspect.

INDEX

Page numbers in **bold face type** refer to major references.